SO-CJE-615

HISTORY AND PHILOSOPHY OF SCIENCE

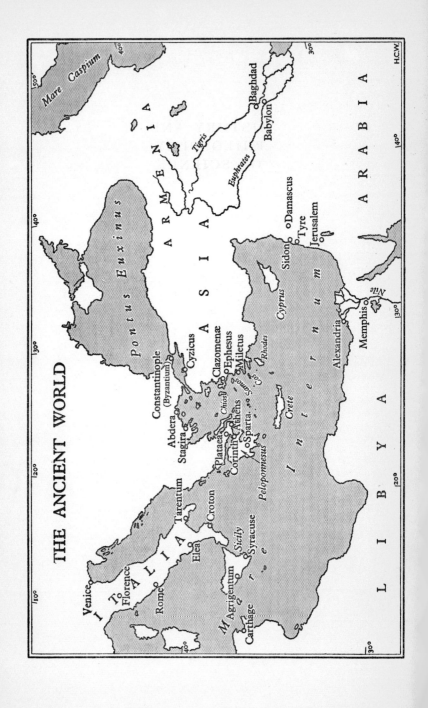

THE ANCIENT WORLD

HISTORY AND PHILOSOPHY OF SCIENCE

An Introduction

BY

L. W. H. HULL

LONGMANS

LONGMANS, GREEN AND CO LTD
6 & 7 CLIFFORD STREET, LONDON W1
THIBAULT HOUSE, THIBAULT SQUARE, CAPE TOWN
605–611 LONSDALE STREET, MELBOURNE C1
443 LOCKHART ROAD, HONG KONG
ACCRA, AUCKLAND, IBADAN
KINGSTON (JAMAICA), KUALA LUMPUR
LAHORE, NAIROBI, SALISBURY (RHODESIA)
LONGMANS, GREEN AND CO INC
119 WEST 40TH STREET, NEW YORK 18
LONGMANS, GREEN AND CO
20 CRANFIELD ROAD, TORONTO 16
ORIENT LONGMANS PRIVATE LTD
CALCUTTA, BOMBAY, MADRAS
DELHI, HYDERABAD, DACCA

© L. W. H. HULL, 1959

First published 1959
Second impression 1959

*Made and printed in Great Britain by
William Clowes and Sons, Limited, London and Beccles*

To the Memory of

H. H. H.

*who loved both Nature
and the Humanities*

93918

PREFACE

THIS is not a detailed history of science. It tries to bridge the gap between science and the humanities by considering scientific ideas in a context of history and philosophy. The gap is of fairly recent origin. It results from unavoidable specialisation in an increasingly technical world. Technicians often lack any coherent philosophical background; while men of general culture lose respect for a science they know all too little about. The outcome is regrettable. Scientific workers may pursue mere technical mastery for its own sake : they may lose sight of human problems. Others are inclined to regard science as no more than the power behind mass production, sanitation, atomic bombs and space travel: they fail to understand its vital contribution to humane thought.

The book is elementary, in that it assumes little scientific knowledge in the reader: but it may not be found altogether easy, as it does not avoid difficult ideas. The material is chosen for the importance of its influence on thought, or for the way it illustrates the genius of an age or man. The choice must depend partly on personal opinion; and most readers will, no doubt, find too little about some topics and too much about others.

In several cases, however, the apparent lack of balance is deliberate. Applied sciences, like medicine and engineering, are only briefly noticed. This is natural in a book whose theme is the relation of science to thought rather than to action. There is not much about the life sciences in the earlier chapters. Their important connection with the development of empiricism is, I hope, sufficiently stressed in the sections on Hippocrates, Aristotle, the Alexandrians and William Harvey. But, before the spread of evolutionary ideas, the influence of biology seems scarcely comparable with that of mathematics and the physical sciences. The balance is redressed in the 19th century, when biology dominates the scene.

Greek science is treated more fully than some other subjects because nearly all the most significant ideas behind modern science have their origin in it. The comparison of Locke and Plato in chapter 7 may also seem unduly long: they are discussed at such length, not only as individuals, but also because they illustrate the conflict of two opposing outlooks—a conflict which pervades the whole history of thought. Two readers have already suggested I am unfair to Plato. But it seems to me that, in this one matter of his attitude to science, he is often unsympathetic and unhelpful. In stressing this point, I remain well aware of his great general merit and importance. In any case, I cannot believe that his reputation will suffer seriously from anything I may say.

I have drawn on the diffuse reading of more than 20 years, much of it done before the book was thought of. It is therefore impossible for me to quote all my sources. My debt to other writers is very great; and I hope its extent is adequately suggested by references in the text, the footnotes and the list of books given at the end.

* * *

My warmest thanks are offered to Dr. A. R. Hall, of Christ's College, Cambridge, who read the first draft and gave his generous advice and encouragement.

I am also most grateful to Messrs. J. B. Fell and C. M. Swaine, of Rendcomb College, for advice concerning their special subjects; to Mr. F. Haywood and Miss C. M. Savage, for help in the preparation of script, diagrams and index; and not least to my wife, for her unfailing support throughout.

Rendcomb, Summer 1958

L.W.H.H.

CONTENTS

ILLUSTRATIONS

'The first generation of teachers of the new science could naturally not learn it in places where the old science, which we call a liberal education, was to be learned. Some of them learned both, with much labour, and searching, and picking up out of stray corners; but some went without a liberal education altogether. And perhaps a few of these, when they found what a demand there was for them and how important they were, may have fallen into a mistake, and taken their half- or quarter-culture for a whole culture.'

W. K. Clifford: *Virchow on the Teaching of Science*, 1878

'The other fault is on the side of those who dislike the new science; it is the fault of being profoundly ignorant of it.'

Ibid.

I

EARLY SCIENCE

THE MOST significant periods of scientific advance are: (1) that of the Alexandrian Greeks; (2) that of the Scientific Revolution in the 17th century; (3) that of 19th-century materialism; (4) the modern period, now with us. None of these can be understood in isolation. The first must be considered in relation to the science of remote antiquity, particularly that of the Egyptians, Babylonians and earlier Greeks. The germs of the second can be seen as far back as the 13th century. Its development extends throughout the 18th. It is connected with the first through a complex series of political, military, economic and religious movements. The third period is distinguished by the rise of chemistry and biology. The progress of the more mathematical sciences in this period was impressive; but the general outlook in these sciences was still that of the Scientific Revolution.

The fourth period exhibits an astonishing technical development as well as an embarrassing growth of pure knowledge. It is not so generally known that there has been at the same time a radical change in the philosophic outlook of the more enlightened scientists. This change has involved departure from the purely mechanistic view of things, an inclination to be less dogmatic, and a suggestion that science should be content to *describe* and *predict*, rather than *explain*, the world. The most striking successes of science have in fact been accompanied by a new modesty and caution among scientists. The new attitude began with certain original thinkers of the 19th century; though the real significance of what these men were doing was not understood in their own time.

Developments in one branch of science often result from those in another. Progress in astronomy and biology, for instance, was stimulated by the optical discoveries of telescope and microscope; progress in medicine by a physicist's discovery of X-rays. The different scientific activities of a particular period must, as far as possible, be considered simultaneously, in order that this cross-fertilisation of one by another may be understood. A period of activity in one branch is likely to be a period of activity in several others. The sciences tend to advance or remain stagnant together. We have also to remember that the different sciences are subject, at a given time, to common outside influences—those of the philosophical, political, social, economic and religious climates of the time. For this reason, also, their modes and rates of progress in a given period tend to resemble one another; and it is desirable to study them together. But we must turn aside, before beginning our historical survey, to consider the nature of science itself. What, if anything, is it that distinguishes science from other pursuits?

The classification of human activities is not usually a profitable occupation. There are no sharp dividing lines, and no pursuit can be undertaken without reference to others. It is impossible to decide the exact point at which logic passes into mathematics, or physics into engineering. The painter's interest in human form may lead him to anatomy; his search for new colours may interest him in chemistry. Music may require the physical study of sound. The historian and philosopher must be ready to take account of everything there is. The work of the hands, in architecture, painting or sculpture, is inseparable from that of the head. There are, however, certain broad categories, sanctioned by custom, which are useful if not too inflexibly applied.

The distinction which most matters here is that between sciences and arts. This is in common use, and has its value; but it is not easy to pin down. The essence of the distinction may perhaps be expressed by saying that the sciences are concerned with discovery and the arts with creation. The scientist turns his attention to the external world, which he supposes to exist independently of himself; exploring and recording it, and looking for a pattern in its behaviour. His attitude to it is mainly passive and receptive. The criterion of his success is that of truth. His statements must survive the scrutiny of independent observers. His pattern, however pleasing, must be rejected as soon as an observation appears for which there is no place in it. The artist, on the other hand, presents a more active attitude to the world. His object is to alter it by adding something to it. His work must be judged by its usefulness or its aesthetic value; that is, by the extent to which it satisfies some human need. The question of its truth does not arise.

No pursuit is exclusively a science or exclusively an art. The scientist is an artist in so far as he creates delicate instruments and refined methods for the accomplishment of his purpose of discovery: the artist is a scientist in so far as he seeks knowledge of the world for the accomplishment of his purpose of creation. All we can say of a given activity is that it is *predominantly* a science or *predominantly* an art. The distinction is one of motive rather than of subject-matter. The etymologist and the poet both deal with words: the one scientifically, seeking knowledge of their derivations; the other artistically, creating something from them. Marble is handled with different purposes by geologist and sculptor. The sifting of documentary and archaeological evidence is a science; but the writing of history is an art. Mechanics, the study of rest and motion, is a science; engineering is an art based mainly upon it. Engineering is a 'mechanical' or 'useful' art, and may be expected to depend much upon science. The dependence in the case of the fine arts is not so pronounced. But we may remember the geometrical study of proportion and perspective by artists of the Italian Renaissance; or the dissection of human bodies by Leonardo; or the optical experiments of the French Impressionists, placing primary colours side by side instead of mixing them on the palette.

There are other reasons for thinking that the distinction between sciences and arts, though significant, is less clear-cut than many people suppose. Some will appear as we go on. In following the history of science we shall consider most of the subjects popularly *called* sciences, although some of these may perhaps more properly be called arts. Physics, astronomy, chemistry, biology are unquestionably sciences. Their aim is to obtain knowledge of the nature and behaviour of the world. The so-called applied sciences, such as engineering, navigation and medicine, are useful arts. Their ultimate purpose is the alteration and control of man's environment. They are carried on by men of action, rather than by men of contemplation. The pure and the applied sciences, however, are so closely related that they must be considered together. Applied science is founded on the knowledge gained by pure science, while pure science, in its turn, is advanced by the technical devices of applied science.

Another subject commonly associated with the sciences is mathematics. It has other associations, and it occupies a position of peculiar importance in the history of thought. Its influence has at times been beneficial and at times iniquitous. You may approve of it or you may not. But you cannot afford to ignore it—any more than you can afford to ignore Aristotle or Mohammed or the Roman Catholic Church—if you want a balanced picture of human development. The history of mathematics must certainly be included in the general history of science, because science could have done little without mathematics. The two have grown up in company, and each has promoted the growth of the other. The pre-existence of a suitable mathematical method has often accelerated an advance of science; while the pre-existence of a scientific problem has often encouraged the invention of appropriate mathematical methods. Mathematics is, however, capable of an independent existence. It has then some of the characteristics of a fine art. As well as noticing its connections with science, therefore, we shall pay some attention to it on its own account.

*   *   *

OUR REVIEW of ancient science is in three parts. In the present chapter we shall deal with the beginnings of science, among the Babylonians, Egyptians and Phoenicians; and with Greek science from about 600 B.C. until the rise of Athens after the Persian Wars. In chapter 2 we consider the growth of science during the period of Athenian greatness—i.e. until the Macedonian conquests of the 4th century B.C. These conquests ended what is usually called the Golden Age of Greece. Alexandria took the place of Athens, as centre of the scientific world, because of them. Astronomy and mathematics were well established before the Athenian decline. Biology, and a mainly speculative physics, had begun. Of the applied sciences, medicine had made the most progress. Engineering, especially as an aid to architecture and irrigation, had also made some. But the Golden Age of Greece was not the golden age of Greek Science. The most admirable and permanent scientific work of antiquity was chiefly that of the Alexandrians, whom we consider in chapter 3. Throughout these periods the history of science is mainly that of astronomy and mathematics. These two subjects are predominant almost until modern times. It is only recently that others have begun to exert a comparable influence.

*   *   *

THE BABYLONIAN and Egyptian civilisations were in many ways similar. It is likely that they had a common oriental origin. In each of them science was the monopoly of a highly organised priesthood. This science was practical and prosaic. The driving forces behind it were everyday necessity and material gain, rather than detached curiosity and interest. There were systematic observations and records in plenty, upon some of which empirical generalisations were founded. All this was truly scientific; but the bare chronicle of fact is only one side of science. There was no tendency to look for reasons or to invent unifying theories. The ancient records were, nevertheless, very valuable to the more imaginative scientists of later antiquity, some of whom were inspired by contact with Babylonian and Egyptian knowledge. In any case we should not despise this priestly work for its deficiencies. It would be absurd to expect a mature procedure among such pioneers.

We need not be surprised at the early rise of astronomy. The heavens are obvious and astonishing. Their regularity of movement cannot escape notice. This regularity provides men with the means, essential to civilisation, of measuring time and constructing calendars. It also gives, to those who study it carefully, the power of predicting celestial events. Now certain celestial events were found to coincide year by year with occurrences, such as harvests and the flooding of the Nile, which were of great significance in daily life. It was therefore natural to suppose that the heavenly bodies could influence mundane affairs; and that those who could foretell the behaviour of the sun, moon and stars could also foretell things of more immediate concern to men. Here was a splendid opportunity for an entrenched priesthood, if it could keep accurate and private astronomical records, to increase its power and influence by fortifying the popular belief in astrology. Successful astrologers could hold high positions at court; and it was natural that they should seek them. But it would seem, from Nebuchadnezzar's admonition to the Chaldeans,[1] that the profession offered risks as well as prospects.

[1] Daniel 2:1–6.

2

The heavenly bodies, and especially the sun, were natural objects of worship for primitive men. Astronomy therefore had religious uses; as, for instance, in the alignment of temples and other buildings of religious significance, such as the Great Pyramid of Gizeh. Finally we should note the connection of astronomy with navigation. This was of special interest to the Phoenicians, who were great sea traders.

It is easy also to find reasons for the development of mathematics. Astronomical observation involves angular measurement; and the results of measurement are expressed in numbers. Geometry and arithmetic are therefore necessary companions of astronomy. Some knowledge of arithmetic is needed also in commerce; while geometry is important to the builder and surveyor. The Egyptians had an annual land-surveying problem, in redefining boundaries obliterated by the Nile floods. The original meaning of 'geometry' is 'earth-measurement'.

The Babylonians and Phoenicians, who were in close commercial touch, were superior to the Egyptians in arithmetic. Egyptian arithmetic is of no particular interest; but that of the Babylonians is important. Their method of writing numbers was very like our own, except that they counted by sixties. Our present notation was brought from India by the Arabs. It may be that the Indians derived the underlying idea from the Babylonians, and that we have ultimately to thank the Babylonians for one of the most important inventions in the history of mathematics. This invention has meant so much to science that it is worth some consideration.

Units in the Babylonian system were denoted by dashes; and 10 by the symbol $<$, supposed to represent a pair of outstretched hands. Thus $'''$ would be 3, while $<<''$ would be 22. So far there is nothing remarkable. The important point about the system is that it was positional—a given symbol could represent various numbers according to its place. When we write 265, it means $2 \times 10^2 + 6 \times 10 + 5$. When the Babylonians wrote $''\ '''''''\ '''''$, it meant $2 \times 60^2 + 6 \times 60 + 5$; i.e. 7565. If the Babylonians wanted to write 39 792, they noticed that it was $11 \times 3600 + 3 \times 60 + 12$; and they wrote $\ll\ '''\ \ll$. They extended their system, as we do, for the representation of fractions; using the sign $\lessgtr$ where we use a decimal point. We write 2·65 for $2 + \frac{6}{10} + \frac{5}{100}$. They wrote

" $\lessgtr$ ''''' ''''' for $2+\frac{6}{60}+\frac{5}{3600}$. Our angular division of the degree into minutes and seconds of arc, and our division of the hour, are evident survivals from Babylonian sexagesimal arithmetic.

The advantages of a positional system are: (1) that it can represent numbers of any size by means of a limited number of different symbols; (2) that it makes possible mechanical methods of calculation, which can be performed quickly with pencil and paper, instead of laboriously on the abacus; (3) that it enables us to see, at once, which of two numbers is the greater. The value of a good notation in arithmetic cannot be exaggerated. The numerical, as opposed to the geometrical, side of mathematics could not have reached its present state of development without the aid of Hindu-Arabic numeration. The Greeks were exceptionally gifted mathematically. We have only to compare the meagreness of their arithmetic with the wonderful growth of their geometry to see how seriously a bad notation can hamper mathematical progress. It is surprising that they did not devise a notation similar to ours. Had they done so, analytical geometry and the calculus might have been invented 2000 years ago in Alexandria.

*   *   *

GEOMETRY AMONG the Egyptians and Babylonians was not an articulated body of knowledge. It was a collection of practical rules for mensuration and land-surveying. This was the only branch of science, except medicine and surgery, in which the Egyptians were ahead of the Babylonians. But the geometrical knowledge of both peoples was fragmentary and crude. The Babylonians, for instance, thought the circumference of a circle was 3 times its diameter. In this they agreed with the Jews.[1] The correct figure is about 3·1416. The famous theorem about the squares on the sides of a right-angled triangle was known to these people long before Pythagoras, though they had no general proof of it. The Egyptians used the converse of this theorem, in the case of a triangle whose sides are in the ratios 3:4:5, for marking out right-angles on the ground. They used a rope, divided in these proportions by knots, which they stretched into the form of a triangle. The angle opposite the longest side was then 90°. They also knew how to find the area of a triangle, and hence that of any rectilinear figure. It is not surprising

[1] 1 Kings, 7:23.

that they could calculate the volume of a pyramid. The construction of the Great Pyramid was a remarkable achievement. The shaping of the huge stones (which are fitted with great precision) in such a way that all the sloping faces of the pyramid should be inclined at the same angle, required considerable skill in practical solid geometry. So also did the marking-out of the square base, with its sides running accurately from north to south and east to west. Some of the stones weigh over 50 tons; so the setting of them in place, even with unlimited slave labour, was a notable engineering feat. Another monumental achievement of Egyptian engineering was the construction of a canal from the Nile to the Red Sea.

*   *   *

LET US now turn to Babylonian astronomy. We shall have to say something of the general aspect of the heavens. The great majority of the stars do not appear to change position in relation to one another. These fixed stars form an unchanging pattern in the sky. The Babylonians gave names to the conspicuous groups, called constellations, of fixed stars. Their division of the stars of the Northern Hemisphere into constellations was similar to ours.

The constellations appear to rotate in circles, about a point called the pole of the heavens. Those near the pole can be seen to perform complete circles. Those farther from it disappear below the horizon for part of the time; but we assume they complete their rotations out of sight. The time they take to make one complete turn is called a sidereal day. The pole is closely marked by the bright star Polaris, easily found from its relation to the conspicuous constellation Ursa Major.

There are, however, seven celestial bodies, visible to the naked eye, whose positions vary in relation to the fixed stars. These are the sun, the moon, Mercury, Venus, Mars, Jupiter and Saturn. The movement of the moon among the stars is so rapid that it can be noticed in a few hours. That of the planets can be detected if they are observed on successive nights. The motion of the sun among the stars cannot be so directly observed, because the stars cannot be seen when the sun is shining. But if we watch the constellations rising immediately before the sun each morning, we notice that these vary according to the time of the year. Suppose that one morning the sun appears to follow the constellation Taurus into the sky. We see Taurus rise just before dawn. Soon afterwards the sun rises from the same place. We can now no longer see Taurus, because the sun dazzles us. But we suppose it is still there, leading the sun across the sky all day. A month later, we shall find that Taurus no longer rises immediately before the sun; but that it is followed by Gemini, which now leads the sun into the sky. In another month's time, Taurus leads Gemini, Gemini leads Cancer and Cancer leads the sun. At the end of six months, Taurus will be so far ahead that it is setting as the sun rises. After a year it will be back in its original position, just ahead of the sun. Thus, although the sun, like the fixed stars, appears to circle the earth from east to west, it continually lags behind them. It takes about 4 minutes longer for its daily journey than they do. It therefore seems to move backwards—i.e. from west to east—across the pattern of the fixed stars. Its path across this pattern is called the Zodiac. The Zodiac is marked out by the constellations which successively lead the sun into the sky at dawn—i.e. by the parts of the pattern over which the sun seems to pass. When Taurus leads the sun, Gemini, though invisible, must rise with the sun. The sun is then said to be 'in Gemini'.

The Babylonians traced the Zodiac, and divided it into twelve constellations, which they named. The Latin names, now used, and the astrological signs of these constellations are: Aries♈, Taurus ♉, Gemini ♊, Cancer ♋, Leo ♌, Virgo ♍, Libra ♎, Scorpio ♏, Sagittarius ♐, Capricornus ♑, Aquarius ♒, Pisces ♓.

> The Ram, the Bull, the Heavenly Twins;
> Next the Crab the Lion Shines;
> The Virgin and the Scales.
> The Scorpion, Archer and He-Goat;
> The man that bears the Water-Pot;
> The Fish with shining tails.

This division of the Zodiac has led to our present division of the year into twelve months.

The time taken by the sun to complete its apparent revolution round the earth is called the solar day. This, as we saw, is about 4 minutes longer than the sidereal day. For ordinary purposes the solar day is the convenient unit of time; for the sun, of all heavenly

bodies, is the one whose behaviour affects our daily life more than
that of any other. For astronomical purposes the sidereal day is the
better unit; and clocks showing sidereal time can be seen in any
modern observatory. Since the sun traverses the Zodiac from west
to east once during the year, it appears to make one revolution a
year less than the stars. Thus the number of sidereal days in a year
is one more than the number of solar days.

There is another peculiarity in the apparent motion of the sun,
which is important because of its connection with the seasons. A
particular fixed star (say Vega) appears to revolve round the pole
of the heavens in a circle whose radius is the same throughout the
year. If P is the pole and V is Vega and O is a terrestrial observer,
the angle POV remains constant. This angle POV is called the
polar distance of Vega. It determines the greatest height reached by
Vega above the horizon. Now the sun's polar distance is not the
same throughout the year. It varies from about $66\frac{1}{2}°$ at midsummer
to about $113\frac{1}{2}°$ at midwinter. The constellations of the Zodiac must
evidently have polar distances lying between these limits. Cancer is
the nearest to the pole, while Capricornus is the farthest from it.
The sun moves with Cancer at midsummer, and with Capricornus at midwinter. At midsummer the sun passes directly overhead at points on the Tropic of Cancer. The other tropic is called
Capricorn for a similar reason. The explanation of these apparent
solar movements is the business of theoretical astronomy. The
Babylonians were content merely to observe and record them.

The apparent motions of the moon and planets in relation to the
fixed stars are more complicated. The Babylonians and Egyptians
kept records of them, but did not attempt to explain them. Nor
could they explain the phases of the moon. But the Babylonians
did succeed in predicting eclipses with some accuracy. An eclipse
of the sun occurs when the moon is between sun and earth; an
eclipse of the moon when the earth is between sun and moon. If
the three bodies moved in one plane, there would be an eclipse of
each kind every lunar month. But they do not move in one plane:
hence the recurrence of eclipses is less frequent, and their distribution in time less simple, than would otherwise be the case. There
is in fact a cycle of eclipses, repeated (with slight variations) at intervals of 233 lunar months. This is called the Saros. It is evident
that careful study of systematic records, kept for a long period,

must reveal the Saros. The discovery was nevertheless remarkable. It illustrates the value of painstaking and detailed observations to science. Such observations may at any time reveal a valuable general law.

It is probably because of this early discovery that eclipses have not caused so much superstitious fear as comets. An eclipse of the sun is intrinsically more impressive than a comet. But that which can be foreseen is never so alarming as that which cannot; and comets remained unpredictable until the end of the 17th century A.D.

*   *   *

THIS SCIENCE of the Middle East began before 4000 B.C. We leave it at about the time (*c.* 600 B.C.) when the Greeks began to apply their active minds to science. It gave them a foundation of factual knowledge upon which to build. It also provided a valuable lesson in procedure, by establishing systematic and patient observation as an element of scientific method. Many later scientists, not least the Greeks, failed to take this lesson sufficiently to heart.

There were civilisations in China and India, as ancient as those of Babylon and Egypt, which attained some scientific development. But these did not directly influence that main growth of science in the West with which we are concerned. Some stimulating oriental ideas were in time brought to Europe by the Arabs. We shall consider these as their effects become felt.

*   *   *

THE ORIGIN of the Greek race is not certainly known. Its importance in the history of science begins about 600 B.C.; but Greek civilisation was established in the eastern Mediterranean some centuries before this. The Greeks were not then confined to what we now call Greece. They also inhabited the western coast of Asia Minor and many Aegean islands. They founded colonial cities of Greek population and culture in Italy and Sicily. We can form an idea of what they were originally like from the Homeric legends of the Trojan War and the wanderings of Ulysses. They were adventurous, imaginative people, full of curiosity and the joy of life. They had no science, but they created a vast mythology instead. Every natural object or event was for them inhabited or caused by some supernatural being. There were gnomes in the earth, nereids in the water, sylphs in the air, dryads in the woods, salamanders in the fire. The sun, moon and planets were living things. The affairs of men were influenced by gods, of engagingly human frailty, who had to be propitiated or defied. But, above all, the world was interesting. It was to be explored and enjoyed, even if you had to risk being eaten by the Cyclops or beguiled by the Sirens or turned into a hog by Circe. It is not surprising that these people, with their curiosity and fresh activity of mind, when once they began to cultivate science, should soon surpass their predecessors.

In 600 B.C. the Greeks were not politically united. They lived in independent city states, such as Athens, Corinth, Sparta, Miletus and Samos. The weakness of these isolated cities excited the ambitions of the Persian kings. Between 546 B.C. and the end of the 6th century Cyrus and Darius conquered the Ionian Greeks of Asia Minor. There was an Ionian revolt, abetted by Athens, in 499 B.C.; but this failed, and the Persians began a further westward advance. Darius was defeated by the Athenians at Marathon in 490 B.C. But the attack on Greece was resumed by Xerxes ten years later. A Spartan force, which tried to stop him, was annihilated at Thermopylae. The Athenians were left to face the invaders alone. Athens was burned; but they succeeded in saving themselves at sea, in the Battle of Salamis, and on land at Plataea. They subsequently liberated the other Aegean cities. Sparta lost prestige by refusing to co-operate in this enterprise. The cities of the Aegean became united, under the leadership of Athens, in the Confederacy of Delos, which later developed into an Athenian empire. Sparta formed a separate alliance of Peloponnesian cities. A pan-Hellenic union was impossible, because of the jealousy between Athens and Sparta. The dominance of the Athenians in the Aegean was eventually broken by Sparta in the Peloponnesian War. But Athens remained independent and powerful until the conquest of Greece by the Macedonians, towards the end of the 4th century.

Greek science began among the Ionians of Asia Minor, as their mercantile enterprises brought them into contact with Egypt, Phoenicia and Babylonia. When the Persians invaded Asia Minor, and while Athens was fighting her war for survival against Persia, Pythagoras and his disciples continued the study of science in

southern Italy. After the war Athens reached, not only the summit
of her military and political power, but also her greatest period of
influence in science, art and letters. Under Pericles she became the
centre of Greek intellectual life. The science of Athenian times was
enriched by the later Ionians, who were associated with Athens in
the Delian Confederacy.

This period is notable for its mathematics, some of which retains
an undiminished significance and charm. But the earlier Greeks
were inferior to the Babylonians as astronomical observers. Indeed, they had two serious scientific faults. They underestimated
the value of observation and experiment; and they supposed they
could obtain knowledge of the outside world by deduction from
general principles based on their personal feelings as to what was
right and proper in a well-conducted universe. Their most important work in astronomy consisted in their attempts to propound
reasonably simple motions for the heavenly bodies, which would
explain the complicated apparent motions. The problem is a geometrical one, likely to appeal to a mathematically-minded people.
It may be fully stated thus:

You have a set of objects, E, a, b, c, ... You know the apparent
motions of a, b, c, . . . , as seen from E. Devise an arrangement of the
objects E, a, b, c, . . . , and a set of relative motions for them, which
shall be compatible with the apparent motions, and which shall at the
same time be as simple as possible.

This was one of the main problems of astronomy for 2000 years.
It was not until Kepler's time that a satisfactory solution was devised. Some of the ancient attempts were beautifully simple, but
did not agree with the observed facts; others agreed tolerably with
the facts, but had to be objectionably complicated to do so. Although the Greeks failed to solve this problem, they did science a
great service by proposing it. The Babylonians drew attention to
the first essential of scientific method—the patient recording of
observed facts. The Greeks drew attention to the second, which
consists in devising a theory (or hypothesis) to fit the facts. This
step, called inductive generalisation, requires imaginative genius.
It is hardly ever the work of one man. Success in it is usually built
upon previous partial successes, which must not be undervalued.
Even when a theory emerges which does at last agree with all the

known facts, it is never final. It may be modified, or even discarded, in the light of new facts. But the imaginative construction of theories is necessary to the advance of science; because a theory which agrees with facts already known is always likely to suggest the existence of, and lead to the search for, facts hitherto unsuspected and unobserved. We shall discuss some of the classic cases later. The Greeks should be given credit for first appreciating the value of theory. The fact that their own theories of celestial motion were not entirely successful is of little consequence. What matters is that they suggested a new and powerful scientific weapon. We shall consider some of their astronomical theories, not only as interesting early specimens, but also because they contain elements subsequently incorporated in better theories.

Physics deals with properties, such as mass, shape, weight and motion, which all matter has in common. Early Greek physics was almost wholly speculative, and intrinsically of little value. It consisted mainly of the fanciful guesses of philosophers, who blandly endowed the universe with the qualities they thought desirable—namely those which justified their own political and moral views. Imaginative speculation of this kind is quite unscientific. It is essentially different from the inductive generalisation above mentioned. In this, the theory, though equally a product of the imagination, is designed so that what is empirically known to be true shall follow from it. The distinction is between disciplined imagination and reckless fantasy.

The physical speculations of the early philosophers had, however, an indirect value. They suggested that there might be far-reaching general principles, relating apparently disconnected things; and that diversity might be more superficial than it seemed. Their opinions as to the nature of the general principles were unfounded and, except for a few lucky shots, erroneous. But they did initiate a line of thought successfully developed by their scientifically less naïve successors.

There was some solid work in biology and medicine. The Athenian period can claim, in Hippocrates and Aristotle, a first-class physician and a first-class natural historian. But over and above the individual scientific achievements of the Greeks we must rate, as regards lasting influence, their new attitude of mind. They were attracted to science by curiosity and intellectual interest.

They developed it for its own sake. They had a talent and an appetite for that abstract thought which they recognised as the most characteristically human of all activities. And they were not priest-ridden.

*   *   *

THE MOST important early Ionian scientist, and the first Greek scientist of note, was Thales of Miletus. He was born between 640 and 620 B.C., and died between 550 and 540. He was a man of business and a man of action, as well as a mathematician, astronomer and philosopher. His interest in science originated in his commercial contacts with Egypt and Babylon. There are two events which may explain the growth of Greek contact with the older civilisations about this time. One was the seizure of power in Egypt by Psammetichus, in 670 B.C., with the aid of Greek mercenaries. Part of the price paid was a relaxation of the traditional Egyptian policy of exclusiveness. The other was the overthrow of Tyre by Nebuchadnezzar about 100 years later, which removed an obstacle to Greek sea power.

Little is known about Thales' life. Even the nature of his work is known only from the testimony of later writers.[1] He was an important innovator in geometry. He introduced the notion of proof. The land-surveying rules of the Babylonians and Egyptians were generalisations from experience—'we have found that so-and-so is true in all the special cases in which we have examined it; let us assume that it is always true'. This is the line taken by children when they first learn geometry. They draw random triangles, measure the angles, and find that the sum is in each case about 2 right-angles. It seems incredible that this should happen many times by chance. They easily become convinced that it must always be the case. But the more mature mind is not satisfied in this way. It asks why the thing should be so. Can it be seen, by the exercise of pure reason, to be necessarily true? Can it be deduced by unassailable logic from something more obvious—or, even, from something so obvious as to be indubitable? Thales asked these questions. He began to make geometry deductive.

Proof consists in showing that a proposition, the conclusion,

[1] Particularly Proclus, who in the 5th century A.D. wrote a commentary on Euclid, in which there is a good deal about the history of early Greek mathematics.

follows from one or more others, the hypotheses or premises. The credibility assigned to the conclusion cannot be greater than that assigned to the most doubtful of the premises. It must always in fact be slightly less, because there may be a mistake in reasoning. This last possibility is remote unless the argument is long and difficult. Having mentioned it, we may ignore it. The truth of the conclusion then depends only upon that of the premises. What are we to do about the premises? Either we must take them for granted, or we must prove them from other premises. It is evident that, however far back we push our reasoning, there must be something, assumed without proof, which we can take for a starting point. The unproved propositions, which are assumed as a basis for deduction, are called primitive propositions.

What should be the nature of the primitive propositions in geometry? The common-sense answer is that they should be so obvious that they cannot be doubted. But this raises two thorny questions: 'What is obvious?' and 'Is obviousness a guarantee of truth?' The question as to what the primitive propositions should be is a difficult one. For the moment, it is enough to notice that something is gained whenever the premises appear simpler and more obvious than the conclusions. It is unlikely that Thales formulated any set of explicit assumptions from which he could systematically derive all his geometrical knowledge. The construction of such a comprehensive system was bound to take time, and the devotion of many minds. But he did succeed in deducing some general theorems from premises which were simpler and easier to accept than the conclusions. In doing so, he took a big step forward —an essential step towards that logically articulated Greek geometry which was the first real mathematics ever created.

Thales' proofs were more convincing than rigorous. His premises were often facts which he considered obvious from the symmetry of figures. An example may illustrate his mode of thought. It is obvious, even to a person without geometrical training, that the diagonals of a rectangle are the same length and bisect each other. It is also obvious that any quadrilateral whose diagonals have these properties is a rectangle. If we draw any two diameters, AOC and BOD, of a circle with centre O, then ABCD will be a rectangle (Fig. 1). Now let us omit the dotted lines from the figure. We are left with the proposition that, if A is any point on the arc of a semi-circle whose bounding diameter is BD, then BAD is necessarily a right-angle. Few people, previously ignorant of this theorem, would think it obvious if presented to them without the preliminary reasoning.

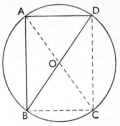

Fig. 1

This first conception of the deductive method is what makes Thales so important in the history of mathematics and the general history of thought. His actual geometrical knowledge was slight. It was, however, wider than that of the Egyptians. He astonished them when he found the height of a pyramid by comparing its shadow with that of a stick. Thus he knew that the sides of equiangular triangles are proportional, whereas they did not.

We must not judge the work of ancient thinkers by modern standards. R. G. Collingwood has some wise words about this in his autobiography. He suggests that much unfair criticism of these thinkers is based on misunderstanding of the questions they were trying to answer. They are accused of failure to do what they were not in fact trying to do, but what their critics mistakenly suppose they were trying to do. We must not belittle Thales because he did not know much, or because his proofs do not comply with modern standards of rigour, or because he did not at once create a complete geometrical system. Some of the geometrical theorems of his time seemed obvious to him. Some, though well established empirically, did not. He asked himself whether those which were not obvious could be deduced from those which were. In assessing him, we should remember that this was the question he was trying to answer. If we do so, we must place him high.

*   *   *

THE MATHEMATICAL work of other early Ionians is negligible. Their physics was entirely speculative; but it has importance, because some of its ideas, though put forward without foundation, suggested valuable lines of thought to later scientists. The most influential of these ideas was the suggestion that the innumerable different substances of which the world is made are not so different as they seem; but that they are really either various forms of a single fundamental element, or different combinations of a few elements. This has become a central principle of modern physics and chemistry.

Thales maintained that everything material is ultimately water. He combined this idea with the animism of his ancestors—the notion that everything is inhabited by a conscious spirit. He may be said to have reduced the universe to spirits and water. Here was an early expression of that dualism of mind and matter which, in various forms, has permeated philosophic and religious thought for many hundreds of years. 'What is mind?' 'No matter.' 'What is matter?' 'Never mind.'

Thales' successors, Anaximenes of Miletus and Diogenes of Apollonia, asserted that the elementary source of all things was not water, but air. Even man's soul, they said, was air—a not unnatural idea, since a man's consciousness fails permanently when he ceases to breathe. For good measure, Heraclitus of Ephesus (*c.* 540–475 B.C.) suggested that all was fire.

The astronomy of these men was no more satisfactory than their physics. Unlike that of the Babylonians and Egyptians, it rested upon no solid basis of observation. Thales was deemed one of the Seven Sages of Greece, because he successfully predicted an eclipse of the sun. But he was able to do this only because he had access to Babylonian records. His prestige, in so far as it depended on this achievement, was won by false pretences. The one really valuable contribution of these people to astronomy was an idea. They had no scientific grounds for this idea; but science is indebted to their imaginative powers. They conceived the notion that the earth might remain unsupported in empty space. This is an extraordinary feat of imagination for men restricted to so small a portion of the earth's surface, and having so little astronomical knowledge. It is repugnant to common sense to suppose that anything, least of all the solid earth, can remain in place without support. It takes a deeper insight to perceive that there is even greater difficulty in supposing that the earth *is* supported. In this case there must be a support for the support, and we have to admit the awkward existence of an infinite regress.

The Homeric picture of the earth imagined the Mediterranean surrounded by a wide belt of land, and this land in its turn encompassed by an unbounded ocean. The belief in a surrounding

ocean had some justification in the travellers' tales of those who had
seen the Indian Ocean or sailed beyond the Straits of Gibraltar.
The Egyptians are even reputed to have sailed round Africa. Thales
began to knock away the solid supports from under the earth, by
supposing it to float upon the ocean instead of merely being surrounded by it. Anaximenes went further. He said that the earth is
'like a broad leaf floating in the air'. It will be remembered that the
air was as essential to Anaximenes as water was to Thales. Anaximander, one of Thales' younger contemporaries, detached the
earth even more completely. He believed that the stars were fixed
to a revolving sphere; and that the earth, which had the shape of a
squat cylinder, remained unsupported at the centre of this sphere,
simply because there was no reason for it to move one way rather
than another. The reason given for this last conjecture has a
strangely modern ring about it. Anaximander was also the first man
to suggest the possibility of animal evolution.

Science practically ceased in the eastern Aegean during the
Persian wars. In assessing what the Ionians had done up to this
time, we must admit that, except in geometry, they had accumulated hardly any positive new knowledge. But we must give them
credit for four permanently valuable ideas. The most important of
these was the germ of the deductive method in mathematics. The
others were: the notion of the earth's freedom in space; the notion
that apparently dissimilar substances might ultimately be the same;
and the notion of evolution. These ideas have influenced the course
of science ever since.

*   *   *

THE WORK was carried on during the Persian wars by the
Pythagoreans in the less disturbed atmosphere of southern Italy.
Pythagoras was born at Samos about 570 B.C. He had advice and
encouragement from Thales and Anaximander. There was therefore no break at this time in the continuity of scientific thought.
After travelling for some years in Egypt and Babylonia, Pythagoras left Samos about 530 B.C. He moved to Croton, a Greek city
on the Bay of Tarentum, where he lectured and founded a learned
society.

The Pythagorean society was almost monastic in the strictness
of its discipline—though not quite, since men and women were

admitted on equal terms, and there was no enforced celibacy. Its most rigid rule was that no member should have proprietary rights in any discovery. Knowledge was to be the common property of members. Credit for the advancement of learning was to belong to the society alone. Nor were the transactions of the society to be revealed to every Tom, Dick and Harry. It was considered undesirable that ordinary folk should have access to the inner mysteries of science and philosophy.

It is understandable that such a society should have become unpopular as its influence grew. The feeling against it was not lessened when it began to meddle with politics. Its political views were what we should now call those of the extreme right. The motive for the political activities of the Pythagoreans is uncertain. It may have been simply a feeling of moral superiority, leading to a belief that the society's destiny was to carry out reforms by means of political power. It may have been, at bottom, a desire to unite the Greek cities of Italy under the leadership of a party which, no doubt, thought itself representative of what was best in Greek culture. The helplessness of the disunited cities of Asia Minor against Persia may well have engendered such a desire in an Ionian exile. Had a union been achieved, able to oppose the rising but still limited power of Rome, the course of history—especially that of thought—might have been much affected. But there was to be no Pythagorean rule. Such a well-organised society, with political aims, could not be tolerated by existing governments. Its exclusiveness excited suspicion among ordinary people. It was forcibly dispersed before its power could spread. It was re-established in Tarentum, as a purely scientific society; and it ultimately became merged in the wider scientific society of which Athens was the focal point.

* * *

WE DO not know how much Pythagoras himself accomplished. The rules of his society were such that it is impossible to distinguish his work from that of other Pythagoreans. But there is reason to suppose that he did a great deal. It is said that Thales had a high opinion of him. His reputation among contemporaries was of the kind that only remarkable men can earn. He was even said by some to be of divine origin, and able to work miracles. We may doubt this: but it is not the sort of thing that is said about an ordinary man. We have seen that, although Thales in fact acquired fame for a false and insufficient reason, he nevertheless really deserved it for other reasons. This is probably also true of Pythagoras. The views attributed to him were probably mostly his; but one should remember that the opinions of others may be mixed with them.

Pythagoras founded a mystical religion as an instrument of moral reform. We need not discuss the details of this religion; but its central notions are important. Some of them were subsequently expounded by Plato; and, although they were not his own, it was mainly through him that they exerted their influence on later thought. The most obvious of these is the society of initiates, based on common property, sex-equality and strict discipline, which was to be the core of the Republic. Another is the idea that a life of contemplation is more blessed than a life of action; and that practical occupations are unworthy of the élite. But the most important is the notion that the world of the senses is less real than the world of the mind. This notion had its fullest development in Plato; but there was more than a suggestion of it in Pythagoras. It has been put forward by a succession of assorted mystics ever since. They have noticed that the sensible world was imperfect—i.e. not as they personally thought it should be. And, being unwilling to believe that God could create an imperfect world, they have convinced themselves that imperfection implies unreality; and that the world of the senses is either a complete illusion or a distorted picture. They have then turned, for reality, to the ideal worlds within their own minds. It has not occurred to them that God's criterion of what is perfect may be different from their own.

We are not concerned with the influence of this belief on religion and morals, but with its effect on science. Its obvious direct effect is harmful. It denies the validity of the observations upon which all genuine sciences ultimately rest. It suggests that scientific knowledge may be got by introspection—by the scientist diligently examining the contents of his own mind. Its indirect effects are more subtle and partly beneficial. For a reason which we shall soon discuss, it directed Pythagoras and his successors to mathematics. As some of them were very able mathematicians, and as mathematics is one of the essential instruments of scientific

3

progress, this was fortunate for science. On the other hand, the very success with which the Greeks cultivated mathematics strengthened the belief, already in their minds, that introspection is a more valuable method of inquiry than observation.

These ideas affected science directly and indirectly for at least 2000 years, and philosophy for even longer. It is not possible to understand the development of European thought without appreciating them. As the thought-connections are involved, it may be useful to summarise them diagrammatically. The only foundation for the three primitive propositions at the top is intuition. The rest are inferred. It will be seen that there is no signpost to experimental science.

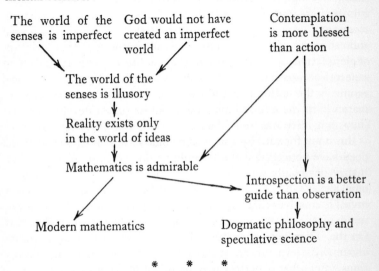

*   *   *

THE PYTHAGOREANS revolutionised geometry. Thales drew attention to the possibility of deducing the less obvious theorems from more easily accepted premises. But his short chains of reasoning were isolated one from another; each proof stood on its own. He was content to derive the theorem of the moment from any set of assumptions which would justify it, and which seemed to him sufficiently obvious to be taken for granted. He did not attempt to derive everything from a single set of assumptions, or to reduce the number of his assumptions to a minimum. Pythagoras and his pupils set about constructing a coherent system, in which all the propositions were shown to follow from a few explicitly stated axioms. If the axioms were true, then so were all the other propositions. There were to be no disconnected scraps of knowledge. The great logical system of geometry later given to the world by Euclid was a revised and extended version of the Pythagorean system, but was not in spirit different from it. There were, no doubt, logical imperfections in the Pythagorean geometry, as there are also in the Euclidean; but it was a deeply significant and immensely influential creation.

The two main constituents of elementary mathematics are geometry and arithmetic. Arithmetic deals with numbers. Geometry is concerned with the distribution of bodies in space, and the distribution of events in space and time. Arithmetic and geometry are connected, because distances and time-intervals can be measured, and can therefore be represented by numbers. The other branches of elementary mathematics do no more than lay stress on particular aspects of geometry and arithmetic. Trigonometry and analytical geometry are methods of applying numbers to geometry. Kinematics is the geometry of motion. Algebra and calculus are extensions of arithmetic.

But to understand what mathematics really is, we must go deeper. We cannot define it convincingly in terms of its subject-matter. We must not say that it consists in doing things with numbers, or being interested in spatio-temporal relations. Bookmaking involves numbers, and cricket an interest in spatio-temporal relations; but neither of these occupations is a branch of mathematics. On the other hand, there are branches of mathematics which are concerned neither with numbers nor with spatio-temporal relations.[1] Sculpture may be done in clay. But it cannot be defined as 'doing things with clay'; for the manufacture of bricks is not sculpture. Sculpture is a particular mode of activity. It may be undertaken with bronze or marble or some recently discovered plastic. It does not consist in dealing with a special substance, but in dealing with any suitable substance in a special way. The same is true of mathematics. You recognise it by the way it handles its material, not by the nature of the material.

It is not easy to define mathematics; but we shall not be too

[1] e.g. Boolean Algebra, which deals with the logical relations between classes.

wide of the mark if we say that it is the study and creation of deductive systems. A deductive system is a body of propositions about certain ideal elements, not necessarily of the kind popularly associated with mathematics. For the purposes of the system nothing is supposed to be known about these elements, except what is laid down about them in an explicitly stated set of axioms. The axioms are accepted without proof; but the only other propositions admitted to the system are those that can be derived from the axioms by strict logic. Whether the axioms are true or not is a question which, so long as we adopt a purely mathematical standpoint, cannot arise. For the word 'true', so far as the system is concerned, is replaced by the phrase 'in agreement with the axioms'. The only restriction is that the axioms must be so chosen that no two propositions of the resulting system can contradict each other. It should not be possible to deduce any of the axioms from the others. If this is possible, the demonstrable axiom becomes redundant; and the system can be improved by a reduction in the number of its initial assumptions. The ideals in such a system are: perfect logical rigour; no tacit assumptions; as few explicit assumptions as possible; no chance of contradiction within the system, however far it may be developed. It is doubtful whether these ideals can ever be attained; but in pure mathematics they are sought. The essential virtue in mathematics is neither utility nor truth, but self-consistency.

The man who creates a deductive system may be unconcerned with its usefulness. But the scientist may find a use for it if he can give it an interpretation—that is, if he can discover a set of physical objects which appear, as a matter of observed fact, to have approximately the characteristics assigned to the ideal elements by the axioms. The logically predictable behaviour of the ideal elements may then furnish a clue to the likely behaviour of the physical objects. A deductive system may have aesthetic value even if it does not possess this kind of usefulness. But most deductive systems turn out in the end to have a scientific use. Some are designed with a scientific use in view. Some occur simply because their authors are mathematicians, just as other men are poets. Good mathematicians, even when they have no conscious interest in the scientific utility of their work, often instinctively create the kind of mathematics which the scientists of the future can apply.

Pythagorean geometry was the archetype of all deductive systems, and therefore the first genuine mathematics. It is easy to see
why the Greek intellectuals found the new geometry so attractive.
In the first place, the perfect circles and straight lines with which
it was concerned were ideas in the minds of geometers. They were
not objects of sense, although there were objects of sense which
crudely resembled them. This naturally recommended geometry
to those who believed that the world of sense was less real than
that of ideas. Secondly, it was possible to obtain geometrical
knowledge by pure thought, without the aid of observation or experiment. Geometry was therefore a congenial pursuit for men who
specially admired the life of contemplation, or who considered
practical work beneath the dignity of gentlemen in a slave-owning
community. Thirdly, mathematics appeared to offer certainty. Up
to a point it does—but not in quite the way that many thinkers
have supposed. Finally; the Greeks pursued deductive geometry
with an astonishing, exhilarating success. It is natural for men to
devote themselves wholeheartedly to anything they can do
particularly well.

*   *   *

THE EXUBERANT growth of geometry among the Greeks was an
important event in scientific history. Although the motive behind
it was not entirely scientific, it was bound in the long run to en-
rich science. It had also, however, an unfortunate effect which we
must not overlook. It was largely responsible for the growth of one
of the most misleading ideas in the history of thought.

The certainty which occurs in mathematics is the logical certainty that some propositions follow inevitably from others. Mathematics never tells us that any particular proposition about the
physical world is true. All it tells us is that *if* certain propositions
are true *then* certain others must also be true. We can be quite sure
that the later theorems of geometry follow from the axioms. But
we have no logical reason to suppose that the axioms tell us anything about the physical world. It is not the business of the pure
geometer either to accept or to reject the axioms as statements of
physical fact. His business is merely to make sure that they are
acceptable—that is, that they do not logically contradict one another—and to discover what consequences must be accepted along

with them by anyone who, for other than purely logical reasons, does in fact decide to accept them. If the suggested axioms lead to contradictory consequences, we can be sure that some of them are false. But the absence of contradiction does not guarantee that they are true—all it shows is that they *may* be true.

There is only one way of deciding whether the axioms of geometry are in fact true of the world; and that is empirically. Empirical knowledge is always open to doubt; because the human senses, even when assisted by scientific instruments, are imperfect. Moreover, each of us depends for most of his empirical knowledge upon the testimony of others; and human testimony is not always reliable. We may be convinced, by pure thought and without any appeal to experience or authority, that the later theorems of geometry follow from the axioms. But we can never be certain that either the axioms or the later theorems are true of the physical world. All we can say is that such experience as we have suggests they may be approximately true.

The desire for certainty is a deep-seated human instinct; and mathematics, as soon as it reached maturity in the form of a logically coherent geometry, appeared to offer certainty. It was natural, therefore, that many thinkers should have regarded geometry from the first with admiration, as the model whose powerful and precise methods should be imitated in all branches of philosophy. This view rested on a misunderstanding of the nature of mathematical certainty. The word 'axiom' meant originally 'something deemed worthy'. Hence it came to mean 'something taken for granted' or 'something assumed as a basis of demonstration'. But it was soon used in a much extended sense. It was taken to mean, not merely 'what is accepted without proof', but 'what is so obviously true that it does not *require* proof'. And 'true' meant 'true of the physical world'. The axioms of Greek geometry owe their apparent obviousness to the fact that they seem to agree with experience. But their origin in experience was overlooked; and it was commonly supposed that they possessed an absolute truth which could be grasped by thought alone, and which needed no empirical support.

It is difficult to believe, considering the depth and subtlety of their thought in other respects, that the greatest Greek geometers —men like Eudoxus and Archimedes—can have made this mistake. But there is no doubt that it was made by many of their disciples and admirers. Its ill effect on thought is easy to see. The modest claim, that the theorems of geometry followed from the axioms, was replaced by the arrogant and groundless claim, that the theorems of geometry were true of the world *because* they followed from the axioms. It was thought that the geometrical properties of the universe could be established without any appeal to experience. And it was believed that all the properties of the universe could be discovered, in the same way, by the mere act of thinking.

Great metaphysical systems arose from time to time, which purported to reveal reality by means of thought alone. They owed their origin, at least partly, to the misunderstanding of what geometers had done, and the consequent attempt to use quasi-mathematical methods where they were not appropriate. The outlook of metaphysicians, from Plato to Hegel, was unscientific. They saw no need for patient, detailed observations. They despised the limited and diffident judgments which men of science were content to found upon such observations. They thought they possessed a more potent method of inquiry. It was unnecessary for them to soil their hands by grinding lenses or dissecting dogfish. Their influence was great, because men are easily deceived by the confident assertion of extravagant claims.

Mathematical methods are of immense value in predicting the consequences of what is already known empirically to be the case. But mathematics is scientifically useless without an empirical starting-point. The mistake of the metaphysicians—impressed by the success of mathematics, but failing to understand its nature—has been to suppose that methods akin to those of mathematics are able *by themselves* to reveal physical truth. The rise of Greek geometry, which was an essential preliminary to serious scientific advance, thus also acted indirectly as a retarding influence, by setting many minds on the wrong track.

Perhaps it was inevitable that this mistake should be made. What is so astonishing is that the mistake should have spread so far and endured so long. The explanation lies mainly in the great prestige of Pythagoras, Plato and Aristotle. We can trace their influence right up to the present day. The geometers of the 19th century did all that was necessary to reveal the true nature of geometry. But their ideas, although gradually spreading, have not yet had time to permeate thought as they no doubt will.

*   *   *

WE MAY now return, from this necessary digression, to the science of the Pythagoreans. Their interest in arithmetic was considerable. Pythagoras attributed a mystical importance to the ordinary whole numbers; and Pythagorean arithmetic was theoretical rather than practical. They were not interested in methods of calculation, but they began what we now call the theory of numbers. This belongs to the artistic rather than the scientific side of mathematics. But we may spare it some attention, because it was associated among the Pythagoreans with a strange view of the nature of things.

They first classified numbers[1] as even or odd; and then according to shapes associated with them. A number with two unequal factors was called oblong.

$$\begin{matrix} \cdot & \cdot & \cdot & \cdot \\ \cdot & \cdot & \cdot & \cdot \end{matrix} \quad (8 = 4 \times 2)$$

If there were two equal factors, the number was called square. The nth square number is the sum of the first n odd numbers.

$$(1) \quad (4 = 2 \times 2 = 1+3) \quad (9 = 3 \times 3 = 1+3+5) \quad (16 = 4 \times 4 = 1+3+5+7)$$

The triangular numbers are 1, 3, 6, 10, · · ·. The nth triangular number is the sum of the first n numbers.

$$(1) \quad (3 = 1+2) \quad (6 = 1+2+3) \quad (10 = 1+2+3+4)$$

[1] Throughout this discussion of Pythagorean arithmetic 'number' is to mean 'whole number'.

Two successive triangular numbers together make a square.

$(3+6 = 9)$

A number with 3 factors was called a solid number.
If the 3 factors were equal, it was called a cube.

$(12 = 3 \times 2 \times 2)$ $(27 = 3 \times 3 \times 3)$

Each pyramidal number is the sum of a series of square numbers.

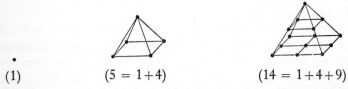

(1) $(5 = 1+4)$ $(14 = 1+4+9)$

This may seem trivial. But it was a first step towards interest in the abstract properties of integers. It was the crude beginning of a beautiful and difficult branch of mathematics. Our concern here is with another aspect of it. The connection of numbers with geometrical figures suggested to Pythagoras that every shape, and hence every natural object, might have its own characteristic number. Superficially, perhaps, this notion is just plausible. The patterns remind one, for instance, of the arrangements of atoms in crystals. But it became an obsession with Pythagoras. As well as believing that numbers determined the *forms* of things, he seems also to have thought that numbers were in some mysterious way the ultimate *material* of which things were made. This was perhaps the most far-fetched of the Greek physical speculations. Even God, according to Pythagoras, was numerical. Similar views of God have been held by others. Plato's version is that God ever geometrises. Sir James Jeans suggests that the Great Architect of the universe may be a pure mathematician. The appropriate comment on such

opinions would seem to be Dean Inge's: 'I find this rather dis-
quieting; a mathematical deity would certainly plough me.'

Wild fantasy and profound thought are strangely mixed in
Pythagorean philosophy. The quaint number-mysticism, just described, was reluctantly abandoned because of a mathematical discovery of the first importance. The length of a line AB is said to be
'measured' by a given unit when that unit is contained an integral
number of times in AB. Let us now consider two lines, AB and
CD, both measured by the same unit. Suppose that AB contains
the unit 5 times and CD contains it 8 times. Then the lengths of
AB and CD are in the ratio 5:8. It would seem at first sight that
we can compare the lengths of any two lines in this way. If we take
progressively smaller units, we must surely come at last to a unit
which fits an integral number of times into each line. But this is
not the case. There are pairs of lines such that no unit, however
small, can measure both. The Pythagoreans discovered that this
was true of the side and diagonal of a square; and it shook them.
The proof is simple.

Suppose there is a unit which is contained p times in each side
of a square, and q times in the diagonal. We may assume that p and
q are not both even; because if they are, we can divide them both
by 2—i.e. we can double the size of our unit. The Theorem of
Pythagoras tells us that $q^2 = 2p^2$. Now p is a whole number. Hence
p^2 is a whole number. Hence $2p^2$ is an even number. Hence q^2 is
an even number. Hence q is an even number, because, if it were
odd, its square would also be odd. As q is even, we may call it $2n$,
where n is an integer. Hence $(2n)^2 = 2p^2$, i.e. $4n^2 = 2p^2$, i.e. $p^2 = 2n^2$.
This means that p must also be even. Hence the valid assumption
that p and q are not both even is contradicted. The only conclusion
we can draw is that there is no unit which can measure both
diagonal and side.

The most astonishing aspect of this fact is that, if the sides of a
square are exactly an inch long, then, no matter how finely the
inches of a ruler are divided into equal parts, it is impossible for
both ends of the diagonal to coincide simultaneously with marks on
the ruler. Two such magnitudes, which cannot be measured by the
same unit, are called incommensurable. We cannot express one as
a fraction of the other. This fact,[1] that the side and diagonal of a

---

[1] Bertrand Russell calls it 'a challenge thrown out by nature to arithmetic'.

square are incommensurable, invalidates the Pythagorean belief in the power of numbers. Here is something which numbers cannot do. The Pythagoreans tried (unsuccessfully) to suppress this remarkable discovery. Such is the tenacity with which men cling, in the face of reason, to the false beliefs they cherish.

Another instance of the connection between mysticism and mathematics among the Pythagoreans is their interest in the regular solids. A polygon is a plane figure, bounded by straight lines. It is regular if all its sides are the same length and all its angles equal. A regular solid is bounded by plane faces, all alike; each face being a regular polygon. The same number of faces meet at each vertex. There are only five such solids (Fig. 2). The Pythagoreans, as mathematicians, were understandably pleased with

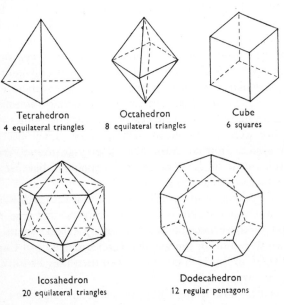

Tetrahedron
4 equilateral triangles

Octahedron
8 equilateral triangles

Cube
6 squares

Icosahedron
20 equilateral triangles

Dodecahedron
12 regular pentagons

Fig. 2

them, especially the dodecahedron, which they themselves discovered. But there was no foundation for their belief that the regular solids played an important part in the design of the universe. Yet this idea persisted for centuries.

*   *   *

PYTHAGOREAN ASTRONOMY was speculative, like that of the Ionians. It contained important suggestions, later revived. But few serious scientific reasons were advanced for these suggestions, and they were entangled with much valueless conjecture. The Pythagoreans believed the earth was spherical. They put forward two arguments for this. The first was reasonable, if not entirely convincing: namely, the argument from analogy with the sun and moon. The second was mystical. The sphere, they said, was the most perfect of figures—more perfect even than the dodecahedron. Therefore all the heavenly bodies must be spherical. There was really no need to look and see.

They also thought that the earth was not the centre of things. Together with the sun, moon and planets, it moved round a central fire. The orbits were necessarily circular, because the circle was as perfect in two dimensions as the sphere in three. The sun, the moon, the earth, the central fire, and the five planets then known, make nine. The Pythagoreans were convinced that, apart from the fixed stars, there should be just ten heavenly bodies. They had a particular affection for the triangular number ten. They therefore added to their system an imaginary counter earth. They believed that the distances of the various bodies from the central fire were in simple numerical ratios. They also believed that the system emitted music like a merry-go-round. We do not notice this music of the spheres, they explained, because our ears are so habitually accustomed to it.

Their three most important ideas were that the earth was spherical, that it was not at the centre of the universe and that it moved. The first of these became general among Greek scientists. The other two were not on the whole taken seriously until Copernicus revived them in the 15th century. Even then they had difficulty in making headway.

The central fire is puzzling. It has been suggested that the Pythagoreans really thought the sun was at the centre, but would not say so because they were afraid of persecution. If this is so, they nearly anticipated Copernicus. It is not clear *why* anyone should have wanted to persecute them for giving the sun a central position. But Anaxagoras was later persecuted for his astronomical opinions; so it is possible that their fears were not groundless. However, since no one ever saw the central fire or the counter earth, Pythagorean astronomy was not widely accepted. Even its good points were forgotten.

* * *

OBSERVATION, AS a method of discovery, was less fashionable with the early Greeks than with their Eastern predecessors. It is therefore surprising to find the first signs of experimental physics among the Pythagoreans. Experiment is more than observation. It is observation in circumstances arranged by the observer. Recording the movements of Jupiter is a matter of simple observation, because the observer cannot control Jupiter. But a man who notices what happens to a substance as he slowly heats it is performing an experiment. The difference is between passively attending to Nature, and actively asking her questions.

The Pythagoreans made experiments to find the relation between the length of a vibrating string and the pitch of the sound it gives. Their belief in the importance of numbers was strengthened by their discovery that lengths in simple numerical ratios correspond to notes at harmonious musical intervals. A note, its fifth and its octave, for instance, correspond to lengths in the ratios 6:4:3. These experiments were not important in themselves. Their significance is that they *were* experiments in an age infected with baseless speculation.

2

THE ATHENIANS

THE GREEK cities were scattered among the mountains and islands of southern Italy and the Aegean. There was no natural line of communication, like the Nile in Egypt or the Euphrates in Mesopotamia, to unite them under one government. The fellow feeling, founded on language, religion, participation in the Olympic Games and reverence for the Homeric traditions, did not prevent rivalry and war among them. Few remained entirely loyal to the Greek cause during the half century of war with Persia. Athens was the most important of them to do so. It was natural that she should emerge with a buoyant spirit, and become leader of the confederation which followed. She was fortunate in finding an outstanding ruler. Her constitution was, in form, democratic. Every citizen had a say in the government; but it must be remembered that many of the inhabitants were not citizens. Pericles became head of the elected government soon after the war, and ruled for over 30 years (*c.* 466–428 B.C.). He was an able statesman, and a patron of science, art and literature. Athens was rebuilt in his time as the finest city in Greece (Plate 2). Men of talent, from all parts, were encouraged to visit it. It became, for nearly 150 years, the place where an able man went naturally to make a name for himself—just as, at other times, men of science went to Alexandria, musicians to Vienna, or painters to Florence, Rome and Venice. At no other time can so many notables have been assembled over so short a period within so small a population. There were the philosophers, Socrates, Plato, Aristotle and Epicurus; the great architect and sculptor Pheidias; the dramatists, Aeschylus, Sophocles, Euripides and Aristophanes; Herodotus, the historian; scientists and mathematicians, such as Anaxagoras, Hippocrates and Eudoxus.

Pericles brought wealth, as well as talent and political power, to Athens. According to the terms of the Delian Confederacy, the members were bound to contribute ships or money. As most of them contributed money, Athens built the ships. She acquired a naval supremacy by which she increased her trade and reduced the Confederacy to an Athenian empire. The rich and liberal-minded aristocracy, which flourished under this system, supported Pericles in his attempt to make Athens a cultural and intellectual centre. There were many people, with time, inclination and the aristocratic contempt for convention, ready to appreciate new art and take an interest in new ideas.

This system was threatened by the less enlightened elements of the democracy; and the fall of Pericles was hastened by the outbreak of the Peloponnesian War (431–404 B.C.), in which Sparta destroyed much of the Athenian power. But Athens remained the intellectual centre of Greece for some time. Her leadership in philosophy was recognised throughout the great days of the Roman Empire. In science and mathematics she gave way to Alexandria after the Macedonian conquests. The atmosphere of Athens was always more favourable to philosophy and mathematics than to natural science, though the achievements in science were not negligible. But the Athenian philosophy of the Golden Age affected thought, and with it science, so profoundly that we must consider it.

*   *   *

ALTHOUGH THIS period is rightly called Athenian, its great men were not all native Athenians. Its scientists mostly came from abroad. Ionian influence entered in two ways : directly, from the liberated cities of Asia Minor ; indirectly, through the later Pythagoreans, from southern Italy and Sicily.

Pythagorean ideas reached Athens mainly through the agency of Empedocles, Parmenides and Zeno. All three influenced the Athenians, and all were acquainted with Pythagorean ideas. They do not, strictly, belong to the Athenian circle; but, as intermediaries, they may be considered here.

Empedocles of Agrigentum made some contributions of his own to science. He lived from about 500 to about 440 B.C. ; but he took to science only in later life. He is famous for his belief that the four elements were earth, water, air and fire. All things, he thought, were combinations of these elements in various proportions. This theory was widely accepted. Traces of it persisted until modern chemistry was developed towards the end of the 18th century. Perhaps it was due to the Pythagoreans; but Empedocles made it widely known. It agreed more closely with observation than any earlier Greek speculation; and it deserved the attention it attracted.

Earth, water and air represent matter in its solid, liquid and gaseous states. A viscous liquid, like honey, is supposed to contain more earth and less water than something more fluid, like milk. The addition of fire will account for differences of temperature. When things burn they are supposed to give up the fire of which they are partly made. Earth and water have weight, while fire has levity. If some substances are lighter than others, therefore, it is because they contain greater proportions of fire. This agrees with the fact that inflammable material is usually comparatively light. These and other arguments make the theory plausible. Quantitative experiment would soon have revealed its shortcomings; but the technical resources for such experiment were not possessed by Empedocles. He did genuinely attempt to design his theory with the facts in mind. It is superior, for that reason, to the rather wild guesses of his predecessors.

He was the first man to regard air as a substance. This view goes naturally with his theory of the elements. He demonstrated it by holding his finger over one end of a tube, and dipping the other end into water. The water did not enter the tube, being kept out by the imprisoned air, until he removed his finger and allowed the air to escape. He attributed a finite velocity to light; but this was only a shot in the dark.

His biological theory was less convincing. Its only merit was that it suggested chance variation and the survival of the fittest. The idea was that originally there were odd parts of animals—arms, legs, eyes and so on—distributed chaotically. These came together in random combinations, forming various strange beasts. But only those whose luck had constituted them suitably survived. He seems, however, to have had some practical ability in this field. He had observed the existence of sex in plants. He founded a Sicilian medical school, in which dissection was practised, and which influenced Athenian medicine. He had a theory, taken up later by Aristotle, that the seat of intelligence was the blood at the heart. He inferred that moral character depended upon the constitution

(a) Hippocrates of Cos

(b) Aristotle

(c) Archimedes

PLATE I

The Acropolis of Athens, a reconstruction

PLATE 2

of the blood, and he prescribed change of diet as a cure for moral depravity. He believed that the body was permeated by a subtle, life-giving fluid. This idea may have suggested the 'humours' of Hippocrates and Aristotle.

Parmenides and Zeno lived at Elea in southern Italy. The life of Parmenides overlapped the lives of Pythagoras and Socrates. According to Plato, Parmenides and Zeno visited Athens, and had a discussion with Socrates, then a young man. It is not certain that this meeting took place; but Plato's account of it, whether fictional or true, shows that Parmenides and Zeno influenced Athenian philosophy. It is likely that they brought some Pythagorean ideas with them. Parmenides was one of those who held that the senses are not to be trusted, and that reality is to be found only among ideas. In consequence he believed that truth was to be discovered by argument alone. He probably derived these notions from Pythagoras. He is important in scientific history for having introduced them into Athens, where they flourished to the disadvantage of science.

Zeno is best known for his paradoxes. He must not be confused with the more famous Zeno of Citium, founder of Stoicism. The purpose of the paradoxes was to support Parmenides, who denied plurality, and asserted that all is one. The denial of plurality cuts at the root of the numerical philosophy of Pythagoras, which Parmenides and Zeno were trying to refute. The attempt to resolve these paradoxes led eventually to the modern theory of the infinite. It led also to the construction of an arithmetic sufficiently subtle for the purposes of geometry. (We have seen that the arithmetic of integers and fractions cannot even represent the relation between the side and diagonal of a square.) Zeno's paradoxes, therefore, are more important than might be supposed from their original purpose. We need only consider the most famous of them; namely that of Achilles and the tortoise. Zeno used this to show that the conception of a line as consisting of many points—as involving plurality, that is—implied a contradiction, and was therefore untenable. The most important considerations arise from the error he committed.

The argument is as follows. Let Achilles, starting from A and moving to the right, pursue the tortoise, which starts from T and also moves to the right (Fig. 3). Let Achilles overtake the tortoise

4

at X. Then Achilles, during the chase, is once and once only at every point between A and X; while the tortoise is once and once only at every point between T and X. At a given instant, Achilles

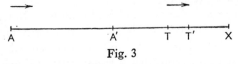

Fig. 3

is at a definite point A'; and he is never there again. At the same instant, the tortoise is at a definite point T'; and he is never there again. To each point A' of AX there corresponds, therefore, one and only one point T' of TX—namely the point where the tortoise is when Achilles is at A'. Hence there are as many points between T and X as there are between A and X. We cannot escape this conclusion, which seems absurd, unless we deny one of the assumptions which led to it. Either we must admit that AX and AT do not consist of points, or we must admit that Achilles cannot catch the tortoise. Zeno supposes that his opponents, aware that Achilles will catch the tortoise, must admit that the lines are not composed of points.

Galileo first understood the nature of the fallacy. The conclusion that AX and TX, although different in length, contain equal numbers of points is *not* absurd; and he saw this. We can therefore admit that Achilles catches the tortoise, without having to deny that AX and TX are composed of points. This is possible because the points of AX form an infinite class. So also do those of TX.

To avoid trouble, we must be clear what we mean when we say that two infinite classes contain equal numbers of terms. We cannot count the terms. But this is unnecessary if we can show that each term of one class corresponds to one and only one term of the other. There is then said to be a one–one correspondence between the members of the two classes. When there is such a correspondence, we say that the two classes contain equal numbers of terms. According to this definition, it is possible for an infinite class to have the same number of terms as a part of itself. The example given by Galileo is that of the whole numbers and their squares. Each whole number has a square, and each square number an integral square root. There is one and only one whole number corresponding to every square number:

Whole numbers	1	2	3	4	5	6	7	.	.	.
	↕	↕	↕	↕	↕	↕	↕			
Square numbers	1	4	9	16	25	36	49	.	.	.

Thus, according to our definition of equality, there are just as many square numbers as integers. But the class of square numbers is only a part of the class of integers.

Zeno, in his argument, established a one–one correspondence between the points of AX and those of TX, thereby showing that the two lines contained equal numbers of points. He observed that TX was only a part of AX. He then thought there was a contradiction, on the ground that the part cannot be equal to the whole. But, when he thought this, he was using the word 'equal' in another sense—as denoting equality of length. It is true that part of a line is never equal *in length* to the whole; but it is false to suppose that part of an infinite class is necessarily unequal *in number* to the whole.

A class which has the same number of members as a part of itself is called reflexive. Cantor, originator of the modern theory of infinite numbers, took this property of reflexiveness for his starting-point. As the problem of infinity is connected with the equally important problem of continuity, Zeno's paradox, although it failed in its direct purpose, was not unfruitful. Zeno is important because he represents a type. Such destructive philosophers are valuable to science. When right, they expose errors. When wrong, they still do good; because they make other people think, if only in self-defence.

*   *   *

THE ASTRONOMY and physics of the Athenian period are best considered together. There was no clear boundary between them, and both were entangled with philosophy. Many conflicting opinions were expressed; some strikingly suggestive, others valueless. But most of these opinions were little more than their authors' prejudices. Even when reasons were adduced, these were seldom convincing. The opinion which carried most weight was often that of the man whose public reputation, for reasons unconnected with science, stood highest. There was little judgment by impersonal scientific standards. The shrewdest conjectures were mostly those of Ionians. They were made by men who allowed their moral and religious views to depend upon their scientific theories.

Unfortunately these men were on the whole less influential than those who framed scientific theories to support their moral and religious views.

The Athenians had their first taste of scientific philosophy from Anaxagoras, an Ionian of Clazomenae. He spent some 30 years in Athens, at the invitation of Pericles, whose friend and instructor he became. His astronomical views were materialistic. He believed that the sun was a mass of incandescent metal,[1] and that the moon had mountains and valleys like the earth. He noticed that the bright part of the moon was always that which faced the sun. He deduced that the moon was cold and shone only by reflected light. This led him to the correct explanation of the moon's phases, which are due to its change of position in relation to the sun and earth (Fig. 4).

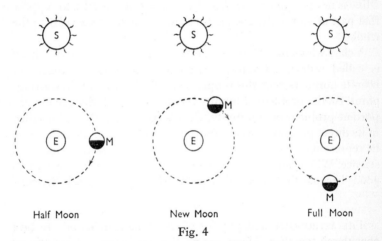

| Half Moon | New Moon | Full Moon |

Fig. 4

He also interpreted eclipses correctly; pointing out that lunar eclipses occur when the moon is in the earth's shadow, and solar eclipses when the earth is in the moon's. He had a crude nebular hypothesis, which suggested that the heavenly bodies were formed by condensation from a chaotic, whirling mass. He believed that there were inhabited worlds other than our own.

His physics involved elements of strangely different kinds. There were many more in his system than in those of his predecessors.

1 A large meteorite fell in daylight at Ægos Potamoi in 467 B.C. It is said that Anaxagoras supposed this to have fallen from the sun, and formed his notion of the sun's nature accordingly.

These elements need not now be enumerated. Their diversity is shown by the remark that fire, blood, colour and lead were among them. Mind was another of his elements. He thought it was a constituent of all living things. But he made as little use of it as possible, preferring material explanations when he could find them. Socrates and Plato, with whom mind was supreme, had a poor opinion of him for this reason.

Anaxagoras was involved in the first recorded clash between scientific scepticism and religious orthodoxy. He was condemned to death for atheism, because of his refusal to see anything miraculous or divine in the heavenly bodies. The more superstitious Athenians were not prepared to forgo their traditional gods. The feeling against him, however, was not entirely religious. Many Athenians at that time were tired of Pericles. They began their attack on him through his friends, of whom Anaxagoras was one. Anaxagoras was saved from death by the intervention of Pericles, but spent his few remaining years in exile.

The atomists, Leucippus and Democritus, evolved theories similar to those of 19th-century materialism. They had no means of checking their beliefs experimentally; and these beliefs had at the time as little foundation as those of other Greek speculators. It is an accident that much of what they said has since received confirmation. Little is known of Leucippus, except that he was a Milesian who flourished about 440 B.C. He was the originator. Democritus, who came from Abdera in Thrace, and was young when Anaxagoras was old, was responsible for developing the system and making it known. He visited Athens, where Socrates was his contemporary, but attracted little notice there. It is possible that the neglect of atomism in Athens was due to the influence of Socrates and Plato, who would certainly have disapproved so materialistic an outlook. Aristotle, who came from the same district as Democritus, was acquainted with his views, but disagreed with them.

These views are as follows. The atoms are indivisible and indestructible. They move about in all directions in otherwise empty space. Atoms and space are all that exists. There are different kinds of atoms, distinguished by differences of shape, but individual atoms are too small to be noticed by the senses. The things we touch and see are made by the arrangement of atoms in groups.

Change consists in nothing but their rearrangement. There is no alteration in the atoms themselves. The motion of an atom persists until checked—presumably by collision with another atom, since the theory itself denies the possibility of any other cause. This is the most significant of the atomists' ideas. It foreshadows the Law of Inertia, enunciated by Galileo. This states that motion needs no cause to preserve it. The cause is necessary only to produce *changes* of motion. If a thing is moving, it will continue to move, without change of speed or direction, until something forces it to slow down, accelerate or deviate from its path. This notion, upon which Newtonian mechanics is founded, is opposed to Aristotle's view, that a body comes to rest unless there is something to keep it going. Unfortunately the Aristotelian view held the field for nearly 2000 years. The progress of mechanics and astronomy might have been more rapid if the atomists had been attended to.

Once the atoms have been given a start, say the atomists, their subsequent motions are determined by invariable mechanical laws. The state of the universe at any time depends only upon its previous states. Its future is decided by its present. Here is the philosophy of determinism in its extreme form. The moral implications, arising from the necessary denial of free will, are obvious and disturbing.

Aristotle (Plate 1b) finds fault with atomism for omitting to say how the atoms acquired their original velocities. What he wants is the admission of some First Cause or God. He fails to see that this only pushes the difficulty one step back. To be consistent, he must next demand a cause for God. Scientific determinism, like mathematical deduction, must have a starting point about which no questions are asked. By starting where they did, and remaining silent about the cause of the initial motions, Leucippus and Democritus tacitly admit the limitations of science. They thereby show the superiority of their scientific insight. Aristotle's mistake does not consist in wanting to begin one step farther back; but in his condemnation of the atomists for not explaining *everything*. No system which depends on a causal chain *can* explain everything. The defect of starting *somewhere*, cannot be avoided by starting somewhere else.

Whatever we think of the atomists in other respects, we must admit their genius for spotting the kind of theory likely to be useful to science. They hit upon the Law of Inertia, the notion of universal cause and effect, and something like the atomic and kinetic theories of modern chemistry. They did all this without the data possessed by modern scientists. If Greek science had followed their line, it would have advanced much more quickly. We need not be surprised that atomism was overlooked. A theory, however good, is of no use to science by itself. People must be persuaded to accept it as a working hypothesis. The atomists lacked the necessary means of persuasion. The atomic theory seems plausible to us, because we have grown up with it and seen the success of its predictions. But it would be hard to imagine a notion superficially less acceptable to common sense. Leucippus and Democritus could offer no convincing reasons for their theory; nor had they the prestige by which Plato and Aristotle were able to enforce questionable opinions. We can hardly blame their contemporaries for not having that second-sight with which the atomists themselves were gifted.

Plato's physics and astronomy are negligible. Those of Aristotle, though largely incorrect, are not negligible. In his own time, and throughout the Middle Ages, Aristotle's less fortunate scientific opinions exercised an influence out of all proportion to their merit. The wiser parts of his doctrine were often overlooked. He was born, in 384 B.C. at Stagira, son of the physician to the King of Macedonia. He studied for 20 years in Plato's Academy: he later travelled, and became tutor to Alexander the Great. He returned to Athens to write and teach in his school, the Lyceum. His disciples were called Peripatetics, from his habit of walking about while lecturing. He contributed to every important branch of learning except mathematics. He wrote on ethics, politics, literature, metaphysics, physics, astronomy, medicine and natural history. He created formal logic.

A most significant element in his philosophy was the importance he attached to final causes. The final cause of something is the future purpose which it is supposed to serve. The efficient cause of something is the agency which brings it about. Thus lightning is the efficient cause of thunder; whereas gain is the final cause of commerce. If eggs are being fried, the final cause may be somebody's breakfast; but the efficient cause is the flame under the pan. A detective may be interested in both kinds of cause. He asks

'Why did X die?' The answer 'Because he consumed arsenic' reveals the efficient cause: the answer 'In order that Y might inherit his estate' reveals the final cause. Final causes appear only where mind is involved. They may be important in criminology or psychology or biology. They are irrelevant in physical science, which deals with inanimate things.

Aristotle attributed to everything a 'nature', by which its behaviour was directed to some purpose. Had he been asked why an egg turns into a chicken, he would have answered simply that this is what an egg is for. This explanation would have satisfied him. He would not have thought it necessary to consider the chemical reactions which accompany the change, or the warmth provided by the sitting hen. Had he been asked why stones fall, he would have said that the purpose of stones is to form the central core of the universe, and they are predisposed by 'nature' to approach it. He may have thought that inanimate objects are actually conscious of the final causes for which they exist; for he must have been familiar with the animism of the recent past. He was an eminent naturalist; and his mind was perhaps conditioned by preoccupation with the behaviour of animals, whose actions are evidently sometimes decided by purpose. The teleological view, that everything makes for a preordained end, is naturally acceptable to theologians. No doubt this is one reason why Aristotle's philosophy was taken up by the medieval Church. The study of final causes may be important in some fields; in physical science, however, it leads to a dead end.

We need not enter upon the philosophic or religious question, whether there is purpose throughout the universe or not. What matters is, that the search for efficient causes has proved a more powerful scientific procedure than the search for final causes. Scientists have succeeded by attending to the one notion, but not usually by attending to the other. Aristotle's concentration on final causes—his attempt to introduce the idea of 'nature' into physical science—was more harmful than any of his other mistakes. It was not just another incorrect statement: it set fictitious value on a fundamentally wrong method. Science should proceed on the assumption that all things have efficient causes which it is the business of the scientist to seek.

Aristotle assumed the four elements of Empedocles. He also

held the opinion, then general, that the design of the universe was based on the perfect figures of the sphere and circle. Earth and water tended 'by nature' to move towards the centre of the universe, earth having that tendency more strongly than water. Air and fire, but fire the more vigorously, tended 'by nature' to move away from the centre. Earth and water, that is, possessed different degrees of gravity; air and fire different degrees of levity. The result was four concentric spheres: first that of earth, next that of water, next that of air and finally that of fire. Outside these another sphere revolved, to which the moon was attached. Everything sublunary was subject to change and decay. Beyond the sphere of the moon revolved those of Mercury, Venus, the sun, Mars, Jupiter, Saturn and the fixed stars. These heavenly bodies were not made of fire, but of a fifth element, the quintessence, which was more refined than the sublunary elements and did not suffer change or decay. Outside all this was yet another sphere, the ultimate heaven, containing the prime-mover, God, who kept the spheres of the stars and planets in motion. The celestial spheres were transparent. In order to explain the irregularity of planetary motions, this system of spheres had to be greatly elaborated. We shall consider this elaboration in connection with Eudoxus.

We have already noticed Aristotle's fundamental mistake in mechanics. He made other mistakes, which careful observation would have detected, but which nevertheless held the field for centuries. The two most glaring were, that heavy bodies always fall more quickly than light ones, and that a projectile moves horizontally until it stops, and then falls vertically. Purging European thought of false Aristotelian ideas was one of the major operations of the Scientific Revolution.

Eudoxus of Cnidus and Heraclides of Pontus are the only other astronomers of this period whom we need mention. Eudoxus lived from 408 B.C. to 355 B.C., and was therefore a younger contemporary of Plato. He went to Egypt with Plato, and afterwards founded a school at Cyzicus. He later lived for a time in Athens, but was not well received there.

Plato was puzzled by the irregularity of apparent planetary motions. The only kind of motion which he thought entirely respectable was uniform circular motion. He would not believe that other kinds of motion could exist in the heavens. But the apparent

motion of a planet is far from uniform. We have seen that a fundamental problem of astronomy is to account for the apparent motions
of the heavenly bodies. This is a very difficult problem. Plato added
artificial difficulty to it by insisting that the earth should be at rest,
and that all the motions must be combinations of uniform circular
motions. Eudoxus attempted a detailed solution of the problem in
this form. The better-known Ptolemaic solution was a modification
of his plan.

The mechanism adopted by Eudoxus was that of spheres rotating uniformly within spheres. The outermost sphere F, with the
earth E fixed at its centre, rotated once a day from east to west
about an axis NS (Fig. 5). This sphere carried the fixed stars. The
points N and S were the north and south poles of the heavens, and
the line NS passed through the north and south poles of the earth.

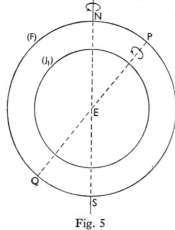

Fig. 5

Four spheres were needed to
give a single planet, say Jupiter,
something like its correct motion.
Let PQ be a diameter of the
sphere F, describing a cone as F
rotates. Let the sphere J_1 concentric with F, rotate about PQ
as axis. Let another sphere, J_2,
rotate similarly about a diameter of
J_1. Let J_3 rotate within J_2, and J_4
within J_3. Let Jupiter be attached
to this innermost sphere J_4. By
varying the rates of rotation and
the inclinations of the axes of
these successive spheres, Eudoxus
could approximately reproduce the observed motion of Jupiter.
He was a keen observer; and one must admire the ingenuity with
which he adjusted his fantastic machinery to fit the facts. Each
planet required a set of spheres like Jupiter's. He found himself at
last with 27 concentric spheres: one for the fixed stars, three each
for the sun and moon, and four for each planet. More accurate
observations later led to an increase in this number.

Heraclides (388–315 B.C.) slightly simplified the system. He supposed that the inner planets, Mercury and Venus, revolved round
the sun instead of revolving, like everything else, round the earth.

Their apparent motions can thus be explained more conveniently. He also suggested that the sphere of the fixed stars was motionless, and that the daily motion of the heavens was an illusion due to the revolution of the earth about its axis. Copernicus cites him as a precedent in this.

*   *   *

THE MATHEMATICAL work of Thales and Pythagoras was epoch-making. By proposing a logically coherent geometry, they offered their successors a vast programme of detailed development. The mathematicians of the Athenian period were mainly occupied with this programme. We need only discuss them briefly. They did not lack originality; but most of what they did had more bearing on the technical development of mathematics than on the general course of scientific thought. By the end of this period Greek geometry, as it appears in Euclid's *Elements*, was broadly worked out. There were a few outstandingly important new ideas, to which we must pay more attention. The school of Eudoxus at Cyzicus was so closely related to the Athenian school that we may treat them as one.

Hippocrates of Chios was born about 470 B.C. He must be distinguished from Hippocrates of Cos, the famous 'Father of Medicine'. He came to Athens about 430 B.C. and, while there, became interested in philosophy and science. He developed the geometry of the circle, and he wrote a textbook, which probably served Euclid as a model. He was the first geometer to use letters for points on his diagrams—a device of great value, which has been used ever since. He gave much time to the problem of squaring the circle, which he failed to solve. This is one of three famous problems of antiquity. These problems have not much intrinsic importance. But valuable work was done, incidentally, in the effort to solve them. Frequently in the history of science important discoveries have been made, by the way, in the pursuit of what we should now regard as trivial ends.

The squaring of the circle meant more than just calculating the area of a circle. It meant drawing a square equal in area to a circle, given no instruments other than compasses and straight edge. In this form the problem was never solved. It has been proved in modern times to be insoluble. There are nevertheless still those who try to solve it. This is also true, under the same conditions, of the other two problems. One was the trisection of an angle. The other was the duplication of a cube—i.e. to find the length of one edge of a cube whose volume is twice that of a given cube.

This third problem is equivalent to constructing a length equal to the cube root of 2. We may take an edge of the original cube as our unit of length. This cube will then have unit volume. If an edge of the new cube is of length x, then its volume will be x^3. Hence $x^3 = 2$; i.e. x is the cube root of 2. The Greeks could not find the cube root of 2 arithmetically. Their progress in arithmetic was restricted by their inconvenient way of writing numbers. There was, therefore, some point in their efforts to solve this problem geometrically. Their hopes were probably raised by their easy success with the corresponding problem of duplicating a square.[1]

The duplication of the cube is called the Delian Problem. It is said that in 430 B.C. the Athenians asked the oracle, in the temple of Apollo at Delos, how they could rid themselves of a pestilence. The answer was that they should double the size of the cubical altar in the temple. They tried making the edges twice as long, which made the volume 8 times as great. They also tried placing a second cubical block beside the first. This doubled the volume, but spoilt the cubical shape. The plague continued, because of their stupidity, and had to run its course. The priests responsible for the oracle's reputation showed considerable low cunning in selecting a problem which, though superficially like one that had been easily solved, was in fact very difficult. The Delian Problem, and that of trisecting an angle, were both solved by the Greeks; but not, of course, by constructions involving only straight lines and circles. The less conservative mathematicians were led, in solving them, to study important curves other than the circle. They thereby opened a new and almost limitless field of research. The attempts to find the area of a circle led to a method not unlike the integral calculus.

With the possible exception of Aristotle, Plato is the most celebrated of Greek thinkers. He was born in 429 B.C., of an aristocratic Athenian family. He was the pupil and friend of Socrates, after whose death (399 B.C.) he left Athens for some time. He travelled with Eudoxus in Egypt; whence, by way of North Africa, he reached Italy in his pursuit of knowledge. While there, he met

[1] See page 201.

the Pythagorean Archytas. This meeting was another of the means by which Pythagorean ideas entered Athenian philosophy. It may also partly explain Plato's reverence for mathematics. He returned to Athens in 380 B.C., where he founded the Academy. He died in 348 B.C.

His attitude to mathematics was pedantic, and his influence on it reactionary. There were two main reasons for his interest in it. Firstly: he was the man, of all men, who most admired it for its other-worldliness—its preoccupation with ideas rather than material things. He altogether misconceived its significance in science. He beheld its purely intellectual apparatus of development, and thought he saw the God-given pattern of success in every branch of learning. He was not interested in the detailed application of mathematics to the results of observation. We need not find fault with him for thinking that mathematics is worth while, to those who love it, for its own sake. For such people it is, like the other arts, a source of refined pleasure. But he was narrow-minded in his dislike of its practical application; and mistaken in supposing its deductive methods universally, or even widely, applicable.

Secondly: he regarded it as the best of all instruments of education. At the entrance of his Academy he placed a notice which said 'Let none ignorant of mathematics enter my door.' He prescribed mathematics as the first of studies fit for the Guardians, who were to be the ruling class in his Republic. He thought of mathematics as an academic discipline; and he established a code which laid down what respectable mathematicians should not do. They should not stoop to applied mathematics.[1] They should not consider curves other than the circle. Plato called such curves 'mechanical', which with him was a term of abuse. It followed that the only legitimate instruments in geometry were the straight edge and compasses. There is here an obvious trace of the mystical Pythagorean admiration of the circle.

It is the pedant who creates artificial difficulties like these, instead of breaking new ground. Such restrictions had no justification but Plato's fiat. His attitude, in matters mathematical, was:

> I am the Master of this College;
> What I don't know isn't knowledge.

[1] Except, oddly enough, for purposes of war.

No subject can retain its freshness and vigour under such treatment; and mathematics wilted under Plato. His reputation in other ways was so great that his repressive influence on mathematics was considerable. This influence was increased through the medium of Euclid, who on the whole accepted the Platonic code. Euclid's *Elements* remained a standard text until the end of the 19th century. Fortunately there were men of genius like Archimedes, outside Athens, who allowed themselves such liberty as they thought fit. It was the Athenian School that withered away. The mathematical merits of Archimedes and Plato are about as comparable as the musical merits of J. S. Bach and Ebenezer Prout.

Eudoxus was the greatest mathematician of this period. His astronomical theory alone is sufficient to suggest this. In one respect this theory was reactionary. It disregarded the Pythagorean idea that the earth might move; and it fixed the earth again at the centre of things. But there was then no good reason for thinking that this suggestion of the Pythagoreans was more than another of their fanciful guesses. The great merit of Eudoxus was that he worked out the celestial motions *in detail*, with constant regard for the findings of observation. This was something new. It implies mathematical ability of the first order. It also shows he understood the proper place of mathematics in the scientific scheme. It expresses the results of observation in a manageable form, and reduces them to order: it is not a means of finding out about the world by detached ratiocination. What is known of his other mathematical work confirms the view that he was exceptionally gifted.

Much of Greek geometry depends upon the idea of proportion. One of its fundamental theorems, for example, was that the sides of equiangular triangles are proportional. Let ABC and PQR be two such triangles; with angle A equal to angle P, angle B equal to angle Q, and angle C equal to angle R. Then the theorem states that QR, RP and PQ are proportional to BC, CA and AB. If one were asked to explain what this means, the natural answer would be that QR is the same fraction of BC as RP is of CA or PQ of AB. But the Pythagoreans, as we saw, discovered the awkward fact that it may be impossible to express one line as a fraction of another. If, then, QR is not a fraction of BC, our simple answer ceases to have a meaning. Is it possible in this case to attribute any meaning to our theorem? And, even if a meaning can be found, is the theorem still true? If not, the theorem, and all that depends on it, must be abandoned. Eudoxus was able to answer both questions affirmatively. His answers are unfortunately too technical to be discussed here. Anyone who is curious will find them in Books V and VI of Euclid's *Elements*. His theory of proportion was one of the greatest achievements of Greek thought. His ideas still underlie modern mathematical analysis, and serve the specialist as a good introduction to it.

The other strikingly advanced notion of Eudoxus was his method of exhaustions. This contains the germ of the integral calculus. We may illustrate it by considering how it is used to find the volume of a pyramid.[1]

Let V be the volume of a rectangular block, having the same height and base as the pyramid. Imagine the pyramid formed approximately by tiles, of diminishing size, set one above another, as in Fig. 6. The total volume of these tiles evidently exceeds that of the pyramid. But the excess can be reduced by increasing the num-

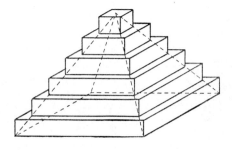

Fig. 6

ber of tiles, so that the 'steps' become smaller. Eudoxus proved that the total volume of the tiles was always greater than $V/3$; but that, by increasing their number indefinitely, he could bring it down as near to $V/3$ as he liked. This showed that the volume of the pyramid was not greater than $V/3$. By considering a pile of tiles fitted *inside* the pyramid, he showed (similarly) that its volume could not be less than $V/3$. Hence it must be $V/3$.

---

[1] The Egyptians could find the volume of a pyramid, but they obtained their formula empirically. They had no general method for solving problems of this kind.

The essence of the method consists in enclosing the required quantity between two others, which can be calculated, and which can be shown to approach each other indefinitely.

Eudoxus discussed curves other than the circle, but it is not certain what they were. He was unfortunate as regards his reputation, which has not been commensurate with his achievements. His writings are lost; and his work is known only through that of others, more famous than himself, whom he influenced—notably Euclid, Archimedes, Hipparchus and Ptolemy. He incurred the hostility of Plato before leaving Athens. This is not surprising; for he certainly failed to toe the conservative Platonic line in mathematics. Eudoxus was in spirit, though not in time and habitat, the first of the great Alexandrians.

We must also mention Menaechmus (375 to 325 B.C.) of the school of Eudoxus, another tutor of Alexander. He was the first to study conic sections. These curves are plane cross-sections of a cone. Let the base of the cone be a circle with centre O (Fig. 7).

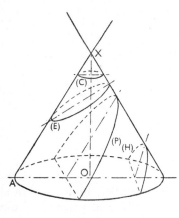

Fig. 7

Its axis is the line XO, perpendicular to its base. X is its vertex. Any line, XA, from the vertex to a point on the circumference of the base, is called a generator. If we cut the cone at right-angles to its axis, the cross-section is a circle (C). If we cut it by a plane parallel to a generator, we get a parabola (P). An oblique cut, not so oblique as that giving the parabola, gives the ellipse (E). A cut more oblique than that giving the parabola will give the hyperbola (H).

The geometry of the conics had no scientific utility when first created. It was cultivated by generations of Greeks for its purely mathematical interest. In the 17th century it was unexpectedly applied with great success in astronomy. If it had not existed, the Scientific Revolution might have died young. One could argue, with some force, that the scarcely known Menaechmus affected history more than Alex-

Veronese; *Feast in Levi's House*

PLATE 3

(a) Pazzi Chapel, Florence

(b) Santa Maria Novella, Florence

PLATE 4

ander, Julius Caesar, Charlemagne and Napoleon together. This
is one of the classic cases in which purely academic mathematical
work has found unforeseen physical interpretation.

*   *   *

THE MEDICINE and biology of antiquity were not separate subjects. Biological discovery usually had a medical purpose, and was
undertaken by those who practised medicine. The first Greek
medical work of a seriously scientific nature was that of the Ionian
schools at Cos and Cnidus, and the Sicilian school of Empedocles,
already mentioned. This work certainly owed something to pre-
Greek civilisations, particularly the Egyptian.

The early history of Greek medicine is uncertain. Ionian physicians probably made their first studies in the Asclepions, or
temples of Aesculapius. In remote antiquity disease was usually
attributed to the anger of some god, and divine relief was sought.
Aesculapius was a god, supposed to possess special powers of healing; and the sick resorted to his temples. There was no fee; but it
was customary for anyone who recovered to leave an offering in the
temple, with a record of his name, his disease and the manner of
his cure. There is no evidence that the priests acted as physicians.
Their function was merely that of intermediary between patient
and god. But it was natural for laymen who took an interest in
medicine to frequent the Asclepions, where they could observe sick
people and read the case-histories. This would have led in time to
the establishment of secular medicine, and the gradual abandonment of religious observance as a means of cure.

Those who do not accept this theory point out that Homeric references to medicine contain no hint of priestly intervention.
Homer speaks of Aesculapius, not as a god, but as a Thessalian
king who was noted for his healing powers. They contend that
secular medicine was established before Aesculapius became a god.
The temple cult was a mere incident, superimposed upon continuous scientific progress. Whatever the truth may be, it is certain that for a time the cure of disease was popularly associated
with religion. The history of the Delian Problem confirms this
view. It is also probable that, even if secular medicine existed before the general resort to Aesculapius, the secular physicians
nevertheless learnt much by observation in the Asclepions.

5

Ancient medicine was dominated by Hippocrates of Cos (Plate 1a). He was born in 460 B.C.; so that he was contemporary with Pericles, Socrates and Plato. He was a little later than Empedocles. He had outstanding merits. He was an upright character, who put his work before what he could get out of it. He thus began the tradition of professional integrity which has ever since been observed by the best medical men. He insisted that disease had natural causes, and that it must be cured by natural means. He steadfastly rejected current superstition. Indeed, he succeeded in giving medicine so firm a scientific foundation that the belief in miraculous cures, though not destroyed, was permanently shaken.

Hippocrates believed, above all, in the importance of clinical study—patient observation at the bedside. He thought that the body was made of the four elements of Empedocles; earth, air, fire and water. With these were associated the four humours; black bile, yellow bile, blood and phlegm. These humours should exist in the body in certain proportions, and each in its proper place. Disease consisted in their disproportion, displacement or impurity. The body had a natural tendency to cure itself, by getting rid of superfluous, misplaced or impure humours. Disease became serious only when such humours could not be discharged rapidly enough. The physician, Hippocrates argued, could not prevent the original misbehaviour of the humours. His business was to watch the course of the disease, notice how nature was trying to rid itself of the unwanted humours, and then do his utmost to assist nature by the appropriate drug or treatment. An essential element of success was correct timing of his action. He had to identify, from his patient's symptoms, the moment of crisis[1] at which his help would be most effective. He had to know when nature was about to make her effort, so that he might be ready to reinforce it. Hence the virtue of clinical study. Acute observation of the case in hand, together with experience of previous cases, was the only reliable foundation for the necessary prognosis—the foreknowledge and recognition of the decisive moment.

Hippocrates paid some attention to preventive medicine, prescribing a proper diet and exercise as means of avoiding disease.

---

[1] The original meaning of 'crisis' is 'separation'. The crisis was, for Hippocrates, the moment when the separation of the troublesome humours from the body should take place.

His practice, which exhibited the touch of the artist in science, was strikingly modern in spirit. It depended uncompromisingly on observation. It ruled out both superstition and the common Greek tendency to base action on fanciful general principles. It had the flexibility and susceptibility to changing circumstance which characterise truly scientific procedure. It was, indeed, the most thoroughly scientific thing of its time. It may be contrasted with the practice at Cnidus. The procedure there was first to attempt a diagnosis; then to carry through, without subsequent modification, a prescribed treatment. Hippocrates maintained that the initial nature of the disease did not much matter. The important thing was to watch developments, and adjust one's action accordingly.

It was in subtlety of method that Hippocrates excelled. His theory of the humours was crude and unimportant. It could hardly be otherwise, since he lacked the necessary knowledge. The sciences upon which medical theory is mainly founded are anatomy, the study of bodily structure, and physiology, which considers the *functions* of bodily organs. Hippocrates' knowledge of physiology was superficial and inaccurate. In anatomy, he had some knowledge of the bones, but little else. He probably dissected animals, but not human bodies. Many writings were attributed to him; some spuriously.

Much of Aristotle's best work was in natural history. This was the one activity in which he made real use of observation. After leaving the Academy, and before becoming Alexander's tutor, he spent some time in Asia Minor studying and dissecting animals and plants. He also studied embryology and heredity. He later wrote on several aspects of zoology and botany. His knowledge is remarkably accurate when founded on his personal observations. But he used some less reliable observations, brought back from the East by scientific followers of Alexander. Aristotle founded comparative anatomy, and began the systematic classification of living things according to their structure. His classification was current till the 16th century. It was the starting point from which the modern system was developed by John Ray and Linnaeus. He contrasted blood-holding with bloodless animals, these classes corresponding to the modern vertebrates and invertebrates. The blood-holding animals were divided into four subclasses:

mammals, birds, reptiles, fishes. There were four subclasses also of the bloodless animals: soft-bodied animals, soft-shelled animals, shell-bearing animals, insects. From his classification of animals Aristotle derived the notion of a 'Ladder of Nature'. The more complex a creature's structure, the higher its place on the ladder. We still speak of higher and lower animals. But Aristotle did not suggest an evolutionary interpretation of his ladder.

It is surprising that observation, to which the Greeks paid little heed in their early astronomy and physics, should have figured so prominently in their biology and medicine. The explanation almost certainly lies in the complexity of living things. This exempted them from mathematical treatment, and tended to make them the province of non-mathematicians. Hippocrates and Aristotle, the two Greeks of this period most interested in the life-sciences, had little to do with mathematics. In this they were unusual among Greek philosophers. Mathematics, as we have seen, turned men's thoughts away from experiment and observation, towards the view that knowledge could be deduced from axiomatic principles. The absence of this mathematical influence was no doubt responsible for the early development of biology and medicine on the right lines. In astronomy and physics, where he inherited a tradition from his mathematically-minded predecessors, Aristotle was as unscientific as anyone. But he approached biology as a pioneer, without prejudice.

It is worth while to consider the reason, given above, for the irrelevance of mathematics at this time in biology and medicine. Mathematics owes both its difficulty and its scientific limitations to its artificial simplicity. It is difficult precisely because it is simple enough to be *completely* understood. It is elaborated by each generation of thinkers; and it represents, at any given stage, just that degree of complexity which the best minds of the day can reach and comprehend. Because it is a human creation, it remains always within the powers of human understanding, but extends always to the limit of those powers. The universe is probably too complex ever to be entirely understood by men. Even small parts of it are more complex than any structure so far created by them. But, as mathematics grows, it becomes applicable to increasingly complex natural phenomena. It has been applied to astronomy, physics and chemistry in turn. Its sphere of influence grows with its subtlety. It is now in the early stages of its application to biology. But its complexity must remain finite, because of its human origin; and its scientific value, though spreading, must always be limited. The Greeks were inclined to suppose that it was Nature's duty to conform to the simplicity of their elementary mathematics. They could not wait for mathematics to grow until its complexity bore some relation to that of the simpler natural phenomena.

The limited complexity of mathematics has another aspect. When the relationship of mathematics to the fine arts is discussed, the conversation is apt to wander blithely to the arithmetic of musical intervals, or the persistence of Golden Section[1] in Italian architecture and painting. But these are trivial matters. There is an altogether deeper affinity. Mathematics and the fine arts can (in at least one respect) satisfy the same need. There is pleasure in the contemplation of what is complex; provided it is not too complex to be *fully* understood. This pleasure is greatest when the complexity is within, but only just within, the power of thorough comprehension. There is much in daily experience which we cannot hope to understand fully, and much else that we can understand too easily to be interested by it. That degree of complexity which gives the most pleasure does not appear of its own accord. One function of the fine arts is to create it. Mathematics is peculiarly suited to this purpose. It proceeds by constructing complex relations out of simpler ones. A man who takes the trouble to pursue it far enough can always reach, or create for himself, the degree of complexity which just satisfies him. Music attains the right complexity in a similar way, synthetically, by combining relatively simple structures. The painter usually attains it analytically. He begins with a subject which is too complex to be fully comprehended, and reduces its complexity, by selection, until it is just within the limits of complete understanding. Bach's *Musical Offering* and the Greek theory of proportion, which are aesthetically satisfying, have complex but completely understandable structures. The structure of a random noise is too complex. That of 'Baa, Baa, Black Sheep' is too simple.

* * *

[1] *Euc.* II, 11. This mode of division gives aesthetically satisfying proportions. Artists tend to use it unconsciously. In Renaissance art its use was often deliberate. It is closely approached by Nature in certain botanical forms.

ATHENIAN PHILOSOPHY affected science in various ways. Athens became the clearing-house for the exchange of ideas. Astronomical and physical speculations, as well as ethical systems, from all parts of the Greek world came together there. A class of philosophers arose whose business was not the creation of new systems, but the comparison and criticism of existing systems. These sophists assumed a function not unlike that of modern literary critics. They undertook to guide public opinion in the understanding and assessment of the many doctrines presented to it. They acted also as the tutors of wealthy young men.

When the different speculative systems were reviewed together, the disagreement became obvious. Not more than one of them could be right; and it seemed likely they were all wrong. Even if one of them *was* right, what criterion was there for knowing which? These difficulties naturally induced a sceptical outlook in the sophists. Their teaching was pragmatic. They put usefulness before truth, as the standard by which knowledge and accomplishment should be judged. The aim of education was not enlightenment, but success in litigation, politics or business. Hence rhetoric, the literary and logical art of persuasion, became the main subject in their curriculum. They advocated outward conformity with traditional religion and morals as a social asset.

The effect of such opinions on moral standards, on disinterested learning, and on religious faith, was unfortunate. The term 'sophist' became one of abuse. But the impartial critic may find much good in sophism. The practice of rhetoric helped to improve the Greek language. This may seem a small thing; but it will not be underrated by anyone who understands the dependence of thought upon the adequacy of language. The scepticism of the more reputable sophists was a genuine expression of intellectual honesty. Such scepticism must arise wherever there is toleration of widely divergent opinions. The religious toleration of Rome, for instance, where many religions put forward conflicting claims at once, led to much religious scepticism there. The sophists were presented with a wide variety of speculative views, and had no means of deciding between them. They can hardly be blamed, and may even be thought wise, for withholding judgment. Scepticism has the great merit of making men examine the frequently insufficient foundations of their opinions. By destroying much that is worthless, it may open the way to a fresh start on better lines. It has certainly done science no harm. Robert Bridges says of the sceptic:

> Like some medicinal root in pharmacy, whose juice
> is wholesom for purgation,—so is he.

The Opposition is concisely represented by Sydney Smith:

> An open mind is like an open sewer.

What inference should have been drawn from the justifiable scepticism of the sophists? Surely this: that the speculative method in science was futile, and that some new method should be tried. Socrates, the implacable opponent of the sophists, did not take this line. He despised them for their worldliness. He, also, taught young men; but not in the same way, and not for money. Much of his time with his pupils was spent in exposing the worthlessness of sophistic teaching and the incompetence of people in high places. The unpopularity he thus earned was the main reason for his condemnation, though it was not among the charges on which he was tried. He shared the scepticism of the sophists with regard to science, but he did not therefore seek a new scientific method. Instead he decided that science was a waste of time. He retained the speculative method, but applied it to a new purpose. He believed that its failure in science was a matter of no importance; but that it could be successful if put to its proper use—the study of moral and aesthetic questions. Such questions, he believed, were the only ones that really mattered to men.

We need not decide the relative merits of ethics and natural science as subjects of human study. There seems no good reason why either should take pride of place, or why students of one should look down upon those of the other. Nor need we consider the teaching of Socrates in detail. As a moralist he no doubt deserves high praise. But his influence was anti-scientific. He belittled science, and widened the gap between philosophy and science, which is only now being closed again. He gave a new lease of life to the speculative method, which might have been more quickly superseded in science if he had not so heightened its prestige in moral philosophy.

Plato had more influence, and did more damage to science, than

Socrates. He agreed with Socrates in thinking moral philosophy more important than natural science, but not in thinking mathematics and science altogether trivial. He knew something of mathematics and astronomy. By praising them for their educational value, he did at least grant them a certain respectability. We have seen that they were expected to pay for this respectability by conforming to a rigid code which restricted their natural growth. But it was Plato's Theory of Ideas which did most harm to science.

The word 'fish' connotes many similar objects, of which no two are quite alike. Such a word is called a universal. Why is it possible to apply the one word to a number of different objects? Plato would have answered that it is because the everyday fishes we perceive with our senses share in the quality of fishiness. This quality exists independently of any individual fish. In fact, fishiness must necessarily exist before there can *be* any fishes. An individual fish is no more than a poor imitation or shadow of this pre-existent quality of fishiness. A quality such as this, from which a universal derives its meaning, is called by Plato an Idea. The Idea is perfect, permanent and unchanging. Plato says it has the property of 'being'. The individual fish is an imperfect imitation of the Idea; it has the property of 'becoming'—by which he means that it strives with only partial success for the permanence and perfection of the Idea to which it owes its existence.

This was a development of the teaching of Parmenides. It led to the belief that the senses could not yield knowledge. Knowledge consisted in acquaintance with the Ideas, which alone had reality. This acquaintance could be had only by the exercise of mind. The senses could reveal only the misshapen and misleading image of reality. One cannot imagine a theory more opposed to observation and experiment, or more obstructive to science. This theory was propagated by perhaps the most influential of all thinkers. Plato's own words show the uncompromising force with which it was put forward. I quote from Lord Lindsay's translation of the *Republic* (Book VII). Astronomy is being discussed. The words are put into the mouth of Socrates; but the views are Plato's:

> If anyone attempts to learn anything which is perceivable—his open mouth may yawn upwards or his closed mouth purse downwards, it makes no difference. He, I declare, will never learn. For such things do not admit of knowledge.

Astronomy, then, like geometry, we shall pursue by the help of problems, and leave the starry heavens alone; if we hope truly to apprehend it, and turn the natural intelligence of the soul from uselessness to use.

Notice, in view of what we have already said about the insidious influence of misunderstood mathematics, the significance of the words 'like geometry'. Notice also, that we are not to make even a subsidiary use of observation. We are ordered simply to 'leave the starry heavens alone', if we want to know anything about them; and, instead of looking at the sky, to use 'the natural intelligence of the soul'.

Aristotle's philosophy was less harmful to science. His treatment of universals was directly opposed to that of Plato. He would have said that the notion of fishiness is derived from the comparison of observations, which reveal a set of objects having many common properties—properties they do not share with other things. Universals are merely labels for the classes into which observed likenesses cause us to collect natural objects. They are the result of abstraction. They represent what is supposed to be common to, and drawn from, many special cases. When we say, 'this is a fish', the word 'fish' does not imply an independently existing Idea, to which 'this' bears a crude resemblance. It is simply a linguistic device for condensing much detailed information.

Aristotle naturally formed this view as a result of his truly scientific work in biology. It is just the view which a modern scientist would take of universals. It is analogous to the more general notion of the inductive method in science, also understood by Aristotle. This consists in making many observations of the same kind, and then formulating a probable general law from the results. It asks what premises will yield certain established conclusions; whereas the deductive method asks what conclusions can be inferred from certain established premises. It is illustrated by the Babylonian discovery of the Saros or the astronomical theory of Eudoxus.

Aristotle did not live up to these correct principles, except in biology. The inductive method is sound but slow. Years of patient work may be necessary before any valuable general result emerges. Even then, the result will be applicable only to a limited range of phenomena; it will be only an approximation to the truth; it will be liable to modification. Aristotle had his share of the impatience and ambition which were usual in Greek philosophers. He was not content with the little solid progress that could be made in a lifetime by honest toil. It was the fashion, then, to produce an all-embracing scheme. As there was no hope of doing this by sound methods, Aristotle speculated. This was unfortunate for science. But we must be fair to him; he did point out a new and better approach to scientific problems, and in one department at least he practised it. He must not be unduly blamed for the extent of his harmful influence, since this was mainly due to the bigotry of some who later adopted his system. It is unlikely that he would himself have clung to speculative opinions, as some of his successors did, even against the overwhelming contrary evidence of the senses.

We must not overlook Aristotle's logic. Just as in biology he classified animals according to their structures, so in logic he attempted to classify arguments according to their structures. He saw that the structure of an argument can be divorced from its subject matter. An argument is valid provided the conclusion really follows from the premises. Its validity depends only on its structure. Consider the argument: '*Some men are not liars. All thieves are liars. Therefore some men are not thieves.*' In deciding whether this argument is valid, we need take no notice of the fact that it deals with men and thieves and liars. It has the same structure as the argument: '*Some drinks are not intoxicants. All spirits are intoxicants. Therefore some drinks are not spirits.*' We can assess it by studying the empty form of which it is a special case: '*Some A's are not B's. All C's are B's. Therefore some A's are not C's.*' Aristotle's aim was to enumerate such forms, and set up rules by which their validity could be decided.

The validity of an argument does not guarantee the truth of the conclusion. We cannot infer the truth of the conclusion unless we also know that the premises are true. Formal logic is concerned only with the validity of the argument; not with the truth of the premises. The latter has to do with the subject-matter of the argument, and has usually to be decided empirically. Formal logic has, in this respect, much in common with pure mathematics.

Aristotle did not carry logic far. There are many forms of argument which he did not consider; and some of his views were mistaken. But he took a big step in suggesting such a study of abstract forms. For 2000 years logic remained much as Aristotle left it. This was just as well for science; because, had logic grown like mathematics, it might have had the ill effects of mathematics without the redeeming usefulness. During the last hundred years it has grown enormously and given rise to important developments in mathematics and philosophy.

The derivation of one abstract form from many particular arguments again illustrates Aristotle's inductive method. Plato would have regarded the particular arguments as slightly disreputable descendants of an eternal form. The same contrast occurs in political science. Plato created his imaginary Republic by reasoning from general principles. Aristotle formed his views by analysing the political systems of actual states.

The Athenians were defeated by Philip of Macedon at Chaeroneia in 338 B.C. The terms granted them were generous in every way save one. Athens suffered little material loss; but she had to accept Philip as the leader of united Greece. This was humiliating for the city which had done so much for Greek unity and had become so accustomed to leadership. Material loss came later—with the drain on Athenian resources caused by Alexander's Eastern adventures. The mood of Athens changed. The carefree spirit of intellectual enterprise gave way to heart-searching and a sense of failure. Science, already losing its vigour in the face of increasingly antagonistic philosophy, now seemed unimportant. Men turned away from those thinkers who offered knowledge. They looked instead to those who offered comfort, and a way of life, in times of difficulty and disillusionment. It became the business of philosophers to show how unavoidable evil might be calmly suffered. Even now we refer to this aspect of philosophy, when we speak of bearing trouble 'philosophically'.

Zeno of Citium, founder of Stoicism, preached salvation by an adjustment of the will. The way to happiness in adversity was not to strive after a state one wished for, but to make oneself wish for the state one happened to be in. Zeno was Phoenician; there was an oriental passiveness in his philosophy. Epicurus, his chief rival, recommended the rational pursuit of pleasure. He believed there was no life after death. One should therefore make the most of this life. 'Eat, drink and be merry, for tomorrow we die' is not a fair description of his teaching. He recommended refined pleasures, such as friendship. And, if the pursuit of pleasure is rational, it must be conducted with moderation. The man who overeats will have a stomach-ache to spoil his enjoyment. At its best, among those, like Epicurus himself, who found pleasure in kindness and pleasant human relations, the Epicurean philosophy was not the base thing it is sometimes supposed to be.

Epicureanism and Stoicism survived for centuries as practical philosophies. Stoicism inspired many of the finest characters of antiquity. It did much to prepare the way for Christianity. But, in science, Zeno and Epicurus are chiefly interesting as outstanding examples of men who shaped their opinions, without regard for truth, according to the needs of their ethical systems. Epicurus adopted atomism; not for its scientific merit, but because its materialism supported his denial of a spiritual life after death. The Roman poet Lucretius was an eminent follower of Epicurus. He did much, by his poem *De Rerum Natura*, to make atomism known.

The Stoic theory of the universe reverted to the old Ionian notion of a single element. This element was rather like the fire of Heraclitus; but it was a rational living thing, identified with God. Part of this primitive fire had been condensed into the ordinary fire, earth, air and water of which common things were made. Thus the universe was made, not only *by* God, but *of* God.[1] Part of the divine fire retained its original quality, and was the spirit which governed the universe. The human soul was a speck of the divine fire. From time to time there were conflagrations, in which everything became again the primitive fire from which it was originally made. After each conflagration the process of condensation began again; so that the material universe was repeatedly destroyed and re-created. The material universe was rationally ordered for the best, during its periods of existence, by its ruling spirit. Thus, in adjusting himself to whatever was, a man was identifying his will with that of God, and was therefore doing right. He was striving, during life, for the reunion with God which would in any case take place at the next conflagration. Such beliefs may have helped men to follow the Stoic rule of life. But we must look elsewhere for serious science.

*   *   *

---

1 Such identification of the universe with God is called pantheism.

ATHENIAN PHILOSOPHY permanently affected thought. In trying
to sum up its effect on science, we must again stress the conflict of
opinion that arose from the difference between Plato and Aristotle
concerning universals. This was not just a disagreement about how
words acquire their meanings: it was the clash of two fundamentally different intellectual approaches to the world, which are even
now not altogether reconciled.

Whoever made the famous remark 'Pigs is *rightly* so called!' was
consciously or unconsciously a Platonist. He believed in the independent pre-existence of an Idea denoted by the word 'pig'. He
was convinced that this Idea had an immutable, eternal being; and
that it was in the mind of man, ready to be applied whenever his
senses should reveal an appropriate object. The appearance of
certain dirty, grunting animals agreed closely with this pre-
established Idea. They might not attain the full perfection of the
Ideal Pig; but the resemblance was near enough. They were at
once recognised as passable imitations of the Idea. A satisfying *use*
had been found for the word whose meaning was, independently
and intellectually, already known.

The Aristotelian view is that the word acquires a meaning only
after observation has shown the need for it. We notice natural
objects whose likenesses are more striking than their differences.
We thus form the notion of a class, or species, in which we group
them together. It is convenient to have a name for the species,
which we should otherwise have to describe by tedious enumera-
tion of the common qualities observed in its members. We introduce the word 'pig' for this purpose.

Belief in the Platonic theory is likely to produce the *a priori*
thinker, who tries to fit Nature to a preconceived intellectual
scheme. Belief in the Aristotelian theory will produce the empiricist, who constructs his intellectual scheme to fit what is observed
in Nature. We take it for granted nowadays that the natural
scientist will be an empiricist. But the final triumph of empiricism
over apriority, in scientific method, was neither quick nor easy.

3

THE ALEXANDRIANS

Two YEARS after Chaeroneia, Alexander became ruler of all Greece. Within a few years he conquered the whole Persian Empire, including Egypt and part of India. While in Egypt he founded Alexandria, which he populated with Greeks, Egyptians and Jews. It was to be his new capital, the finest city in the world. He chose the site, and left a Greek architect in charge of the work. He did not live to see it finished. He died in Babylon, on his way back from the East, in 323 B.C. After his death his empire was divided among three of his generals. Ptolemy Soter, who settled in Alexandria as ruler of Egypt, is the only one with whom we are concerned.

Alexander's short career had a profound effect on Greek intellectual life. It put an end to most of what was left of Athenian prosperity and hegemony. Many of the able men, who might otherwise have remained in Greece to preserve the Athenian tradition, saw more outlet for their ambitions under Alexander. They travelled and fought with him, or were scattered abroad in the garrisons he left in conquered cities. Alexandria, splendidly placed for communication with East and West, had strategic and commercial advantages. It gathered trade at the expense of the Athenians. These material misfortunes, loss of man-power and loss of trade, following the humiliation inflicted by Philip, turned Athenian thought away from the disinterested pursuit of knowledge. Philosophy became a drug, whose purpose was to enable men to suffer adversity. Science almost ceased for a time; but in the long run it indirectly gained far more than it directly lost. For Alexander's campaigns brought Ptolemy Soter to power in Egypt. He founded the dynasty which ruled Egypt until it became part of the Roman Empire. The last of his line was Cleopatra, whose interests were not exclusively cultural. But the earlier Ptolemies did much for learning, and particularly science.

Alexander was little interested in philosophy or science. But he had some respect for the Greek culture which he could not fully understand. He also had a sense of his responsibility, as political leader of Greece, for supporting and extending Hellenic civilisation. This appears, for instance, in his willingness to take on his campaigns a number of scientific men, of no military use, to collect information for Aristotle. The efforts of his distinguished educators were therefore not entirely wasted on him. Nor was he the only man to be influenced by Aristotle and Menaechmus at the Macedonian court. Ptolemy, in particular, derived lasting literary and scientific interests from them.

After establishing himself firmly, Ptolemy set about making Alexandria the new centre of Greek learning. He began collecting a vast library, which was extended by his son, Ptolemy Philadelphus, and which became one of the wonders of antiquity. Large sums were spent on the library. Buyers of books were sent abroad, and many copyists employed. It became the central feature of the Museum, or Temple of the Muses. This was not a museum in the modern sense; it was the World's first university. It had lecture-rooms, astronomical instruments, dissecting rooms, botanical and zoological gardens. There were four departments; those of literature, mathematics, astronomy, and medicine. The last, as was then usual, included natural history. Appointments to the staff were at the royal disposal. These appointments offered every facility for teaching and research, as well as a luxurious life, to those who held them. The Ptolemies themselves attended the liberal banquets which had already become a feature of academic life, and at which the conversation must have acquainted men of different faculties with one another's doings. The ablest men of the day were attracted to the Museum. These were the Greek thinkers and men of letters who, in other circumstances, might have met in Athens. For centuries, all the most distinguished men of science were connected with the Museum, as students, teachers or correspondents. We may call such men Alexandrians, just as we call members of a more modern society Oxonians. But, although the atmosphere of the Museum was predominantly Greek, its presence in a city of mixed population gave it contact with non-Hellenic cultures—particularly the Hebrew. And there was one appointment which, at first, was wisely not given to a Greek. The titular head of the

Museum, in its early days, was a representative of the ancient Egyptian hierarchy; in order that long-standing religious feelings might not be hurt by the intrusion of Greek scientific scepticism. For 200 years after the foundation of the Museum—from about 300 to about 100 B.C.—Greek science flourished with astonishing brilliance and vigour. This period produced three astronomers and three mathematicians of the highest class. One of the mathematicians, indeed, has scarcely had an equal. There was no comparable work in astronomy or mathematics until the 16th and 17th centuries. The progress of biology and medicine, though less marked, was considerable.

Before studying the work of these two centuries, we must notice the intellectual atmosphere in which it took place. It is evident that men of genius, finding the amenities of the Museum at their disposal, could hardly fail to do something worth while. And it is a fact that a number of men of great genius appeared during the first 200 years of the Museum. But why was it that so many of them used their ability, at just this time, in one particular way? Why was it that men whose talents might have been used with equal distinction in philosophy or letters should have turned to astronomy and mathematics with such unanimity?

We must look back for a moment to the Athenian sophists. Their comparison of one physical system with another had drawn attention to the failure of the speculative method in science. The pursuit of science by some other method was the obvious corollary; but the great influence of Socrates and Plato was opposed to this. They preserved the speculative method at the expense of science. In biology, politics and logic, Aristotle had evolved a new method. He attacked specific problems by observation, comparison and classification. He obtained reliable knowledge, within limited fields, by a systematic procedure. But in astronomy and physics, which were not his main interests, he followed the conventional line. It was still supposed in Athens that these subjects should be studied exclusively 'by the natural intelligence of the soul'; and they did not thrive.

The founders of the Museum were inspired by Aristotle. He was read and admired there. His new methods became widely known in a place where there was no philosophic disapproval of their application to the older sciences. It is significant that there was no

Department of Philosophy in the Museum. Science was uprooted by Alexander's wars. It was replanted where there was no Platonic code commanding men to 'leave the starry heavens alone', or forbidding them to study conic sections. Astronomy then dealt with the simplest of natural phenomena. It therefore offered the best chances of scientific success. It immediately became, when released from the bondage of philosophy, an attractive field of research for the best minds of the age. A race of astronomers arose who no longer wasted time constructing imaginary universes. They carefully examined portions of the sky, as Aristotle had examined plants and beasts. They set out to solve clearly formulated problems by systematic programmes of observation. They used their imagination to create *methods*—not, as their speculative predecessors did, to invent 'facts'. Determination to examine the universe in detail superseded the arrogant belief that one man, by shutting his eyes and using his small mind, could produce a full account of it.

Mathematics was bound to flourish beside astronomy. Those who created the mathematics that astronomy required, were not content to do only this. They did more because it delighted them. But they had the sense to keep mathematics in its place. They knew that it could not by itself produce physical knowledge. But they understood its value as a means of tracing the subtler implications of what had been empirically discovered: they saw that it could help to extend the results of observation. In carrying it further than was necessary for this purpose, they may have guessed that their work would be scientifically useful in the future. It is more likely they pursued it as one of the fine arts that make life worth living. This more moderate view of the scope of mathematics was typical of the balanced outlook which prevailed in the Museum. It went with the realisation that the problems of science were immense, and could yield only to the patient work of generations. The great Alexandrians attained a sense of proportion which their forerunners lacked, and which their successors often forgot.

The good result which was to be expected of sophistic scepticism—namely, an altogether new approach to science—was prevented by the conservatism of philosophers in Athens. It appeared in Alexandria; where those Athenian influences which favoured it were predominant, and those which opposed it were unrepresented.

6

It is important that Alexander was born just when he was. A few years earlier, and he might have had Plato as his master; a few years later, Epicurus or Zeno. In either case the Museum would have had a very different spirit. The influence of Aristotle at this crucial point in scientific history was overwhelmingly good. It only later became harmful.

Many writings of the Alexandrians have survived, in the original Greek or in Arabic and Latin translations. Much is known, through the later Alexandrian commentators, about writings which have been lost. There is, however, little biographical information. The lives and characters of the great men are less known than their discoveries. Much of their work is too technical to be discussed in detail here. We shall refer only to those results, and discuss only those ideas, by which they most influenced later thought.

*   *   *

EUCLID WAS the first head of the mathematical department in the Museum. He lived from 330 to 275 B.C., and was at Alexandria from about the year 300. Little is known of his life or character. He is thought to have had Phoenician blood. He was educated at Athens, possibly in the Academy. He was one of the very great men of his time, and was particularly suited to the position he held. Although not the most original of the Greek mathematicians, he was an inspiring teacher with a thorough knowledge of the mathematics of his day. Through him, all that was best in the mathematics of the past was made available in Alexandria. He did a great deal to lay the firm foundation upon which so much was built.

His most important work, the *Elements*, was one of the most influential books ever written. It gave a systematic account of all the Greek geometry of circle and straight line, and of the theory of numbers as then known. It dealt also with the three-dimensional geometry of the plane, sphere and regular solids. The subject-matter was mostly due to such earlier mathematicians as Pythagoras, Eudoxus and Hippocrates of Chios. Euclid's own contribution appeared mainly in his genius for organisation and logical arrangement. He fitted the theorems together, filling gaps and re-casting proofs where necessary, into one great deductive system. He greatly reduced the number of unproved propositions upon which the rest depended. He set a new standard of rigour, and sometimes also of elegance, in demonstration. He created an expository style which was not despised by Newton 2000 years later. In respect of *method*, therefore, he made a valuable contribution to the progress of mathematics, even though the material he handled was not all his own. This was not the only merit of the book. It was a work of reference containing most of the important conclusions so far reached by mathematics. As such, it was of great use in a university where research and discovery were vigorously conducted. It was used as a textbook in schools and universities until the end of the last century, though it is really too difficult for beginners.

Modern criticism has revealed defects in the *Elements*. There are assumptions which are not explicitly stated. Much of the subject-matter has lost the significance it had when the book was written. Much that is now important is not included in it. It presents conclusions, with deductive proofs, but without a hint of the analysis by which the results and proofs were discovered. But, in fairness to Euclid, it should be said that he probably intended his pupils to use it only as a supplement to his lectures; and he did in fact write another book in which methods of analysis were discussed. He was influenced by Plato, but not overawed by him. He certainly accepted Plato's view that Mathematics was worth while for its own sake. But there is no record of his despising its application. In the *Elements* he followed Plato in disallowing instruments other than the straight-edge and compasses. It is likely that he did this with the artist's instinct for economy of means. He wrote a separate book on conic sections which shows that, unlike Plato, he would not hold mathematics back because of a prejudice against 'mechanical' curves.

It is an astonishing feat to have written a book which played an active part in the development of mathematics for 2000 years, and which will never lose its appeal, as a classic, to those who enjoy the subject. Many celebrated mathematicians have owed their first interest to the *Elements*. Time and again, in reading the history of mathematics, one finds some such remark as: 'He came across a copy of *Euclid*, and was at once attracted by the incisiveness and clarity of the proofs.'

There is much of logical interest in the *Elements*. One of Euclid's favourite methods is the *reductio ad absurdum*: '*If A is false, then B is true. But B is false; therefore A is true.*' It may occur with ornamentation, as in the proof of *Euc.* I, 19, of which the structure is: '*A, B and C are not all false. But B implies X, which is false; and C implies Y, which is false; therefore A is true*'.[1] Another version is: '*If A is false, then B and C must both be true: but B and C are incompatible; therefore A is true.*' The calibre of the man may be judged from his use of this weapon to attack an apparently difficult problem in arithmetic. His solution is well known, but it may bear repetition here. It is one of the few pieces of first-rate mathematics that can be appreciated without technical knowledge.

A number which has any factor (other than itself or unity) is called composite. A number which is not composite is called prime. Every composite number is the product of a set of primes. Thus $165 = 3 \times 5 \times 11$ and $343 = 7 \times 7 \times 7$. Every composite number is therefore divisible by at least one prime. If we follow the number-series, picking out the primes, we find that they occur less frequently as we proceed. If we have the patience to go far, we shall encounter long stretches of the series without any prime at all. Shall we ever reach a point beyond which there are no more primes; or is the number of primes infinite? This question can obviously not be settled by trial. But Euclid proved elegantly that the number of primes is infinite.

Suppose it is *not* infinite; and that the greatest prime is N. Now consider the number, K, which is greater by 1 than the product of all the primes; so that $K = (2 \times 3 \times 5 \times 7 \times 11 \times \ldots \times N) + 1$. Let us now try to divide K by any prime number, p. It is evident that p will divide exactly into the number within the brackets, since p (being prime) is one of the factors of this number. Hence when p is divided into K, there must be 1 over. Hence K is prime, since it is not divisible by any prime. But K is greater than N. Hence K is composite, since N is the greatest prime. And so our supposition, that the number of primes is finite, leads to the incompatible conclusions 'K is prime' and 'K is composite'. Hence the supposition is false; and the number of primes is infinite.

This exhibits the qualities of the great artist: the certainty and delicacy of touch; the perfect sense of fitness in the choice of method; the strange power to find more in the material than would

---

[1] It should be remembered that the words 'true' and 'false' are here to be interpreted as 'agreeing with the axioms' and 'contradictory to the axioms'.

seem possible. It reveals one facet of an admirable mind to anyone
who has the sensibility to understand it. It has absolutely no other
use whatever.

Euclid wrote books on astronomy and music; but nothing is
known of their contents. He also wrote on optics, though his work
in this was not outstanding. He was unfortunate in his theory,
which supposed that light was a kind of tentacle put out by the eye
to grasp the thing seen. He knew the Laws of Reflection. Let light
be reflected at the point A of a plane or curved surface (Fig. 8). Let
AN be the perpendicular to the
surface at A. Let PA and AQ be
the incident and reflected rays.
Then:

    (i) PA, AN and AQ are all
in one plane.

    (ii) PA and AQ make equal
angles with AN.

Euclid's main concern in optics
was to examine the consequences

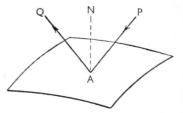

Fig. 8

of these laws—i.e. to predict the behaviour of rays of light reflected
from body to body. Once the laws are established, this becomes a
purely geometrical problem, devoid of physical interest.

*   *   *

ARISTARCHUS OF Samos, born about 310 B.C., was an Alexandrian only in the broadest sense. He was certainly the first important astronomer of the Alexandrian period, and his discoveries
soon became known in Alexandria. He began the epoch of astronomical progress with which we are now concerned. He was
educated by a disciple of Aristotle, and had the same free spirit as
the other great astronomers of the Alexandrian school. Their work
was a direct continuation of his, and cannot be discussed apart
from it. But he was never resident in Alexandria, and there is no
record of his ever visiting it. He may be thought the greatest astronomer of antiquity. His cosmological views were certainly more
advanced than those of any other ancient astronomer; and they
rested upon daringly imaginative observation, not upon aesthetic
or moral prejudice.

We have seen that the Alexandrians had a sense of proportion in matters intellectual. They did not allow mathematics and speculative philosophy to exert undue influence outside their proper spheres. They understood the nature and magnitude of the scientist's task. Aristarchus drew their attention to proportions of another kind—the geometrical proportions of the universe. A glimpse of these proportions was no doubt partly responsible for the growth of their more balanced outlook in other matters.

Aristarchus explained his work in a book on the sizes and distances of the sun and moon. He began by accepting the explanation of the moon's phases offered by Anaxagoras. E, M and S (Fig. 9) represent the centres of earth, moon and sun. When the moon's

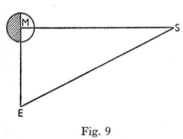

Fig. 9

disc appears exactly half illuminated, the angle EMS is a right-angle. Aristarchus saw, therefore, that he had only to measure the angle MES, at the instant of half-moon, in order to find the shape of the triangle MES. He estimated the angle MES at 29/30 of a right-angle, which is 87°. He knew no trigonometry; but, by an ingenious geometrical argument, he calculated that ES was between 18 and 20 times EM. Although his method was correct, his numerical result was much in error. The angle MES is in fact about 89° 51'. The comparatively small error of 2° 51' in his measurement makes a big difference to the ratio ES:EM, which is really about 400:1. His inaccuracy is easily explained. He had no instrument of precision with which to measure the angle; and he could not judge the instant of half-moon with certainty. But his result was qualitatively, if not quantitatively, very valuable. It showed that the sun was much more distant than the moon. It also showed that the sun was much larger than the moon; since, despite their different distances, they look about the same size. According to Aristarchus, the sun's diameter was about 20 times the moon's. In fact it is about 400 times.

Aristarchus next compared the sizes of the earth and moon. He made use of lunar eclipses to do this. Fig. 10 shows how the earth obstructs the sun's light. All the light is cut off in region I, part of it in regions II, III and IV, and none in regions V and VI. The

central cone of complete shadow, I, is called the umbra; the regions
II, III and IV are those of penumbra. The moon becomes noticeably eclipsed only when it enters the umbra. Because of the sun's

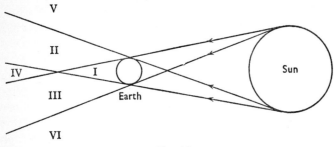

Fig. 10

great distance, the rays from different parts of it are nearly parallel.
Thus the umbra tapers very slowly; and the shadow cast by the
earth on the moon, during an eclipse, has a diameter nearly equal
to that of the earth. By comparing the apparent radius of the moon's
disc with that of the earth's shadow, Aristarchus estimated the
moon's diameter as about half that of the earth. The correct figure
is about a quarter. His method was again correct; but he had not
the technique for using it precisely. He learnt, however, that the
moon, though smaller than the earth, was much larger than his
predecessors had supposed. He learnt also that the sun was much
larger than the earth.

Anaxagoras was thought to exaggerate when he suggested that
the sun was as large as the Peloponnese. This last discovery of
Aristarchus was therefore especially significant. It suggested, for
the first time, the astronomical unimportance of the earth. The
idea that the earth might move round a fixed sun, rather than the
sun round a fixed earth, would naturally occur to a man who had
some notion of their relative sizes. And, according to Archimedes,
Aristarchus did in fact suggest that the sun was at rest in relation to
the fixed stars, while the earth moved round it in a circle. Such a
view was likely to meet opposition from the anthropocentric prejudice of ordinary men. But the serious scientific objection to it was
that, if the earth moved, then the fixed stars should appear to
change position in relation to one another, like fixed objects seen

from a moving ship. When the objects are very far from the ship, however, so that the movements of the ship are negligible compared with the distances of the objects, these changes of relative position become imperceptible. The valid answer to the objection is, therefore, that the distances of the fixed stars must be so great that the diameter of the earth's orbit is insignificant by comparison. This, again according to Archimedes, Aristarchus also suggested. If he really did so, his insight was astonishing and admirable, considering the meagreness of the resources at his disposal. The Pythagoreans forestalled him with the notion that the earth moved. But with them it was a fortunate guess, while with him it was a sober scientific judgment.

Aristarchus, then, did much to reveal the *proportions* of that part of the universe which is the earth's immediate neighbourhood. But he made no absolute measurements. The next step was to obtain one of the absolute magnitudes. From this several others could be deduced. If, for instance, the size of the earth could be estimated, it would at once be easy to calculate the actual sizes of the sun and moon, and their actual distances from the earth. This step was taken by Eratosthenes (275 to 194 B.C.). He was born at Cyrene, and educated in Alexandria and Athens. He had athletic and literary, as well as scientific, ability. For most of his adult life he was chief librarian at Alexandria. In old age he became blind, and committed suicide by voluntary starvation because he could no longer read.

For several reasons—e.g. the analogy with sun and moon, the evidence of lunar eclipses, and the disappearance of ships below the horizon—educated men had believed for some time that the earth was spherical. Eratosthenes determined its circumference as follows.

He supposed that Syene, some way up the Nile, was due south of Alexandria. He knew that Syene possessed a deep well, in which the sun was reflected on Midsummer Day. This meant that the sun was directly overhead at Syene at noon on that day. He therefore measured the inclination of the sun's rays to the vertical at that same instant at Alexandria, finding it to be $7\frac{1}{2}°$. This is illustrated in Fig. 11. A is Alexandria, S is Syene, O is the earth's centre, and OAN is the vertical at Alexandria. The sun's rays, PA and QS, are practically parallel. Thus the angle PAN, known to be $7\frac{1}{2}°$, is equal

to the corresponding angle SOA. Since $7\frac{1}{2}°$ is 1/48 of 360°, the arc
AS must be 1/48 of the earth's circumference. The distance AS,
being known, has only to be multiplied by 48 to give the circumference of the earth. Its diameter is then easily calculated. The

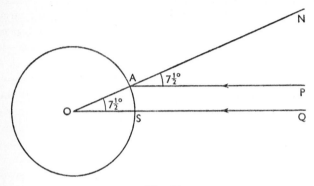

Fig. 11

greatest practical difficulty, for Eratosthenes, was the measurement of the distance AS. It is probable that he did not know this
very accurately. Syene is not in fact due south of Alexandria, and
the sun is not quite overhead at Syene on Midsummer Day. There
were therefore three sources of error. Eratosthenes was lucky. The
effect of one error was nearly cancelled by the effects of the others;
and his result was very nearly correct.

Eratosthenes made a map of the known world. Considering
the limited means of locomotion in his time, his mapping of the
Mediterranean area was remarkably good. The outlying parts
of his map were inaccurate, as he lacked data for them. He still
believed in the circumfluous ocean of Homeric myth.

He suggested the calendar, known as Julian, in which every
fourth year has an extra day. This assumes the year contains
exactly $365\frac{1}{4}$ days. It was adopted by the Romans, under Julius
Caesar, in 45 B.C. Since the year really contains rather less than
$365\frac{1}{4}$ days, this calendar led to an error of about 3 days in every
400 years. The Gregorian Calendar, introduced by Pope Gregory
XIII in 1582, but not adopted in England until 1752, set matters
right by omitting 3 leap years in every 4 centuries. Under the old
scheme, any year was a leap year if its number was divisible by 4.

Under the new scheme, years whose numbers are divisible by 100 but not by 400 are not leap years. Thus 1800 and 1900 were not leap years; but 2000 and 2400 will be. This reduces the error to about 1 day in 4000 years.

The plane in which the earth revolves annually about the sun is called the ecliptic.[1] It is so called because eclipses can take place only when the moon is in it. The earth's axis, on which it turns daily, is not perpendicular to the ecliptic. Thus the plane of the earth's equator (being perpendicular to the earth's axis) is inclined to the ecliptic. This tilt, called the obliquity of the ecliptic, is of great importance because it causes the seasons. Eratosthenes measured it. It is about $23\frac{1}{2}°$; but his estimate was slightly in excess of this.

*   *   *

WE MUST now return to the mathematicians. Two very great ones, Archimedes and Apollonius, were contemporary with Eratosthenes. Archimedes (Plate 1c) is chiefly famous for jumping out of his bath and running naked through the street, shouting 'Eureka'. This, though possibly his most diverting achievement, was not his greatest. He was the finest mathematician of antiquity, and perhaps the finest intellect of any kind prior to the Renaissance. His class is that of Shakespeare, Newton, Michelangelo and J. S. Bach. It is not easy to do him justice, because his work can be fully appreciated only by those with a fair knowledge of mathematics. To understand his amazing depth of mind, it is necessary to solve, by the methods of modern mathematics, some of the more difficult problems he solved without them. He was probably related to the royal family of Syracuse, where he was born in 287 B.C. and murdered in 212 B.C. He therefore came from the region of the last surviving Greek city states. He was educated in Alexandria, and corresponded regularly with his fellow scientists there; but he lived most of his life in Syracuse.

He made inventions and discoveries in four fields: geometry, arithmetic, physics and engineering. In geometry he dealt mainly with a problem which was very difficult in his time: the mensuration of figures enclosed by curved lines and surfaces. In this work

---

[1] Most of the ancients, of course, would have said it was the plane in which the sun revolves about the earth.

he used, with astonishing skill, the method of exhaustions invented by Eudoxus. We may consider briefly how he used it to find the circumference and area of a circle. Let us inscribe a regular hexagon, ABCDEF, in the circle (Fig. 12). By drawing tangents to the circle at A, B, C, D, E and F, we may form another regular hexagon, PQRSTU, which circum-

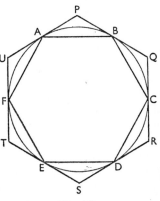

scribes the circle. The perimeters of the outer and inner hexagons are respectively greater and less than the circumference of the circle. Hence, by calculating these perimeters, we can set upper and lower limits to the circumference of the circle.

If, instead of hexagons, we use polygons of 12 sides, we shall find that the perimeter of the inner polygon is greater than before, and that of the outer polygon less. Thus the limits set to the circumference of the

Fig. 12

circle are closer than they were. If we use 24-sided polygons, we can narrow the limits still more. By using inside and outside polygons of 96 sides, Archimedes showed that the circumference of a circle is more than $3\frac{10}{71}$ and less than $3\frac{1}{7}$ times its diameter; i.e. that π is between $3\frac{10}{71}$ and $3\frac{1}{7}$.

It is worth while to notice why he chose 96 as the number of sides. Let O (Fig. 13) be the centre of a circle. Let XY be a chord, for which the angle XOY is α. We may call XY 'the chord corresponding to an angle α', or 'the chord of α'. If $\alpha = 60°$, the triangle XOY is equilateral. Hence the chord of 60° is equal to the radius of the circle. Archimedes found that, by the theorems of current Greek geometry, he could calculate the length of the chord for $\alpha/2$ if he knew that for α. He could thus

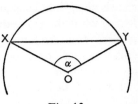

Fig. 13

calculate the chords of 30°, 15°, $7\frac{1}{2}°$, $3\frac{3}{4}°$, etc. The sides of a 96-sided polygon are chords of $3\frac{3}{4}°$, since $3\frac{3}{4} = 360 \div 96$. He could therefore find them. He could, in theory, have obtained a better approximation to π by using polygons of 192 or 384 sides. But the arithmetic, difficult in any case by Greek methods, would have been prohibitive. All this was important for the subsequent invention of trigonometry.

The areas of the polygons are easily calculated when their sides are known. The approximate area of the circle can thus be found without further difficulty, being greater than that of the inner polygon and less than that of the outer.

By the method of exhaustions, Archimedes proved other important results. He found the area of an ellipse. He found the area cut off from a parabola by any chord. He found the volume and surface of a cone. But the theorem of which he was proudest was that which gave the volume and surface of a sphere. Let the sphere be fitted into the smallest cylinder that will contain it, as a ball fits into a tin whose diameter and height are equal to the diameter of the ball. His theorem states that the volume of the sphere is just 2/3 that of the cylinder; while the surface of the sphere is equal to the curved surface of the cylinder. He expressed a wish that the sphere surrounded by a cylinder should be engraved on his tomb. He was killed by a Roman soldier at the fall of Syracuse, although orders were given for him to be spared. In erecting his tomb the Romans complied with his wish.

Generality is a feature of high-class mathematics. It may be illustrated by Archimedes' approach to the old problem of trisecting an angle. He did not just give another solution: he solved the general problem of dividing an angle into any number of equal parts. To do this, he introduced the spiral which goes by his name. Let a line turn uniformly, like the hand of a clock, while a fly crawls along it at constant speed. Then the curve described by the fly, which is the curve drawn by a steadily expanding pair of compasses, is an Archimedean spiral. The essential property of the curve is that equal angular movements correspond to equal increases of radius.

Let AOB be the angle we wish to trisect. Draw an Archimedean spiral, with O as the pivot of the clock-hand, cutting OA at P and OB at Q (Fig. 14). Draw a circle with centre O and radius OP, cutting OQ at X. Find points Y and Z, dividing XQ into 3 equal parts.[1] Draw circular arcs YL and ZM, with centre O, cutting the

[1] *Euc.* VI. 9.

spiral at L and M. Then angles LOP, MOL, QOM are equal, since they correspond to equal increases of radius. It is clear that AOB can be divided into any number of equal parts by this method.

Archimedes did other first-class work in geometry; but most of it is of purely mathematical importance and illustrates no new principles. We shall consider his arithmetic later. His best known contribution to physics was his principle of floatation. It states that, if a body is immersed in still water, then the water exerts an upward thrust on the body; and this thrust is equal to the weight of water displaced by the body. A body whose weight is less than that of an equal volume of water

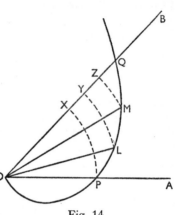

Fig. 14

will experience an upthrust greater than its own weight. It will therefore rise to the surface, unless held down.

The argument supporting this principle is ingenious and simple. The various forces exerted by the surrounding water on the body A (Fig. 15) depend only on its shape and position. They do not depend on the nature of the substance of which A is made. Even if A were itself made of water, they would still be the same. But in this case A would remain at rest, since we know from experience that water left to itself does not move. The forces exerted on A by the surrounding water must in this case, therefore, combine

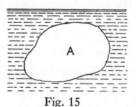

Fig. 15

to neutralise A's weight. They are together equivalent, that is, to an upward thrust equal to the weight of water which fills the space A.

Here is an example of genuinely scientific argument. The reasoning is mathematical. But the outcome does not depend upon mathematics only. It depends also upon the observation that water, unprovoked, stays still. 'The natural intelligence of the soul' is much in evidence; but it does not operate alone, as Plato would have had it do. The proper function of mathematics in the scientific scheme is to reveal the hidden consequences of observed facts. Here it may be seen doing its own peculiar work.

This discovery is the one which is supposed to have made Archimedes leap from his bath. With it he began the science of hydrostatics. In mechanics, he was much interested in the theory and design of devices giving a mechanical advantage—devices by which a small force can overcome a large one. The simplest of these is the lever, which is essentially a rigid bar turning on a fixed pivot. He wrote an account of the theory of levers. The central principle is that two forces which hold a lever in equilibrium must be inversely proportional to their distances from the pivot. Thus a force of 30 units at a distance of 1 foot from the pivot, O, will balance a force of 10 units at a distance of 3 feet (Fig. 16). If the force of 10 units is slightly increased, it will overcome the force of 30. Whenever a device gives such a mechanical advantage, however, the gain in force is obtained at the expense of a loss in distance. Thus, in order to move the point A through 1 inch, it is necessary to move B through 3 inches. Systems of pulleys accomplish a similar purpose. Fig. 17 shows a system devised by

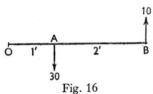

Fig. 16

Archimedes. The effort in this case has to move 8 times as far as the load. Unless there is much friction or unnecessary weight in the pulleys, a given effort will raise a considerably greater load.

His mechanical ingenuity is further illustrated by the Archimedean Screw (Fig. 18). This is a device for raising water from

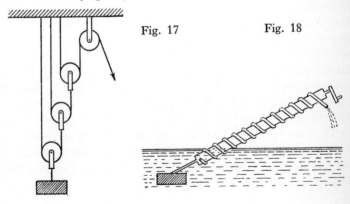

Fig. 17　　　　　　Fig. 18

streams. It consists of a pipe, open at both ends, wound like a screw-thread about a shaft. As the shaft is rotated, the water works its way up the pipe. In order that the device may work, the shaft must be inclined to the vertical at an angle greater than the angle of pitch of the screw.

Archimedes was not greatly interested in the practical application of his knowledge. But, when consulted by Hiero King of Syracuse about problems in engineering, he was usually willing to help. On one occasion a ship was built for Hiero, so big that it could not be launched in the usual way. Archimedes used his knowledge of machines to overcome the difficulty. When Syracuse was attacked by a Roman fleet, he designed catapults which were so effective that the city never fell to frontal attack. It is said that he made concave mirrors, with which he set fire to the Roman ships by concentrating the sun's rays on them; but this story is doubtful. He was, perhaps, the first example of a type now common—the scientist valued by the state for his military usefulness. Science at this time was beginning to have a direct bearing upon affairs, after the modern fashion. On the whole, however, until the Industrial Revolution, its influence on thought remained more important than its influence on action. It has always been, like literature, religion and the fine arts, an ingredient of balanced and refined civilisation. But its important economic consequences, which now for the first time make such civilisation possible for a fair proportion of the human race, are very recent. So also are the devastating military powers that threaten to destroy the civilisation of which it is a part.

The other first-class mathematician of this time, Apollonius of Perga (*c.* 260–200 B.C.), studied and lectured in Alexandria most of his life. His chief work was on conic sections. Much of it survives in the original Greek. Menaechmus and Euclid only began this subject. By the time Apollonius had done with it, the geometry of the conics was as extensive and coherent as that of the circle. At that time they were of purely mathematical interest; but it was mainly due to Apollonius that this branch of geometry was ready when it was needed by astronomers.

The proofs given by Apollonius are in the classical Greek form. It is really astonishing that he was able to discover so many new results. Once he knew a theorem was true, it was comparatively easy for a man like Archimedes or Apollonius to find a proof. But the conventional Greek methods were not particularly apt weapons of discovery at the stage which geometry had now reached. Archimedes first obtained some of his results in mensuration by experimental methods, such as weighing. He had a shrewd notion of the answer before he began to construct the mathematical proof. Two solids of the same material have volumes proportional to their weights, so that the unknown volume of one can be estimated from the known volume of the other by weighing. Such a method of discovery would have been anathema to Plato; but Archimedes had assumed a modern freedom. His mathematical proofs, when they came, were, of course, impeccable. Probably Apollonius also had some private way of reaching his results, although he expounded them with orthodox proofs. It has been seriously suggested that he developed methods of co-ordinate geometry. There is no direct evidence for this; but there is no reason to think it beyond him, and it would explain his extraordinary powers of discovery. Such methods were not generally used until the 17th century, when they were introduced by Fermat and Descartes. The brevity of this account must not be taken to imply that Apollonius was of second-rate importance. Archimedes was his only superior among ancient mathematicians: Pythagoras, Eudoxus and Euclid may be thought his equals.

*   *   *

To UNDERSTAND the achievements of Archimedes in arithmetic, we must know something of Greek arithmetic in general. A good notation is essential to success. The Greeks never had a good notation—they had a bad one which they abandoned for a worse. In Athenian times they used a system like the Roman; with symbols for 1, 5, 10, 100 and 1000, which could be combined to represent intermediate numbers. This was adequate for recording results, provided the numbers involved were not great. It is obviously useless for really large numbers; and it does nothing to facilitate calculation. In Alexandria, however, it gave way to an even clumsier notation.

The Greek alphabet of Alexandrian times had 24 letters. For numeration, the Alexandrians reintroduced two obsolete letters: digamma (F), between ϵ and ζ; and koppa (ϙ), between π and ρ. They added the Phoenician letter sampi (ϡ) at the end, to make 27.

They then used the first nine letters for the numbers 1, 2, 3, . . . 9; the next nine for the numbers 10, 20, 30, . . . 90; and the last nine for the numbers 100, 200, 300, . . . 900. When used as numerals, the letters had a dash at the top right-hand corner. Thus: $\delta' = 4$, $\phi' = 500$, $\sigma\lambda\beta' = 232$. If the dash was at the bottom left-hand corner, it had the effect of multiplying the number by 1000. Thus: $\eta' = 8$; but $,\eta = 8000$. The old Attic symbol M, for 10 000, was used with other symbols which were written above it. Thus, since $\lambda' = 30$, $\overset{\lambda'}{M}$ would have meant $30 \times 10\,000$.

The Greeks, thus encumbered, were unable to calculate as we do, by manipulation (according to rule) of the symbols representing the numbers. They had to rely on the abacus. This is a board with parallel grooves. Pebbles[1] or coins are placed in the grooves as counters—up to 9 in each groove (Fig. 19). Each counter in column P represents a unit, each in Q represents 10, each in R represents 100, and so on. In Fig. 19 the number 425136 is shown. Suppose you wish to add 87 to this. You first add 7 counters in column P. There are now more than 10; so you remove 10, replacing them by 1 in column Q. You then add 8 in column Q, remove 10 and replace them by 1 in column R. If you wish to sub-

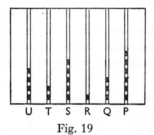

U T S R Q P

Fig. 19

tract 600, you remove a counter from S, replacing it by 10 in R. The subtraction is then possible. The carrying and borrowing processes are, in fact, the same as those we still employ. Multiplication on the abacus is done by repeated addition. Division is done by repeated subtraction. If you wish to divide 476 by 37, you repeatedly subtract 37. After 12 subtractions you find that there is only 32 left. Hence 37 is contained 12 times in 476, with remainder 32.

A more convenient abacus, called the swan pan, consists of parallel wires on which beads can slide. This is still used as an educational toy; but in Greek and Roman times the abacus was a scientific instrument. It was used also by the Aztecs, Indians and Chinese. It was, therefore, almost certainly invented independently

---

[1] The Latin for a little stone is 'calculus'; whence 'calculation'.

7

in three different parts of the world; for it is unlikely the early Middle Eastern civilisations ever had contact with those of America and China.

It seems a short step from the abacus to our present Hindu-Arabic numeration. Each groove of the abacus is capable of 10 different states—it may be empty or contain any number of counters from 1 to 9. We simply substitute, for the actual groove and its counters, a written symbol representing its state. In view of the widespread use of the abacus, it is surprising that this idea did not occur in several places. It is particularly surprising, and it was most unfortunate for Western science, that it did not occur among the gifted Alexandrians. But one essential eluded everyone except the Hindus—the notion of a symbol, zero, to indicate the presence of an empty groove and so keep the other symbols in their proper places.

Even the simpler operations of arithmetic were tiresome for the Greeks, with their unfortunate symbolism. The more complex operations were immensely difficult; and geometrical constructions were developed for performing some of them. We may consider one example. They constructed the square root of 7 as follows. First factorise 7; as $3\frac{1}{2} \times 2$, say. Make $AB = 3\frac{1}{2}$ units, $BC = 2$ units (Fig. 20). Draw a semicircle with AC as diameter. Draw BX, perpendicular to AC, meeting the semicircle at X. Then the length of BX gives the square root of 7. In fact BX is always the square root of the product AB.BC, as Euclid proves.[1]

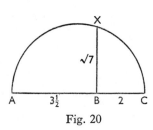

Fig. 20

In estimating the circumference of a circle, Archimedes had to find the chords of successively smaller angles. This involves the calculation of square roots. He could not have found them accurately enough by a geometrical construction, and in any case this would not have satisfied him. He must therefore have had a way of finding them arithmetically. Considering the undeveloped state of arithmetic in his time, the fact that he could do it at all is evidence of his outstanding powers.

His other main arithmetical interest was in the management of

[1] *Euc.* II, 14.

very large numbers. Here again he had to overcome the difficulties inherent in Greek methods. He suggested a notation whereby numbers of any size could be expressed. Numbers up to 100 million—that is 10^8—were to be called first-order numbers. Second-order numbers were to be expressed by using 10^8 as a unit. These second-order numbers could reach $10^8 \times 10^8$, which is 10^{16}. Thus the third-order number $\rho\kappa\gamma'$ was 123×10^{16}. There is no limit to the numbers which can be written by using this system of successive orders. Archimedes expounded its possibilities in an essay called *The Sand Reckoner*. He estimated, using the results of Aristarchus and Eratosthenes, the number of grains of sand needed to fill a sphere whose radius was that of the earth's orbit. He found that this was less than the seventh-order number, $,\alpha$; i.e. less than 10^{51}. Such numbers had no practical significance at the time, though they have now. But Archimedes, like all adventurers in thought, enjoyed going where other men could not, and subjecting something to human power which had previously been beyond it. Playing with large numbers is still an attractive mathematical entertainment. See, for instance, J. E. Littlewood's recent estimate of the odds against a celluloid mouse surviving for a week in Hell.[1]

* * *

To COMPLETE this account of the mathematical sciences in early Alexandria, we need mention only two more distinguished men—Hipparchus and Hero. The former probably flourished about 140 B.C. He studied at Alexandria, but made his discoveries in the island of Rhodes. He rivals Aristarchus for pride of place among ancient astronomers. These two men excelled in different ways. Aristarchus was the greater, more daring theorist. But Hipparchus was the more accurate and prolific observer. His angular measurements were made to 1/15 of a degree, which is astonishing with the instruments he had. The Greeks, who had always outshone the Babylonians in imagination, were now also superior to them as observers.

Hipparchus measured the obliquity of the ecliptic more accurately than Eratosthenes. He determined the length of the year to within 6 minutes. He devoted much time to making a catalogue of 1080 fixed stars and their relative positions. He carried out this

---

[1] *The Mathematical Gazette*, Number 300.

undertaking very thoroughly; for the number of stars that can be seen in Rhodes without optical aid does not greatly exceed 1000. The need for a carefully compiled list of stars was suggested to him by the appearance of a bright new star. This directly contradicted the Aristotelian dogma that the heavens were exempt from change. The reaction of Hipparchus well illustrates the adult scientific sense of the Alexandrians. Although Aristotle was (quite rightly) admired at this time, there was none of that blind admiration which came later. Hipparchus did not bury his head in the sand, like the Aristotelians of the Middle Ages, and obstinately refuse to admit the evidence. He unemotionally noted the mistake; and, in order that his successors might more easily confirm it, he set about the systematic mapping of the sky.

Observation of the fixed stars led Hipparchus to his most famous discovery. The pole, about which the stars appear to revolve, is the point of the heavens towards which the earth's axis is pointed. Earlier astronomers had recorded the positions of some fixed stars. When Hipparchus compared his results with theirs, he found that the position of the pole in relation to these stars had changed. He had in fact discovered that the direction of the earth's axis in space is slowly changing. This movement is called precession. The position of the pole, as plotted on a map of the sky, describes, in about 23 000 years, a circle of considerable diameter. At present the pole is close to the bright star Polaris, and is becoming closer. But, at the time of Hipparchus, Polaris was not so good a guide to the north as it is now. A few thousand years hence there will be no obvious star to mark the pole. The spinning of the earth on its axis is like that of a top which is slowing down. Its axis becomes inclined to the vertical, and turns slowly about the vertical.

The movement of the sun against the background of fixed stars was interpreted by most of the ancients as showing an annual revolution of the sun about the earth. We, like the exceptional Aristarchus, now interpret it as indicating a revolution of the earth about the sun. For the moment let us take, with Hipparchus, the ancient view. If, as he supposed, the motion of the sun is uniform and circular, it is to be expected that the sun will appear to make one quarter of a revolution in each quarter year. Fig. 21 shows the positions, S_1, S_2, S_3, S_4, of the sun, in its supposedly circular orbit, at intervals of one quarter of a year. If the sun's motion is uniform, and if the earth is at the centre C, then the angles S_1CS_2, S_2CS_3, S_3CS_4, S_4CS_1 must all be right-angles. Hipparchus found that this was not the case. He saw that the anomaly could be explained by supposing the earth was not at the centre of the sun's orbit. If the Earth is at E, then the angles S_1ES_2 and S_4ES_1 will be greater than S_2ES_3 and S_3ES_4; and the sun will seem to cover more than half its orbit in one half of the year. Its rate of angular motion, as seen from the earth, will vary. After careful measurement of the angles, Hipparchus calculated the distance CE. He found that it was about 1/24 of the radius of the orbit. This fraction is called the eccentricity of the solar orbit. It measures the displacement of the earth from the centre.

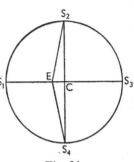

Fig. 21

This means the sun is not a constant distance from the earth. If we take the modern view that the earth moves round the sun, we still need an eccentricity. We must now suppose that the sun is not at the centre of the earth's orbit. This discovery did not, therefore, become obsolete when the Copernican System was adopted. Although Hipparchus did not know it, the earth's motion round the sun is neither uniform nor circular. When this is allowed for, a smaller eccentricity will explain the sun's irregularity. The correct figure is about 1/30.

Hipparchus also kept records of planetary and lunar motions. He made no theory to explain these motions, but he consciously accumulated the data which would enable his successors to do so. Again the Alexandrian scientific sense appears—the understanding that science is more than one man's work, and must progress by laying detail upon detail.

Hipparchus invented trigonometry, but his success depended on the work of Archimedes. There are two distinct kinds of measurement in geometry—distances and angles. The purpose of trigonometry is to relate angular measures to those of distance. The need for this arises frequently in astronomy. In finding the relative distances of the sun and moon, Aristarchus calculated the ratio ES:EM (Fig. 9) from knowledge of the angle MES, which alone he could measure. The eccentricity of the solar orbit, which is also the ratio of two distances, was similarly calculated by Hipparchus from an angle. Aristarchus solved his own special problem by an *ad hoc* argument. But what was wanted was a general method for solving all such problems; for finding the ratios of the sides of a triangle when its angles were known. Since any triangle can be divided into right-angled triangles, the fundamental problem is to relate the sides of a right-angled triangle to its angles.

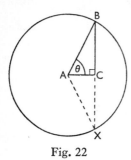

Fig. 22

Consider the triangle ABC, right-angled at C (Fig. 22). Let us take AB as our unit of length, and suppose that we know the angle θ. Our object is to find the lengths of BC and AC. Draw a circle with centre A and radius AB. Extend BC to meet this circle at X. It is evident, from symmetry, that the angle CAX $= \theta$, and that BC is half BX. Thus BC is half the chord of the angle 2θ; and it can be found at once if we have a table giving the chords which correspond to various angles. AC can then be found by Pythagoras's Theorem.

Hipparchus made a table of chords. We have seen that Archimedes calculated the chords for $60°$, $30°$, $15°$, $7\frac{1}{2}°$ and $3\frac{3}{4}°$. His method could be extended to still smaller angles. Hipparchus also used a theorem, called Ptolemy's Theorem, by which he could find the chord of $(\alpha + \beta)$ when he knew the chords of α and β. Thus he could find the chord of $75°$ from those of $60°$ and $15°$; or that of $37\frac{1}{2}°$ from those of $30°$ and $7\frac{1}{2}°$. With patience, he could calculate the chords of angles at quite short intervals.

The table of chords is equivalent to a modern table of sines. If AB is the unit of length, then the length of BC is called the sine of the angle θ. Thus the sine of θ is half the chord of 2θ.

With the help of his table of chords Hipparchus found it easy to relate the sides and angles of any plane triangle. But, like Eratosthenes, he was interested in geography;[1] and the triangles of geography are drawn on the surface of the earth, which is (approximately) a sphere. It is not generally possible to draw a straight line on a curved surface. The nearest approach to it is a geodesic. Suppose

---

[1] He first suggested latitude and longitude for giving position on the earth's surface.

that A and B are two points on the surface; then the geodesic is the shortest route one can take from A to B without leaving the surface. The geodesic may be found experimentally by stretching a thread tightly over the surface from A to B. The geodesics on a globe are arcs of great circles; a great circle being a circle, on the surface of the globe, whose centre is at the centre of the globe. Such a circle may also be thought of as the cross-section obtained when the globe is separated into hemispheres. No circle of greater radius can be drawn on the surface of the globe. Circles of smaller radius can be drawn, and these are called small circles. A line of latitude, other than the equator, is an example of a small circle. It is possible to prove mathematically that, if A and B are not diametrically opposite, then there is only one great circle through them both, and the geodesic between them is an arc of this circle.

If A, B and C are three points on the globe, and if we join each to

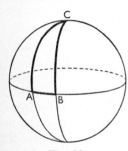

Fig. 23

the others by arcs of great circles, the resulting figure is called a spherical triangle. Such a triangle is shown in Fig. 23, in which A and B are points on the equator, and C is the North Pole. The side AB is part of the equator, while CA and CB are meridians. The properties of spherical triangles are different from those of plane triangles. In the triangle ABC, for instance, the angles at A and B are both right-angles. Hence the angles of the triangle together exceed 180°. The study of spherical triangles is called spherical trigonometry. Hipparchus made considerable progress in it.

Hero, who flourished early in the 1st century B.C., is interesting because he illustrates a tendency which might have grown in Alexandria but did not. He followed Archimedes in attempting to put the resources of science to technical use. This was a sideline with Archimedes; but, even so, Hero was not his equal at it. Most of Hero's ideas remained experimental. There were two good reasons for this. Firstly: the social and economic systems of the time, depending on abundant slave labour, could function without much technical assistance. There was no general demand for the services of the mechanical engineer, though the civil engineer had his uses even then. Secondly: the technique of manufacture in iron, and the general knowledge of materials, essential to the use of mechanical power on a large scale, were defective. The ingenuity of Alexandrian scientists did not, therefore, lead to an industrial civilisation.

Hero's best known invention was an embryonic steam turbine. It consisted of a hollow sphere which could revolve about a horizontal axis. Steam was passed into this sphere through hollow axle-shafts, and expelled tangentially through bent pipes. The reaction from the jets caused the sphere to turn. This is the first known device for converting heat into mechanical energy.

Hero's most valuable suggestion in pure science was that a ray of light, in passing from point to point, takes the path of least distance. This principle may be shown to imply the Laws of Reflection known to Euclid. It was developed by Fermat during the 17th century; and an 18th-century generalisation led to the important physical method known as the Principle of Least Action.

*   *   *

THE WORK of the Alexandrians in astronomy and mathematics was more important, for its intrinsic worth and its subsequent influence, than anything else they did. It was so modern in spirit that the great scientists of the 16th and 17th centuries could carry on quite naturally from the point at which the Alexandrians left off. Hipparchus could have co-operated on equal terms with Tycho, or Archimedes on equal terms with Newton. There were, however, other activities in the Museum which we must not ignore.

The medical school of Alexandria owed much to the statesmanship with which the Ptolemies reconciled Greek, Jewish and Egyptian cultures. It was able to draw inspiration from several different sources in the past, mainly because of the energy and perseverance the Ptolemies devoted to their library. The Athenian contribution, with something from the Sicilian school of Empedocles, appeared in the works of Aristotle and his disciple Theophrastus on botany, comparative anatomy, embryology, heredity and medicine. Ionian medicine was represented in the many works attributed to Hippocrates. Some of these were no doubt his own; but many were fakes. The high prices paid for important books by the Ptolemies set a premium on forgery. Ionian medicine, like

Ionian astronomy and mathematics, owed much to Babylon and Egypt. There was also a *direct* Egyptian contribution to Alexandrian medicine. Egyptian knowledge, especially of drugs and surgery, was considerable. The Ptolemies, by their tact in choosing an Egyptian president for the Museum, made sure it should be available.

This accumulation of biological and medical literature, known as the Hippocratic Collection, was one of the foundations on which Alexandrian medicine was built. The other was an increased activity in dissection. Until this time only animals had been dissected. The Ptolemies, with scientific contempt for the tabus of the past, permitted and encouraged the dissection of human bodies. They also allowed the vivisection of condemned criminals. This may seem barbaric; but in those days there were many equally unpleasant and much less useful methods of execution. Anatomy, as pure science and as an adjunct to medicine, advanced rapidly. Physiology presents greater difficulties. Despite the practice of vivisection, the study of organic function made less progress than that of structure.

The temple of Serapis, adjoining the Museum, was used as a hospital, where students of medicine could practise clinical observation, as they do today. Herophilus and Erasistratus, the outstanding physicians of the early Museum, were contemporaries of Euclid. The former, educated at Cos, used methods similar to those of Hippocrates, whom he admired. Erasistratus owed more to the peripatetics; and he practised milder methods of treatment. Herophilus and Erasistratus were able anatomists. They also made some physiological discoveries. Herophilus attributed the pulse to the action of the heart; and, in opposition to Aristotle, believed the brain to be the centre of intelligence. Erasistratus found that some nerves are connected with movement and others with feeling: but he mistook the function of the arteries, believing them to carry air.

The followers of Herophilus and Erasistratus became increasingly devoted to learned discussion, and less interested in practical medicine. In consequence, a sect called the Empirics arose, founded by Philimus of Cos, a pupil of Herophilus. The Empirics believed the acquisition of purely scientific knowledge was a waste of time. They denied the value of anatomy, physiology and any kind of theory. They claimed that the only sure foundation was a vast recorded experience of actual disease. Their outlook was one-sided. But they were successful physicians, who helped to maintain the balance between theory and practice, which might otherwise have been lost.

The various threads of Alexandrian medicine were tied together by Galen, who wrote and practised, mainly at Rome, in the 2nd century A.D. Alexandrian medicine held sway throughout Roman times. The Romans saw the military value of medicine; but they made little original contribution, except in hygiene. Their attitude to all science was insensitive and utilitarian. The extension of Roman power over the Greek world, though it did not altogether halt science, was a main cause of the decline which preceded the Dark Ages. The ignorant Roman murder of Archimedes, just as the last Greek city states were losing their independence, was poignantly symbolic of the process. In the words of T. R. Glover, 'the Greeks were famous for their brains, and the Romans for their drains'.

The Jews played an active part in the development of Alexandrian medicine. This is significant, because it illustrates the success of a tolerant and far-sighted policy pursued by the Ptolemies— their attempt to unite ancient cultures. The effect of this policy on the development of thought was important and beneficial. Alexander populated his capital with mixed races: the Ptolemies seized this opportunity.

Greek philosophy and science had always been sceptical of the traditional, too human, gods. Polytheism had given way: sometimes to belief in a single, spiritual god; occasionally to outright atheism; but most often to pantheism—the identification of the universe with God. The Egyptians, on the other hand, were still devoted to their ancient religion. The Ptolemies were faced with a problem of reconciliation. We have noticed one step they took to solve it. The other was equally diplomatic. They fostered the worship of Serapis. The idol representing this god was a Greek figure, made of many different substances, which the Greeks could interpret as a symbol of their scientific pantheism. But the Egyptians were persuaded to accept the figure as that of Osiris-Apis—the human form assumed in after-life by their sacred bull Apis. They cheerfully worshipped it beside Isis and Horus.

At the same time, the mingling of Greek and Hebrew cultures

was promoted by the Septuagint, a Greek translation of the Old
Testament, sponsored by Ptolemy Philadelphus. By such devices
the Ptolemies made sure that the mixed population should feel well
disposed to a predominantly Greek civilisation.

*   *   *

DURING THE 1st century B.C. Egypt came under Roman influence and finally under Roman rule. There was little scientific
progress during this period of political uncertainty. But the
Roman government, once established, was tolerant and stable. The
Romans regarded abstract learning with indifference; but they did
not suppress it, or seek to change the essentially Greek character of
Alexandria. Science revived after a time; and there was another
period of progress during the 2nd, 3rd and 4th centuries A.D. It is
not comparable, in genius or success, with the period just considered. But there was some valuable work in mathematics and
astronomy. From being metropolitan, Alexandria had become pro-
vincial. World-wide reputation had now to be sought in Rome,
which had supplanted Alexandria just as Alexandria supplanted
Athens. Rome paid its tribute rather to men of action than men of
science. Scientists were no longer the companions and advisers of
kings. The Greek intellect lost much of its drive, and began to turn
for satisfaction to the contemplation of its own past. There were
now able scholars and commentators where there had once been
great original thinkers.

Claudius Ptolemy,[1] active during the first half of the 2nd century, was the most distinguished astronomer of the second
Alexandrian school. His work in astronomy was similar to that of
Euclid in mathematics. He did not contribute striking new ideas;
but he assembled those of his predecessors in a systematic treatise
which summed up Greek Astronomy. This is known by its Arabic
name of *Almagest*.

The Greeks always assumed that the motions of heavenly bodies
were derived from uniform circular motions. Eudoxus, under
Plato's influence, designed a system by which the behaviour of sun,
moon and planets was carefully explained in this way. Hipparchus
and Ptolemy abandoned his apparatus of concentric spheres, and
introduced the theory of epicycles which was in use until the

[1] Probably not related to the Egyptian royal family.

Scientific Revolution. This was an abstract geometrical description of the heavens. They supposed that certain motions took place, but suggested no explanatory mechanism. The fundamental idea, that of a body moving in a circle whose centre moves in another circle, was due to Hipparchus. So were most of the observations with which the theory had to agree. But he worked out the details of the epicycles only for the sun and moon. The system is justly called Ptolemaic. It was Ptolemy who adjusted the planetary epicycles to fit the facts—a monumental labour—and who wrote a comprehensive account of the theory. Let us consider briefly what required explaining, and how the epicyclic theory sought to explain it.

We must distinguish the outer planets, Mars, Jupiter, and Saturn, from the inner planets, Mercury and Venus. Let us first take Jupiter as an example. He moves, like the sun, from west to east through the constellations of the Zodiac; but he does so more slowly, taking about 12 years to complete his course. He does not move at a constant rate. He moves to the east for a time, then to the west for a shorter time, then to the east again, and so on. His instants of rest are called stations. His motion to the west, between stations, is called retrograde. The cycle of movements, from the beginning of one retrogression to the beginning of the next, takes rather more than a year—there are 11 retrogressions in about 12 years. Besides occupying a shorter time, the retrogression is less rapid than the eastward motion. Thus, on balance, the planet makes way to the east.

We shall see later how this behaviour is simply explained by the

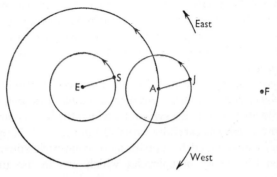

Fig. 24

Copernican hypothesis of the earth's motion. The first essentials of
the Ptolemaic scheme are shown in Figs. 24 and 25. These show

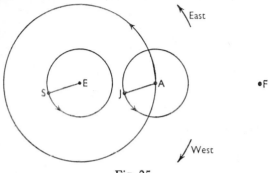

Fig. 25

the motions attributed to the sun and Jupiter in relation to the
fixed earth and fixed stars. We must imagine ourselves looking
down on the earth E from above the North Pole. F is a typical
fixed star. The sun S rotates once round the earth, from west to
east, in a year. The point A moves once round the earth, also from
west to east, in about 12 years. The circle on which A moves is
called the deferent of Jupiter. Jupiter, at J, meanwhile revolves
round A in a smaller circle, called an epicycle, in such a way that
AJ is always parallel to ES. When the arrangement is that of Fig.
24, the motion of J in relation to A is in the same direction as that
of A in relation to F. Thus J, as seen from E, appears to move from
west to east more quickly than A. Six months later the position will
be as in Fig. 25. The sun has made half a turn round the earth,
while the point A has made 1/24 of a turn. AJ has turned with ES;
and the motion of J in relation to A is a backward one. The motion
of J along the circumference of the epicycle is more rapid than the
motion of A along the deferent. Hence J, as seen from E, now
appears to move from east to west in relation to F—but not so
quickly as it previously appeared to move from west to east. The
path actually followed by Jupiter will be as shown in Fig. 26.

While these long-term movements take place on the paper, we
must imagine the daily movement of the heavens to be represented
by a revolution of the paper about E, in a clockwise direction,
every 24 hours.

The arrangement for Mercury and Venus was different. It is shown in Fig. 27. B is a point on ES; and it therefore circles the earth once a year with the sun. Mercury, at M, describes an

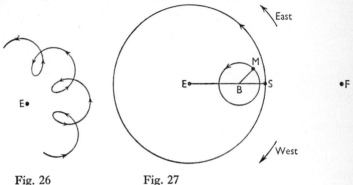

Fig. 26   Fig. 27

epicycle, with centre B, so as to cross EB at intervals of about 116 days. As seen from E, Mercury will then appear to follow the sun through the Zodiac, oscillating from one side of it to the other. This is in fact how Mercury appears to move. Venus does the same, but its oscillations are slower and wider. The same apparent motions for Mercury and Venus could be produced by the simpler expedient of supposing them to revolve round the sun itself. It is not clear why Ptolemy introduced the unnecessary point B.

The theory, as described above, accounts roughly for the main features of apparent planetary motion. But there are discrepancies. In order to account for these, the theory had to be elaborated. Jupiter, for instance, did not exactly follow the point J (Fig. 24). Another point J′ described a smaller epicycle round J, a third point J″ a still smaller one round J′; and so on, as far as was necessary. Jupiter itself described the last of these successive epicycles. By carefully adjusting the sizes and periods of these epicycles, Ptolemy was at last able to reproduce the observed motion of Jupiter. It was also necessary for the earth to be not quite at the centre of the deferent.

The Ptolemaic System, progressively modified, met the needs of astronomers until the time of Copernicus. By then it was so involved that it was becoming unmanageable. Ptolemy admitted that the apparent daily motion of the heavens was most simply understood by supposing the earth to rotate on its axis, as Heraclides had suggested. But it was not generally thought until some time after Copernicus that this rotation really took place. The still more advanced views of Aristarchus were not even considered. To grasp the Ptolemaic motions as they were really meant to be, one has to imagine the epicycles performed year by year on a platform, while the platform rotates daily about an axis through the centre of a fixed earth.

The Greek description of celestial motions appears clumsy beside that of Copernicus and Kepler. But, judged against the background of its time, it seems a fine achievement of imagination, observation and geometrical skill. It embodies the essential principle of an important modern mathematical method. If an object P, moving uniformly in a circle about centre O, is observed from a distant point in the plane of the circle, then the oscillating motion which P appears to have is called simple harmonic motion. If, meanwhile, O revolves in the same plane about another centre O', the apparent motion of P in relation to O' is that obtained by superimposing one simple harmonic motion upon another. The epicyclic motion of a planet, as seen from the earth, must evidently appear as the combination of several simple harmonic motions.

A simple harmonic motion is determined when its period (the time of oscillation) and its amplitude (the width of an oscillation) are known. What the Greeks did, in effect, was to give an approximate description of the complicated periodic motion of a planet by combining simple harmonic motions of different periods and amplitudes.

Now periodic motion—i.e. motion in which a sequence of changes is repeated in successive equal intervals of time—is a frequent occurrence in nature. Simple harmonic motion, the simplest kind of periodic motion, is mathematically easy to handle. A more complicated periodic motion is easier to understand if it can be represented as a combination of simple harmonic motions. This method of dealing with periodic motions, introduced into modern science by the French physicist Fourier and the German astronomer Bessel early in the 19th century, is widely used. It was subsequently proved, by the Prussian mathematician Dirichlet, that the representation of a periodic motion in this way, to any required degree of approximation, is always possible. Like so many mathematical methods, this was in scientific use before the underlying theory had been fully worked out.

*   *   *

PAPPUS AND Diophantus are the only other Alexandrians who need be mentioned. Pappus lived towards the end of the 3rd century. He wrote commentaries on the geometry of the past, from which much has been learnt about the lost work of his predecessors. His original work is not of sufficient general interest to need discussion here. It consisted of new theorems in subjects, like that of conic sections, already well developed. Diophantus, who was at work in Alexandria soon after Pappus, is important as the first serious writer on algebra. But, before considering his work, we must discuss the nature and significance of ordinary algebra. This subject is closely related to a wider one—the connection between language and the growth of thought.

Algebra, which in its earlier days was concerned almost exclusively with the solution of equations, originated in the attempt to solve the inverse problems of arithmetic. A direct problem is one in which we perform certain operations upon a given number, and find the result. The ancients, because of their inept systems of numeration, had difficulty even with quite simple direct problems. It was, for instance, by no means easy for them to find the result of multiplying 17 by 19, adding 147 and then dividing by 5. They had still more trouble with inverse problems. In such problems the result of performing a series of operations upon an unspecified number is known, and we wish to find the number. What number (e.g.) must be doubled and added to 3 times its own square to give 85? It is true that the solution, 5, to this simple problem could be found by trial and error. But, with Greek methods of arithmetic, even this might involve some labour. If 86 were put in place of 85, however, there would be little hope of solving the problem in this way. The solution could now be found only by a complex reasoning process; and it would be a matter of some difficulty to conduct this reasoning through the medium of everyday language.

A striking quality of ordinary language is its flexibility. It can be used for discussing almost any topic or idea. But, just as the equal-tempered clavier, tuned to play in all the keys, cannot give perfect accuracy in any one of them, so the price of versatility in language is a certain lack of precision. This does not matter much except in the technical discussions associated with special activities in a high state of development. In general discourse the able tongue or pen can secure sufficiently fine distinctions of meaning, without undue sacrifice of brevity, by selection and arrangement of the ordinary linguistic devices. But where this is impossible, symbols other than words become necessary. Chemistry, cartography, music, mathematics and logic depend largely upon the use of such symbols. Ballet is a good example of an activity which is in constant danger from not possessing an adequate notation of its own.[1]

Ordinary algebra is the special symbolism of arithmetic. It is a language designed for the sole purpose of expressing relations between numbers. It does this with a clarity far beyond the reach of normal languages, because (to revert to a previous comparison) it is, unlike them, tuned to perfection in a single key. There is nothing far-fetched in calling it a language. All its parts and devices have their unmistakable counterparts in (e.g.) English; though the converse is not true—literary language has many properties neither needed nor possessed by algebra.

The power of algebra resides firstly in the brevity with which it can express complex relations. It enables the mind to grasp at once what would otherwise have to be assimilated in successive doses, with consequent strain on the memory. Thus the essentials of the problem considered a few paragraphs back are much more easily understood from the equation $3x^2 + 2x = 85$, which can be assessed at a glance, than from the cumbersome statement in words. Or again; the rule for finding the surface of a cylinder, expressed in the formula $S = 2\pi r(r + h)$, cannot be so concisely or clearly expressed by any verbal instruction.

But there is a subtler and greater advantage. This arises from the fact that algebra is a language of extreme simplicity, without irregularities. If the steps of an argument are symbolically recorded, each step corresponds to a particular rearrangement of the

---

[1] 'Music has its score, the drama its book, and the paintings of the past can be seen on the walls of museums and to a certain extent in reproduction. Ballet enjoys no such advantages. Cease dancing for 20 years and the damage might well be beyond repair.' (Arnold Haskell, *Ballet*, Chapter I.)

8

symbols. Consider the equation $AY + B = C$. We may argue that the equality is unaffected by subtracting B from each side. Thus $AY = C - B$. We may now argue that the equality is unaffected if we divide each side by A. Hence $Y = (C - B)/A$. Other modes of thought correspond to other modes of rearrangement. We soon learn to recognise those symbolic rearrangements which correspond to valid reasoning processes. We can then make such rearrangements automatically, without perpetually considering their significance. We may be sure that any statement we arrive at by so doing will be true, provided the statement with which we begin is true. By simply observing the rules which the symbolism is known to obey, we may obtain, without intellectual effort, the results of complex reasoning processes. The symbolism acts as a calculating machine, thereby leaving the mathematician free to concentrate on those parts of his problem which require creative thought.

A symbolism which behaves in this way is called a calculus. It can do more than facilitate a reasoning process whose aim is decided beforehand. Tentative rearrangement of the symbols may actually suggest a line of thought which would otherwise have remained unnoticed. It is a truism that language and ideas grow side by side. New ideas make new demands on language; and the increasing subtlety of language in turn promotes the growth of ideas. This process is seen at its most obvious in mathematics.

Conventional language cannot act as a calculus. Its richness, variety and dependence upon idiom—the qualities which give it its literary merit—prevent it from doing so. Because it can say the same thing in many ways, it does not always react in a given way to a given mode of thought, as a calculus must.

Diophantus could solve the problems represented by linear and quadratic equations. His reasoning in each case was similar to ours. But this is not why he is important. The Babylonians did it before him. He is important because he introduced a notation by which he could express his reasoning more shortly than in words. He had special symbols for equality and subtraction, and also for the unknown number and its square and cube. He placed numbers side by side to indicate that they should be added—the device by which we now indicate a product. He could not use letters freely for unknown numbers (or variables) as we do, because in Alexandria the letters already represented specific numbers. This cramped his style in problems which involved several variables, though he nevertheless considered such problems. His notation was not sufficiently developed to become a calculus; but it was the ancestor of modern algebra.

4

THE MIDDLE AGES

THE ORIGINAL contribution of the Greeks to Western thought was essentially complete by about 100 B.C. The decline of philosophy and art began long before this, with the eclipse of Athens. Science enjoyed a further 200 years of immense success in Alexandria. But, even there, the peak was reached by the time of Hipparchus. With the exception of Diophantine algebra, there was nothing really new after this. Important work was done, but it was only the detailed development of existing lines of thought.

The slow death of Alexandrian science had at least four causes. The most powerful was its own senile decay. Its methods in geometry were wonderfully productive. But almost everything that could be done with them had now been done. Further progress demanded new methods, which were not forthcoming. Arithmetic had been pushed as far as was humanly possible without a new notation, such as the Greeks failed to invent. Observational astronomy could do little more without optical instruments of precision; and opticians could not yet provide these. The laws of reflection were known; and it is perhaps surprising that a reflecting telescope was not devised. But refraction was not understood. In any case, the manufacture of good lenses required materials and a manual skill which were not then available.

The possibilities of current theory, like those of observation, were exhausted. The astronomical theory of Hipparchus and Ptolemy was really scientific, in that it was systematically reconciled with the known facts. But it was too complex and artificial to admit of much extension by existing mathematical methods. Theoretical simplicity was needed. This could come only from the daring notions of Aristarchus about a moving earth, for which even Greek thought was not yet prepared.

Disregard for the atomists held back chemistry and physics

Brilliant but isolated discoveries were made in optics and harmonics; and by Archimedes in mechanics and hydrostatics. But there was no satisfactory theory to give direction and unity to physical research—no framework within which a purposeful programme might be conducted from generation to generation. Chemistry existed only as alchemy, which was associated with astrology and magic. It had no genuinely scientific aim. It was little more than a succession of haphazard efforts to convert baser metals into gold. An atomic theory might have given it coherence. But the success of Aristotle's *method* of detailed observation was accompanied by undue respect for his rather sterile theories, which overshadowed those of Leucippus and Democritus. Biology lacked a plausible evolutionary theory. Like astronomy, it needed optical assistance. Wherever we look we find an apparatus of method and theory which has been already to the utmost exploited and can no longer support progress. New techniques and a new outlook are necessary. Greek science now needs what Babylonian and Egyptian science found at the time of Thales—the keen interest of a fresh race whose mind is not set in the traditional mould.

But although the root cause of the decline was internal, there were three significant outside influences—Rome, Christianity and ecclesiasticism.[1] These were only slightly responsible for the onset of the disease, but they accelerated its course and made recovery impossible. The Romans destroyed political liberty and racial ambition in the Mediterranean area. They thus indirectly damaged Greek civilisation, without deliberately attacking it. Subject races tend to contemplate the past in sullen silence, or to give all their efforts to the single purpose of setting themselves free. None among them had the zest to do for Alexandrian science what the Ionians did for that of the Middle East. The Romans alone had the liberty and self-confidence for such a part; but they were too much occupied with practical problems of government and conquest, and had little interest in the pursuit of knowledge as such.

Christian thought affected science as adversely as Roman action. It supposed that the sole purpose of this life was preparation for another. Unquestioning faith was set up as a greater virtue than intellectual curiosity and effort. Future blessedness, alone worth

---

[1] The last two must not be confounded. This point is made delightfully by Boccaccio (*Decameron*, 1st day, 2nd story).

attainment, was reserved for those who had such faith. There was therefore no profit in the vigorous exercise of those qualities of mind which the nobler Greeks had always encouraged men to value. Science dealt only with this world. Philosophy was limited by the imperfections of human understanding. Both, in consequence, were trivial—in so far as they were not misleading. The allegories of Prometheus and Adam show that knowledge obtained by human enterprise and daring had long been recognised as dangerous. Christianity spread the view, never widely held before, that such knowledge was valueless or positively harmful. The attack was conducted with force and ability by St. Paul. He says:

'Beware lest any man spoil you through philosophy and vain deceit.' (Colossians 2:8)
'O Timothy, keep that which is committed to thy trust, avoiding profane and vain babblings, and oppositions of science falsely so called.' (1 Timothy 6:20)

He strikes more shrewdly, if less directly, in the first epistle to the Corinthians (3:21):

'Therefore let no man glory in men.'

This superficially innocent remark is aimed at the vital point. It condemns the underlying humanism—the self-confidence of man —essential to progress in science and the arts.

We need not decide whether this aspect of Christian teaching is true or false. We must observe that it existed, and that it militated against any revival of a sick science. Its influence was far-reaching: for we need not accept Nietzsche's savage judgment of Christianity, as a religion fit only for slaves, to see that there were elements in it to appeal strongly to those who suffered oppression —a vast majority within the Roman Empire. The meek, the poor, the simple and the down-trodden were offered such comfort and future compensation that they could rejoice at not being wealthy, powerful or wise. It would have been surprising if this message of hope had not induced an uncritical acceptance of the accompanying strictures upon philosophy and science.

The development of Greek science was characterised by the struggle between two sharply contrasted methods. There was the philosophical method, inspired by the success of mathematics, according to which knowledge was to be deduced from general principles laid down by moral or aesthetic judgment. And there was the inductive method, in which the general principles, before being used as premises, were derived from observation. The philosophical method was predominant in Athens. The more powerful inductive method triumphed for a time in Alexandria, and has passed into modern science. But, despite their differences, the advocates of these conflicting methods shared a fundamental belief. They never doubted the power of human judgment and reason; they disagreed only about how such judgment and reason should be applied. Christian teaching emphasised an altogether deeper conflict. Authority, backed by supposed revelation, was exalted, in opposition to Reason itself, as the only valid judge of truth or source of knowledge. For a thousand years Authority had the better of the struggle. Reason turned the tables at the time of the Scientific Revolution. It seemed, by the middle of the 19th century, to be approaching final victory. It is now clear that this was not the case; though the most powerful champions of Authority are now neither Christian nor even ecclesiastical.

Its appeal to the underdog was not the only reason for the rapid spread of Christianity. Stories of miracles and the threat of hell strongly influenced the superstitious, who were many. The noble system of ethics, to which the pagan religions offered nothing comparable, attracted educated men reared on the moral philosophies of Plato, Zeno or Epicurus. Such men were also predisposed toward monotheism. Stoicism had opened the way for the idea that every man had in him a share of the Spirit of God, and that men were all the spiritual sons of God. The consequent notion of the duty of brotherly love gave the strength of unity to groups of Christians from the first. Christian unity was further fostered by the Christian attitude to other religions, which was intolerant. The pagan religions existed together without mutual interference or ill will. But the Christian code involved the denunciation of other religions and the conversion of those devoted to them. Christianity was consciously opposed to other modes of life and thought, and the Christian minority developed solidarity and an organisation such as less militant minorities could do without.

The Roman government was disturbed at this growth within the Empire of an organised society whose first loyalty was not to the state. Imperial nervousness appeared in various attempts to weaken Christianity by persecution. The reason for the persecutions was more political than religious. Religious toleration was a feature of Imperial Rome, where religions of every kind were freely practised by those willing to admit the over-riding claim of loyalty to the Emperor. But, whatever the reason for them, the persecutions failed to check, and even served to strengthen, Christianity. Christians won admiration by their readiness for martyrdom. Some even went out of their way to seek it as a means of furthering the Faith.

It was soon clear that violence could not stop the spread of Christianity, even within the army which was the real source of Imperial power. Constantine the Great, in the fight for power with his rivals, allied himself with the Christians, whom he rightly supposed able to turn the scale in his favour. His criminal record[1] made it advisable for him to leave Rome. Early in the 4th century he set up a new capital in Byzantium, which became Constantinople. He established Christianity as the official religion of then Empire, though not himself converted until just before his death.

These events brought a new influence to the forefront in human affairs—that of ecclesiasticism. An Established Church backed by civil authority began to offer its bishops such opportunities of power, wealth and standing as had not existed in the independent Church of the past. High ecclesiastical positions, unlike those of a military and civil kind, were generally open to men of low birth. There were unedifying scrambles for power among unscrupulous and worldly priests, who employed gangs of ruffians dependent on their charity, and who were ready to gain their ends by intrigue, bribery or murder. We may disregard the entertaining and disgusting details. The outcome was a gradual concentration of power in the bishoprics of Alexandria, Constantinople and Rome. The bishops of Rome, by their comparative immunity from Imperial supervision and by the skill with which they played their rivals off against one another, in the end became supreme. It should not be supposed that the leaders of the Church during this period were uniformly disreputable. Some, like Ambrose of Milan, who called an emperor to account for his crimes, were notable for high moral standards and courage. But many who wielded the new power were

---

[1] He murdered his wife, son and nephew.

jealous, ignorant and evil. Nearly all were narrow-minded and intolerant.

The impact of ecclesiastical power politics did much to hasten the decline of science and secular philosophy. Those who fought for high places in the Church were at one, despite their private quarrels, in their dislike of independent thought. The maintenance of episcopal power and wealth, whoever held them, required that the doctrines of the Church should be as generally accepted as possible. It did not really matter what they were, or whether they were true; but it was expedient that they should be universally believed. The authority of churchmen depended on their hold over men's minds. The scientist and philosopher, too inquisitive to be tolerated and too intelligent to be deceived, were also too sceptical to be interested in the promise of heaven or worried by the threat of hell. But, now that Church and State were friends, the independent thinker could be effectively tormented on earth. He could be accused of witchcraft or dealings with the Devil. Ignorant mobs could then be encouraged to demand his execution, or to murder him while pious emperors looked the other way. Thus Constantine was forced to order the death of the philosopher Sopator, who was vulgarly supposed to have tampered with the winds. Hypatia, who lectured on Greek medicine, philosophy and mathematics to fashionable Alexandria, and was the last to maintain the great tradition in public, was barbarously murdered by a gang of monks. This was at the instigation of St. Cyril, the archbishop, who was jealous of her influence.

The early Christian teaching, by its very nature, gained a foothold mainly in the lower stratum of society. Ecclesiastical leaders were quick to see that they could add to their power by still further increasing the number of their easily led plebeian supporters. They did this by judicious use of alms, and by embellishing Christianity with rites and superstitions, like those of the pagans, so that it might have an even wider popular appeal. They became demagogues, able to turn crowds of unenlightened followers against the ancient civilisation they detested.

The mob was not the only weapon now possessed by bold bad bishops. The authority of the State became so bound up with that of the Church that emperors could be persuaded, for the sake of civil security, to suppress Greek learning in its character of accessory to paganism. They could be encouraged by the suggestion that they were saving their own souls in the process. An occasional emperor was uncompliant; but the overwhelming tendency was for State to yield to Church. New laws, in theory directed against the black arts, in practice made it dangerous to enter a temple, own a library or use a scientific instrument. By the end of the 4th century the public practice of pagan religions had been nearly extinguished. What was left of independent Greek thought was being rapidly driven underground. The Temple of Serapis in Alexandria was destroyed by order of the fanatically Christian Theodosius. The archbishop, Theophilus, who carried out the order, at the same time organised the destruction of most of the remaining library.[1] This, and the murder of Hypatia, were decisive blows at science in Alexandria. Some books and a few undistinguished scholars remained. A handful of fugitives kept up the study of Alexandrian science for a time in Athens, whose schools survived precariously until closed in the 6th century by Justinian. Others went to Constantinople, where some records of Alexandrian achievement fortunately escaped destruction.

Greek science, by its scepticism, did much to check belief in the old polytheism. Greek philosophy, unlike the pagan religions, gave rise to moral notions akin to those of early Christianity. Science and philosophy each did something to discredit paganism and clear the way for Christianity. Yet they were persecuted, upon suspicion of their sympathy with paganism, by churchmen who, for worldly reasons, themselves saturated Christianity with pagan ideas.

Philosophical and scientific inquiry, as they died out, were superseded by theological dispute and official dogma. Would-be leaders of the Church often found it convenient to accuse rivals of heresy. Bitter controversies arose about the nature of the Trinity and the status of the Mother of God. Such questions are not amenable to reason; nothing short of divine inspiration can provide the answers. But intellects which might otherwise have served science were now given over to incessant argument about them. The Church was so infected with unseemly wrangling that clear-cut

[1] Many of the books were burnt when the city was taken by Julius Caesar. It is not known whether they were destroyed on purpose, or, like Archimedes, by mistake. Mark Antony—possibly for love of learning, but probably for love of Cleopatra—did his Roman best to repair the loss, by robbing the rival library at Pergamus.

standards of orthodoxy became necessary for its health. Such standards were settled by successive Councils of the Church, called together for the purpose. The decisions of these Councils had the force of law wherever the Byzantine emperors held sway. They had the support of strong moral pressure from the Church over a still wider area. Orthodoxy was from time to time set forth in words which had little meaning for the ordinary man.[1] It became a recognised virtue (as well as an act of prudence) to profess belief without seeking to understand. Throughout Christendom men grew accustomed to having their minds made up by clergymen. Even when the enterprising Fathers of the Church devised a science of their own in place of that which they had persecuted, men were not anxious to contradict them. The new science, which avoided the effete methods of Eratosthenes and Aristarchus, and which did not need the mathematics of Archimedes or Eudoxus, was founded on the axioms of Hebrew scripture and ecclesiastical superstition. The earth was flat. The sun and stars were towed across the sky by angels for the benefit of man. There was ample room for heaven above and hell below. The bones of martyrs and effigies of saints were endowed with such healing power that scientific medicine might be given up as obsolete. Aesculapius was back in office with a new name. Even men of such uprightness and talent as St. Augustine and St. Jerome had so far lost their balance that they relied on obscure Jewish historians for information about natural phenomena, or thought the reading of the Classics a sinful self-indulgence. Nothing could more aptly illustrate the disgrace which had overtaken Hellenic humanism. Mediterranean man had lost his self-respect. Christianity, meanwhile, under worldly masters, acquired an aspect which the Apostles can hardly have foreseen.

*　　*　　*

THIS DISMAL state of things endured for centuries in the west, but was partially alleviated in the south and east. The main causes at this stage are military. The western parts of the Empire were not so easy to govern or defend from Constantinople as from Rome. The Emperors slowly lost their grip in the West. There were two significant results. One was a series of increasingly successful

---

[1] See, for instance, the Athanasian Creed, composed in the 5th century. This may be found, following Evensong, in the Book of Common Prayer.

barbarian invasions; the other was the rise of an increasingly independent ecclesiastical authority in Rome itself. Italy and the western
provinces were devastated by wars waged against invading Huns,
Vandals, Goths and Franks. Millions died by disease, famine and
the sword. Rome changed hands many times. But the invasions
were not permanently held up. The Roman Empire in the West
was destroyed, and the nature of the population in those parts
altogether changed.

The Popes succeeded where the Emperors failed. The new
populations, unlike some they replaced, had no great ancestral
civilisations to look back to. They were not inclined, either by tradition or intellect, to resent the imposition of Church dogmas. The
political condition of Europe was chaotic, and remained so for a
long time. The Church stood alone, as an enduring organisation,
amid change and civil strife. The armed force of ambitious but in-
secure rulers could be acquired for the service of the Church in
return for its influential public approval of their claims. These conditions favoured an extension of ecclesiastical dominion. The opportunities were ably seized by churchmen who were mostly the
bitter enemies of human learning. The alliance of the Popes with
the French kings, who halted the Moorish invasion from Spain
during the 8th century, finally settled the pattern that European
intellectual life should take for some hundreds of years. Charlemagne, the most distinguished of these kings, spread Papal influence, by frankly naked force, over the area now covered by Italy,
Austria, Germany and France. He had his reward when he was
anointed successor to the Roman Emperors in the West, in the
year 800, by Pope Leo III. It became understood that the Church
should sponsor those temporal powers which supported it—and
temporal power without the blessing of the Church was not easily
maintained. Thus ecclesiastical authority was backed by force; and
free thought became unfashionable in Western Europe. Such
scholarship as remained, being almost exclusively monastic, was
devoted to theology and a perennial study of the Fathers. Classical
science and literature lay disregarded or unknown.

The successful attacks on the priest-ridden Roman Empire in the
East came later. They were physically less devastating; but they
produced a greater change of outlook in the regions they affected.
The Byzantine Empire lingered on, steadily dwindling, until the

capture of Constantinople by the Turks in 1453. Its population remained mostly Greek in character and language; but the Greek
virtue had departed, for reasons we have seen. The Syrian,
African and Spanish provinces were over-run by the Arabs in the
7th century and the early part of the 8th. Persia also suffered
Moslem conquest during the same short period. The course of
Western thought was in time deeply influenced by these events.
The tyrant who sets out to order men's deeds is trivial by comparison with the tyrant who wishes to control their minds. The struggle
between Reason and Authority, which rose to prominence with the
growth of ecclesiastical power, and which is still very much alive,
is fundamental in the history of human development. Authority,
the aggressor, had much the better of it in the early stages, and
soon became firmly rooted in the West. It was a long time before
Reason could fight on equal terms. It might have been much longer
if there had been no Moslem conquests.

The rapid military success of the Arabs was partly due to the
fanaticism with which they sought to spread their new faith. It was
also partly due to the discontent and treachery of the African subjects of the Byzantine Empire. Many still had Arian sympathies,[1]
and detested the Catholic supremacy upheld by the Byzantine
government. Others were sick of the continual theological bicker-
ing which had taken the place of Greek philosophy and science.
The Jews, and those at heart still pagan, had a common dislike of
ecclesiastical bullying in Alexandria. It must have seemed to many
that there was little point in resisting a new régime which could
hardly be more distasteful than the old.

In its first phase the Arab rule seemed as much opposed to
secular learning as the Byzantine. Mohammed died while the
Moslem forces were still confined to the Arabian Peninsula; but
the holy war which he began was carried on by the Califs who
followed him. Alexandria fell to the second of them, who ordered
all that was still left of the library to be destroyed; pointing out (it
is said) that books which disagreed with the Koran were mistaken,

[1] The Arian heresy, the not unreasonable belief that the Father existed before
the Son, was condemned at the Council of Nicea (A.D. 323). Its author, Arius,
was an unsuccessful contender for the archbishopric of Alexandria during the
reign of Constantine. He had many supporters in North Africa; and his opinions
concerning the Trinity were widely held after his death, in the face of orthodox
antagonism.

while any that supported it were superfluous. It looked as if one intolerant religious system had merely given way to another.

But the attitude to human learning in the new Moslem Empire was soon changed. The Arabs mellowed as they overran the haunts of ancient civilisations in Egypt and Persia. Enough remained of the past in these places to suggest that the intellectual and social life of great cities could, at their best, offer something well worth while. The Arabs did not renounce their faith in Allah, or cease to take religion seriously. But their fanaticism waned and their sense of proportion grew. They began to understand the merits of humanism. In Syria and Persia they met the Nestorians, driven from Constantinople as heretics because they refused to regard the Virgin Mary as the mother of God. Those willing to suffer loss for the sake of unorthodox opinions are often anxious and able to think for themselves. This was the case with the Nestorians, who took into exile with them a lively interest in Greek science—especially the medicine which was giving way to superstition in Constantinople. They also took precious copies of the works of Greek thinkers, which they translated into the languages of the countries they settled in. Thus the Arabs met ideas of Hippocrates, Aristotle, Euclid, Archimedes, and Hipparchus. They saw the value of these ideas, and their intellectual curiosity was enlivened. They also came across the Indian mathematics which, no doubt, owed something to the Greek influence spread over the East by Alexander. They mixed easily with the Jews in Alexandria, where they learnt much about medicine. Here also they acquired that interest in alchemy which became so characteristic of them. The Ptolemies did much by wise statesmanship to bring races and cultures together in North Africa. This was not the least of their services to learning. For, even at the time of the Saracen invasion, the atmosphere which the Ptolemies had created still favoured the growth of easy intellectual relations between race and race.

The simplicity of the Mohammedan belief—There is but one God, and Mohammed is his Prophet—left no opening for subtle theological dispute. Men's minds were no longer turned aside from useful arts or scientific thought in the attempt to settle questions of divine precedence. Within 100 years of Mohammed's death there was a Moslem empire from the Indus to the Pyrenees, throughout which Greek philosophy and science, with Jewish medicine and Indian mathematics, were being studied, taught, developed and admired. This empire had no lasting political cohesion. But it had a genuine social and cultural unity, which it owed partly to the practice of polygamy, partly to a widespread educational system, and partly to the religious toleration which soon became its policy. Unbelievers had to pay a tax; but, once the first fanaticism had died down, they were otherwise unmolested. Many, seeing less harm in the Faith than in the tax, were converted. But no one worried much about those who remained obdurate. There was no serious attempt to maintain universal orthodoxy, and therefore no reason to restrict free thought. Christians were occasionally maltreated; but this was usually because they were enemies, not because they were Christians.

* * *

THE MOHAMMEDAN civilisation of the Middle Ages, occupying the whole southern border of the Mediterranean, and having a bridgehead on the European mainland in Spain, thus kept ancient science alive. This civilisation was bound in time to influence Catholic Europe. It is important mainly because it did so. The Arabs are not to be compared with their Greek forerunners or their Western successors as originators of ideas. But, without making any revolutionary contribution to thought, they quietly developed the science of the past in detail; and what they added to it, before handing it on, is not negligible. They achieved, at the same time, a sense of balance and a generous way of life such as Europe could not for centuries approach.

Arabian writers on mathematics were acquainted with Greek geometry but added little to it. They developed trigonometry for astronomical purposes, using tables of sines and tangents, such as we use today, instead of the chords used by the Alexandrians. They learnt arithmetic and algebra mainly from the Indian mathematicians Arya-Bhata and Brahmagupta. It is likely that these Indians knew something of Diophantine algebra, and it is possible that their arithmetic was of partly Babylonian origin. But the Arabs were not at first directly influenced by Diophantus, whose work they discovered only later. The most important Arabian mathematician was Alkarismi, who flourished early in the 9th century. It was through his writings on arithmetic and algebra that the

Indian decimal numeration eventually reached Italy, whence it spread over Europe. The word 'algorism', a corruption of Alkarismi's name, was often used for the methods of computation he advocated; while 'algebra' was derived from the first word in the Arabic title of his chief work.

In astronomy the Arabs were content with the epicyclic theory of Ptolemy. Arzachel of Toledo suggested, in the 11th century, that the planets might move in ellipses; but the idea was not taken seriously. Astronomical observation was systematically carried on, and its technique steadily improved. The Arabian observers deserve great respect for their accuracy. The French astronomer Laplace, for instance, found a use, in his *Exposition du Système du Monde* (1796), for several of their observations made in the 11th century. The impression left on astronomy by the Arabs is obvious to anyone who consults a star map: he will find it sprinkled with Arabic names such as Betelgeuse, Algol and Fomalhaut. Several words of Arabic origin—e.g. 'zenith', 'nadir', 'azimuth'—are regularly used in astronomical measurement.

Alhazen, who flourished in Egypt about the year 1000, treated optics from both physical and physiological points of view. His discoveries are among the most important made by the Arabs. He believed, as we now do, that light passes from its external source into our eyes, after being reflected by the objects we see. Until his time the accepted theory was that of Euclid, which suggested that light was sent out from the beholder's eye in search of what he wished to look at. The faults of Euclid's theory are so obvious that its prolonged life among the acute Alexandrians is not easy to understand.[1] It explains why we cease to see things through an obstruction, but it fails completely if we ask why we cease to see things when the sun sets or the curtains are drawn. Alhazen found direct confirmation of his new opinion in the structure of the eye, which he studied by dissection. He discovered a lens at the front, which could concentrate light on a screen, the retina, at the back. He knew that this screen was connected to the brain by an optic nerve. The whole structure seemed admirably suited for reception, but to have nothing whatever to do with transmission. And so he argued from anatomy to physiology; deducing the probable function of the instrument from its design.

[1] Perhaps it was suggested by the shining eyes of the sacred Egyptian cats?

Statue of Copernicus, Torun

PLATE 5

The Alchemist, by Ostade

PLATE 6

Light travels in straight lines in a homogeneous medium; but when it passes from one medium to another it is usually bent. This bending is called refraction. Let XYZ represent the boundary between two transparent media P and Q (Fig. 28). Let LYM be the

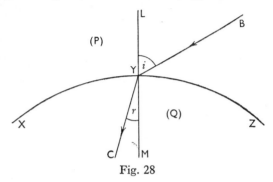

Fig. 28

normal to this boundary at Y. The ray BYC, passing from P to Q, is bent at Y. If, as shown, the ray is bent towards the normal as it enters Q, then Q is said to be optically denser than P. In passing from Q to P the light will be bent away from the normal. Rays near the normal are bent less than those more sharply inclined to it. The only unbent ray is that which has the normal for its path.

Refraction was studied superficially in Alexandria. Alhazen gave it more attention. Rays from a luminous point O, passing through a convex lens L, are refracted when they enter the glass and when they leave it. The rays which pass through the outer parts of the lens meet its surfaces more obliquely than those which pass near its centre, and are therefore more sharply refracted. If the lens is properly shaped, and O suitably placed, the rays from O will converge, after passing through the lens, to a point I (Fig. 29). A screen at I will show a luminous spot, called the image of O. The distance v, from the lens to I, will depend on the distance u, from the lens to O. Alhazen discovered the relation between u and v, in virtue of which the position of the image can be predicted when that of the object is known. This was an essential preliminary to the design of optical instruments, such as microscope and telescope. It was therefore of fundamental importance to science. For any science, if based (correctly) on observation, must gain by the artificial sharpening of the human senses.

9

Alhazen also considered atmospheric refraction, which had been noticed by Ptolemy, and which affects astronomical observations. The upper atmosphere is more rarified, and optically less dense, than that near the earth's surface. The optical density does not

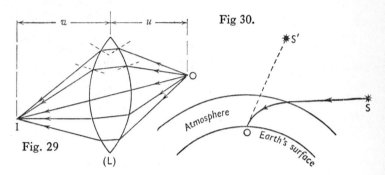

Fig 30.

Fig. 29

(L)

merely increase, but increases at an ever greater rate, as we approach the earth. Light from a star S (Fig. 30), entering the atmosphere obliquely, is therefore bent in a curve whose sharpness increases as it approaches the observer O. The light from S will seem to the observer to come from S'; and S will appear higher in the sky than it really is. When a star is near the zenith, the difference between its real and apparent directions is negligible, because its light enters the atmosphere almost normally. The difference increases as the star approaches the horizon. We may even see a star when it is below the horizon. Alhazen saw that atmospheric refraction could explain twilight. He also used it to explain the oval appearance of the sun just before it sets. The lower edge of the sun, being nearer the horizon, is more affected by refraction than the upper edge. These edges therefore seem closer to one another than they should; and the vertical diameter of the sun is shortened.

The fundamental problem in refraction is to find the relation between the angles of incidence and refraction—angles i and r in Fig. 28. Ptolemy attempted this. Alhazen showed that Ptolemy was wrong, but did not find the correct law. Although this law is simple, it proved elusive. It was at last discovered, early in the 17th century, by the Dutch scientist Snell. It states that $\sin i = \mu \sin r$, where μ is a number, called the refractive index, which has a fixed value for any given pair of media. If P is air and Q is water, $\mu = 1 \cdot 333$. In this case, if $i = 60°$, then $r \simeq 40\frac{1}{2}°$; so that the light is turned through about $19\frac{1}{2}°$. But if $i = 30°$, then $r \simeq 22°$; so that the bending is now only some $8°$.

The Arabs derived their interest in alchemy mainly from the Alexandrian Greeks and Jews, but partly from the Chinese. The purpose of Greek and Jewish alchemy was the discovery of the Philosopher's Stone, which could change base metals into gold. The idea of an elixir of life, or cure for all ills, probably came from Chinese sources. The Arabian alchemists and their European successors were interested in both stone and elixir. Alchemy was an art rather than a science; an art whose purposes were never likely to be achieved. It had in it a considerable occult element, but it was of value to science for its by-products. The alchemists discovered important substances, such as alcohol and the mineral acids, which turned out to have many uses in industry and in the gradual development of scientific chemistry. They also gained valuable knowledge of alloys and metallurgical processes. The development of optical glass was largely due to them. Much of the ordinary apparatus of chemistry, used for distillation, filtration and heating, was invented and improved by the alchemists. Alchemy was unscientific in its purpose; but it was partly scientific in its method, which involved experiment and observation. It was bound to lead to some chance discoveries of importance, even though it did not achieve the end it sought.

Modern chemistry owes much to the alchemists; but the evolution of scientific chemistry from alchemy was long delayed. It did not take place, as might have been expected, in the 16th and 17th centuries, when other sciences advanced at an astonishing rate. This failure of alchemy to change its nature appreciably during the Scientific Revolution provides a striking exception to the general rule that the sciences tend to advance or remain stagnant together. Physics deals with properties, such as mass, weight, extension, temperature and motion, which belong to all kinds of matter. But chemistry deals with properties which distinguish one substance from another. The backbone of scientific chemistry must therefore be a theory which allows one substance to differ from another, but which ensures that all things shall share the subsisting physical properties of matter as such. The atomic theory does just this. The universal physical properties of matter can be attributed to the material, whatever it may be, of which the atoms themselves are made. The chemical differences of one substance from another may then still be explained by supposing that the atoms in different substances vary in size, shape, arrangement or all three. The theory combines uniformity of material with variations of fine structure which *appear* to our imperfect senses as variations of material. Modern atomic theory maintains the idea that the atoms are differently arranged in different substances; but where Democritus made the individual atoms vary in size and shape, we suppose they differ in electrical structure. But the central notion—that chemical variations are structural variations superimposed on material uniformity—remains. The neglect of Leucippus and Democritus did no more than hinder physics; but it strangled chemistry. Newton and Boyle both believed that matter was atomic; but the atomic theory was not systematically adopted in chemistry until it was taken up by John Dalton (1766–1844). Since then chemistry has kept pace with the other sciences.

*   *   *

THUS, ALTHOUGH chaos followed the disintegration of the Roman Empire, the broad outlines of a new pattern had appeared in Europe and the Mediterranean region by about 800. Central and Western Europe were culturally backward and politically fluid, but were to some extent held together by the powerful and growing influence of the Roman Church and its military supporters. Asia Minor and the Balkans still formed a declining Byzantine Empire. Spain, North Africa and most of the Middle East were Mohammedan. It will be convenient for the time being to call these three areas, respectively, the west, the east and the south.

Not much need be said about the east. Some fugitives from Alexandria reached Constantinople with their books at the time of the first fanatical Moslem attack. From that time, until its fall in 1453, Constantinople was the chief resting place for what was left of classical literature in the original Greek. But the east has otherwise no importance in the history of science. There was little creative thought of any kind there during the Middle Ages.

The population in the west was virile but uncouth. It was the west which in the end produced the intellectual equals and worthy successors of the Athenians and Alexandrians. But it had first to be reduced to order. The Church played a big part in the ordering process. Despite the evil lives and violent deaths of many who sought ecclesiastical rank for the sake of wealth and power, it did establish some authority over secular rulers and some Christian standards of conduct among ordinary men. These standards were not always observed, but they stood as a rebuke to those who fell below them. Life under their influence gradually became gentler and less dangerous. The struggle for existence and security became less intense. The west began to acquire cultural and spiritual unity despite political division. While this was going on, the submission demanded by ecclesiastical authority did not seem irksome. The comforting influence of the Church was understood and seen to be necessary. But, as conditions of life became easier, men found time to think for themselves. It was natural that they should then question the Church's claim to expound all it was necessary or expedient for men to know. The growth of independent trading cities, such as Venice, Bruges and Hamburg, produced a powerful merchant class, who had wealth and leisure which they owed to neither king nor pope. The economic independence and influence of such men was accompanied by independence of mind. The previously dormant intellect of the west began to seek employment. It became susceptible to the influences which were ready to revive humanism.

The most important of these influences was that of the south, which entered Europe by several ways. Europeans met Mohammedan civilisation through the Crusades, through the penetration of Moorish influence beyond the Pyrenees, through the Sicilian Court of the Emperor Frederick II, and through trade—particularly that of Venetians and Genoese, whose only contact with the wealth of the Indies lay through the Mohammedan Middle East. Eminent men, kings, and even popes, despite their Christian prejudice, sought Arabian and Jewish physicians, who were more skilful than those of the west. Many of these physicians were deeply read in subjects other than medicine. Men of discernment in Europe were impressed by these glimpses of Mohammedan culture. From time to time, in search of education, they found their way into Moorish centres of learning. Among the ablest of those who did so were Gerbert, later Pope Sylvester II, and Adelhard of Bath, who returned from Cordoba with the first copy of *Euclid* to reach Catholic Europe. The Mongol conquests of the 13th century, and the journeys of Marco Polo to the court of Kublai Khan, further roused European interest in the outer world and the fresh ideas and adventures it offered.

Humanism is the active confidence of men in their own powers. The mythological figure which represents it is Prometheus. Signs of its revival in the west are discernible at least as far back as the 11th century; but for a long time they appear only spasmodically, in a few remarkable individuals. Such were Gerbert, Frederick II, Petrarch, Boccaccio and the Franciscan Roger Bacon. Bacon (*c.* 1214–1294) might have been important in the history of science if his contemporaries had accepted what he said. His strongly expressed opinion, that knowledge of the world must be gained from observation rather than authority, failed to impress the men of his time. It led him into trouble with the Franciscan authorities, despite his friendship with the Pope; and it did not produce the scientific movement he foresaw.

But although there was no obvious general change of outlook during the 12th, 13th and 14th centuries, ancient Greek ideas, coming mostly at third hand from the south, were inconspicuously making themselves felt in a Europe increasingly disposed towards free thought. After the fall of Constantinople (1453) quantities of classical literature reached Europe. In the second half of the 15th century the admiration of pre-Christian thought became open and widespread—first in Italy, and soon throughout the west. Classical scholarship was then recognised for a time as the most valuable of all intellectual accomplishments. It is important to understand, however, that there had been intellectual contact between the Italians and the Byzantine Empire, as well as between the Italians and Arabs, before 1453. The exciting, popular phase of the classical revival—which followed the events of 1453, and which coincided with the great voyages of discovery and the introduction of printing—was the culmination, not the beginning of the Renaissance.

The essential characteristics of the Renaissance are a new breadth of outlook and the development of secular learning—a learning neither practised exclusively by priests nor concerned exclusively with material approved by the Church. Its great men repudiated the narrow outlook so well illustrated by St. Jerome's renunciation of classical poetry. They were ready to be interested in any human pastime from trigonometry to black magic, without fear of the World, the Flesh or the Devil. They disregarded St. Paul, and openly gloried in men. The Renaissance, therefore, cannot fairly be described as a scientific or an artistic or a literary movement. It owed its life largely to the literary talent of its classical scholars, such as Erasmus and More; but the interests it excited were universal. Leonardo da Vinci is remembered as an artist; but he was important also as engineer, physicist, anatomist and mathematician. Copernicus is remembered as an astronomer; but he was also master of six languages, and is said to have been more or less expert in 'mathematics, physics, medicine, law, geography, philosophy, literature, history, biography, philology, finance, engineering, epistolography, painting, estate administration'. His achievements resemble those of Thackeray's Prince Giglio at the University of Bosforo.

Ecclesiastical leaders could not ignore the revival of humanism. At an early stage, when the first signs of southern influence appeared in Europe, the Church sought, by setting up its own philosophical system based mainly upon Aristotle, to make itself leader and controller in the new movement it foresaw. It was thus that the false scientific conclusions of Aristotle acquired a prestige which the leaders of the Scientific Revolution had to fight bitterly to overcome. Aristotle's inductive method had been used in Alexandria to the great advantage of science; but science in the west at the time of the Renaissance was held back by too much reverence for his conclusions.

Humanism may find an outlet on the one hand in philosophy and science, or on the other hand in art. As the Renaissance gathered force, the Church, continuing its struggle against independent thought, encouraged art as the less dangerous outlet.[1] We need not regret the astonishing result, for which a century of scientific progress, had it been demanded, would have been a small price. In fact, however, Renaissance art flourished without detriment to science. The Church failed to control the growth of secular learning. The Renaissance took a form unfavourable to ecclesiastical

---

[1] One need only consider the architecture of Renaissance churches, and the paintings of biblical subjects with classical backgrounds, to appreciate the diversion of an essentially pagan art to ecclesiastical purposes at this time (Plates 3 and 4a).

authority in intellectual matters. In Italy, with such men as Machiavelli, it became frankly pagan. In the more serious and moral north it led to the Reformation. But everywhere it encouraged individual liberty of thought and expression. It thus cleared the way for renewed activity in science, as well as stimulating interest in science by disinterring the science of the Ancients.

There is some resemblance between Renaissance Italy and Periclean Athens. In each there was a gathering together, and an unprejudiced comparison, of conflicting ideas from many sources. Men's minds were unsettled. The unsettlement led ultimately to a weakening of authority, and a great advance of science carried through by men with an essentially new outlook.

*   *   *

IN ASSESSING ancient and medieval science, we should beware of certain snap judgments. Greek science is often undervalued, because of its too speculative nature. There could be no greater mistake. We have had to stress the lack of empiricism among the Greeks, because the conflict between empirical and *a priori* methods is a great issue, pervading the history of thought, which must be understood. The triumph of empiricism was necessary for science. But speculation was an essential first step, and the debt of science to the Greeks cannot be exaggerated. They gave us the spirit of intellectual curiosity and free inquiry; they conceived the possibility of a rational, coherent scheme of natural knowledge; they created mathematics. Without these there could *be* no science. Their speculation, however unscientific, suggested nearly all the pregnant ideas of the Scientific Revolution. We inherit from them the true love of Nature, and the love of knowledge for its own sake. They teach us to be content only with the best in thought. Aristotle and the Alexandrians began a genuinely empirical science. It was not their fault that history prevented the immediate development of their work.

Another error we must avoid is to regard the Middle Ages in the west as a mere barbaric interlude. It is truer to say they were a necessary period of probation. There was no race ready to carry on the Greek tradition. The Romans *preserved* Greek culture for a time, but added nothing intellectually new to it. Roman engineering feats may still be seen, but there were no Roman scientific ideas. The Arabs took more interest in abstract thought, but had no great originality. The necessary intellectual force was latent in the new populations of the west after the fall of Rome, but centuries of gradual civilisation were needed before it could bear fruit. These centuries show little scientific achievement, by Greek or Renaissance standards. But they were not entirely wasted, because they were used by the west in growing up. The Dark Ages (*c.* 500–1000) were taken up in establishing a modicum of law and order. The insecurity of daily life was such that intellectual progress was scarcely possible. Europe's debt to the Roman Church at this period is immeasurable. The Church has often been the bitter enemy of independent thought; but its civilising and unifying influence in the Dark Ages did much to build a Europe in which such thought could emerge.

Intellectual activity increased rapidly in the later Middle Ages, when ecclesiastical influence was at its peak. Study was based mainly on the theology of the Fathers, the ancient lore retailed by Pliny and Boethius, the logic of Aristotle and some fragments of Plato. Its outlook was strictly limited, because its ultimate purpose was nearly always the fuller interpretation of Scripture or the better management of church services. But the habit of thought was revived. Centres of learning grew up in the schools, of cathedral and monastery, from which scholasticism takes it name. These embryo universities fostered the fruitful contact of mind with mind. Their outlook broadened as translations from the Arabic versions of Greek works became available. Craftsmen were all the time acquiring technical knowledge which would later prove invaluable to science. Thus the necessary skills of head and hand were ready when the Renaissance came.

G. K. Chesterton (*St. Francis of Assisi*, Chapter II) suggests an interesting interpretation of the Dark Ages. He regards them as a period of purgation. Greek science sprang from a love of Nature which, at its best, was priceless.[1] But it became polluted. Every animal and plant and star was connected with some obscene story in the *chronique scandaleuse* of mythology. The human intellect needed purification, by centuries of wandering in the wilderness, before it could again contemplate natural science without shame.

[1] See Sir D'Arcy Thompson's delightful essay on Aristotle in *The Legacy of Greece*.

St. Jerome and the early Christian hermits represent this point of view. They renounce the pleasures of the mind as severely as those of the flesh. St. Francis is the symbol of a returning gentleness, of which there are many traces in the art and thought of his age. His attitude to Nature indicates that the long penance is over. The stain is removed, and men are fit to study Nature with innocence again.

There is, perhaps, an element of fancy in this. But it may serve us as a warning. For modern science also has its taint. It is associated, not with harmlessly salacious legends, but with destruction and the abuse of power.

5

CELESTIAL GEOMETRY

THE PROGRESS of science since the Renaissance has been a continuous evolution. It is now, therefore, that we begin the study of modern science. The main lines of development were laid down during the period from Copernicus to Newton; i.e. between the middle of the 16th century and the end of the 17th. This phase is called the Scientific Revolution. The scientists of the 18th and 19th centuries were mainly occupied in performing the vast programme outlined for them at this time.

Science has made itself felt, since the Scientific Revolution, in two ways—technically and intellectually. Technical developments in engineering, agriculture, medicine and war have profoundly affected the fate of societies and the daily life of individuals. This direct influence of applied science is obvious. It is essentially modern. The technical influence of ancient science was always slight. Signs of technical advance did appear in Alexandria, but science was submerged before they came to anything. The science of Greek and Roman times never seriously affected economic life. The weapons it devised did not decide great wars. We shall notice from time to time the discoveries from which great technical achievements sprang; but the effect of technical advances on history seems so clear that we need not discuss it in detail. We shall concentrate on the less direct and less obvious, but possibly even more important, effects which pure science has had on thought and outlook.

With the revival of humanism there was a renewal of the struggle between Authority and Reason. Scientists were prominent in this struggle. Astronomers, particularly, were in the thick of it. The astonishing success of astronomy in the 17th century did more than anything else to restore confidence—and later, perhaps, to create over-confidence—in the power of human reason. Astronomy altogether changed the opinion which men held of their place in Creation. It changed their view as to how they could best cope with their environment. It led the other sciences, and put heart into them. We must therefore give it special attention.

*   *   *

THERE WERE two stages in the astronomical advance; the first geometrical, the second mechanical. The geometrical stage was accomplished by Copernicus, Tycho Brahe and Kepler. These men, each with a contribution characteristic of his particular talent, gave a beautiful solution to the problem posed, but never satisfactorily solved, by the Greeks: to deduce the arrangement and relative motions of the heavenly bodies from their bewildering apparent motions. The chief phenomena to be explained are: (i) The daily circling of the Pole by all the heavenly bodies (Chap. 1). (ii) The backward motion of the sun across the pattern of fixed stars (Chap. 1). (iii) The stations and retrogressions of the planets (Chap. 3). (iv) The seasons.

Copernicus, who took the first most daring step, was a Pole, born at Torun (Plate 5) 1473, died at Frauenberg 1543. As well as being an active churchman, he served his country as economist and diplomat. He received much of his education in Italy. His universal scholarship was typical of the Renaissance; and it was partly his wide reading in Greek that prepared him for his scientific work. In this reading he met the notion that the earth might move. He had the scientific sense to take this suggestion seriously. He also had the mathematical ability and perseverance to examine its implications in detail. In the published preface, which dedicates his book *De Revolutionibus Orbium Coelestium* to Pope Paul III, the Pythagoreans and Heraclides are cited as suggesting that the earth moves. There is no mention of Aristarchus, but no doubt Copernicus knew of him. Robert Record,[1] writing eight years after the death of Copernicus, speaks of him as having 'revived the opinion of Aristarchus Samius'. If Record had heard of Aristarchus in 1551, it is unlikely that so complete a scholar as Copernicus was unaware of him a few years earlier. Moreover, Heraclides considered only a rotation of the earth about its axis; while the Pythagoreans thought of the earth as revolving about a central fire

[1] Well known for introducing the symbol ' = ' into mathematics.

—not the sun. It was Aristarchus who suggested the
sun as the centre of the earth's
orbit; and this was the idea
at the root of the Copernican
theory. There is reason to
believe that the preface was
not published as Copernicus
wrote it.

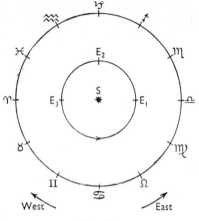

Fig. 31

The Ptolemaic System,
modified in accordance with
continued observation, had
become so involved that some
simpler interpretation of planetary motions was absolutely
necessary. Copernicus retains
the outer sphere of fixed stars; but he reduces it to rest, and
puts the sun at its centre. He supposes the planets move in concentric circles round the sun; their order, from the sun outwards,
being Mercury, Venus, Earth, Mars, Jupiter, Saturn. The moon
meanwhile circles the earth. The planets nearer the sun move more
quickly, and have smaller orbits, than those farther from it. Thus
Mercury completes its orbit in about 3 months, while Jupiter takes
nearly 12 years.

The apparent daily rotation of the heavens about the Pole is explained by supposing that the earth each day makes one complete
rotation about its own axis. The earth has also a third motion—
that slow change in the direction of its axis, called precession,
discovered by Hipparchus.

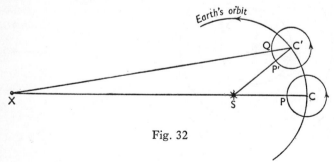

Fig. 32

The apparent annual motion of the sun among the stars is illustrated in Fig. 31. The outer circle must be imagined at a very great distance from the sun S. This circle is that in which the plane of the earth's orbit meets the sphere of the fixed stars: the constellations of the Zodiac are marked on it. When the earth is at E_1, the constellations ♓, ♈, ♉ will constitute the sun's background; while ♍, ♎, ♏ will be opposite the sun and will appear in the night sky. Three months later, when the earth is at E_2, the sun's background will be ♊, ♋, ♌; while ♐, ♑, ♒ will be seen at night. After 6 months, when the earth is at E_3, the sun will be in ♎ and we shall see ♓, ♈, ♉ at night.

Fig. 32 shows why the solar day is longer than the sidereal day. S is the sun, C the earth's centre, P an observer on the earth's surface, and X a fixed star—very distant compared with the sun. The earth's orbital and axial motions are suggested by arrows. The observer's noon occurs when C, P, S are in line. By noon on the next day the earth's centre will be at C'; and the earth's axial rotation must carry the observer round to P' to complete his solar day. To complete his sidereal day, however, he has only to reach Q.

The apparent retrogression of the planets follows naturally from the Copernican Theory. In circling the sun S, the earth takes up positions E_1, E_2, E_3 in the course of a year (Fig. 33). Jupiter, who moves less quickly, meanwhile takes up corresponding positions J_1, J_2, J_3. Let us suppose that the lines E_1J_1, E_2J_2, E_3J_3 lead, respectively, to the fixed stars B, A, C. When the earth is at E_1 and Jupiter at J_1, Jupiter will have B as his background. His background

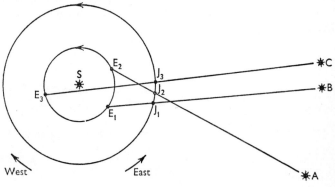

Fig. 33

when the earth is at E_2 will be A. He will have C as background when the Earth is at E_3. His apparent motion among the stars will therefore be from B to A and then from A to C. That is he will

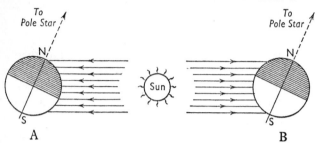

Fig. 34

appear to take a westward step followed by a longer eastward step. This process will be regularly repeated; so that Jupiter's apparent motion will be overwhelmingly, but not continually, eastward through the Zodiac. His stations, or moments of standing still, will occur whenever his apparent direction of motion is about to change.

The seasons depend on the tilt of the earth's axis. The view in Fig. 34 is that of an observer in the ecliptic, who sees the earth's orbital motion from the side, instead of from above as in previous diagrams. N and S are the earth's north and south poles. When the earth is at A the sun's rays fall more vertically in the northern hemisphere, and more obliquely in the southern hemisphere. We then have northern summer and southern winter. Six months later, when the earth is at B, this state of things is reversed, since the earth is on the opposite side of the sun, while its axis NS still points in the same direction.

Copernicus was thus able to account for the main planetary and solar phenomena without difficulty. As we saw with the atomists, however, it is not enough merely to invent an ingenious theory. Your theory will advance thought only if you can persuade others to adopt it as a working hypothesis. It is here that the merit of Copernicus chiefly lies. His idea was not original. He had the sense to see it was a good one; but it was not essentially his own. His real contribution lay in the years of patient work he devoted to the details. He realised that his system had no hope of general accept-ance on the grounds of simplicity and elegance alone. These might be recommendations; but the theory would convince no one unless it accounted for every known feature of planetary behaviour, however insignificant. Before publishing it, therefore, he undertook the tedious work of modifying it until it should agree with all such observations as he could make himself or find in the records of others.

His scholarly conservatism made this harder for him than it need have been. It was natural he should retain some of that respect for authority which had become ingrained in men by centuries of submission. The Renaissance did not at once substitute original thought for dependence on authority. What it did, rather, was to encourage recognition of more than one authority. Men of that time still felt bound to quote pronouncements of the past in support of what they said—the change consisted in their now often being ready to prefer the support of the Classics to that of the Fathers. Original thought was certain, in time, to follow the comparative study of conflicting authorities; but the serious growth of original thought in science did not appear until after Copernicus. He accepted, without question, the Greek assumption that celestial geometry must be dominated by the figures of sphere and circle. This meant that he could reconcile his theory with the facts only by reintroducing some of those epicycles which were the bane of the Ptolemaic System. He did not need the largest of them; but enough remained to spoil the simple beauty of his original theory. This must have disappointed him. But he was sufficiently sure of the virtue of his central idea to persevere with it; and *De Revolutionibus* was published in 1543, the year he died.

*   *   *

BEFORE CONSIDERING the reception and influence of the Copernican theory, we must see how it was improved by Tycho Brahe and Kepler.

Tycho, a Dane who lived from 1546 to 1601, did not himself accept the Copernican theory. His own system was a compromise. The earth was fixed at the centre of the universe,[1] while the sun and moon revolved round it. The orbits of the other planets, however, had the moving sun, and not the fixed earth, as centre.

---

[1] I.e. at the centre of the supposed sphere of fixed stars.

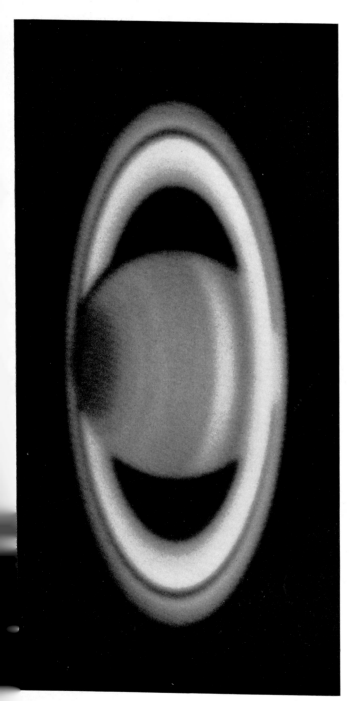

Saturn's rings

PLATE 7

(a) A typical spiral nebula

(b) A cluster of extra-galactic nebulae

This Tychonic System did not gain acceptance. Indeed, Tycho was never celebrated as a theorist. His fame depends on his skill and patience in observation. He was born of a noble family, but had no liking for the traditional occupations of his class. At the University of Copenhagen he read law; but his attention was soon diverted to astronomy. He was attracted by its astonishing power of prediction, and set out to construct planetary tables more reliable than any made before. He made instruments, and soon became well known as an observer. Fortunately for science he received the patronage of Frederick II of Denmark, who gave him a pension for life and a large sum of money with which to build an observatory on the island of Huen near Copenhagen. He called the place Uraniburg—Castle of the Heavens. He lived there, with his magnificent collection of instruments, making vast numbers of observations, from 1576 until 1592. He became the most famous scientific man in Europe. He dabbled in alchemy and astrology; but his genuinely scientific work was not vitiated by his deviations into the occult.

Tycho's angular measurements were the best ever made without optical aid, being reliable almost to 1/60 of a degree. It is surprising that he could do so much better than the Alexandrians, of whom the most accurate—Hipparchus—measured only to 1/15 of a degree.

After the death of Frederick II, Tycho failed to retain the royal favour. Those who were jealous of him engineered his eviction from Uraniburg. He never recovered from this blow; though, for a few years, he was re-established in an observatory at Prague by Rudolph II of Bohemia. Here Kepler, as a young man, became his assistant. Tycho's misfortune was thus ultimately good for science; because Kepler completed the new planetary tables—published, after Tycho's death, as the Rudolphine Tables—and, in doing so, had access to the records which made his own peculiar contribution to astronomy possible.

Kepler (Plate 9a), whose life was marred by poverty and ill health, differed from Tycho as much in talent as in background. Poor sight made him an indifferent observer; but he was an imaginative theorist, and a first-class mathematician with an almost Pythagorean belief in the mathematical simplicity of Nature. He was convinced that the planets moved according to simple

10

geometrical laws, and that these laws could be abstracted from the mass of figures accumulated by Tycho. Like many of the Greeks, he assumed that the natural laws he sought could be expressed in terms of existing mathematics. As it fortunately turned out, his naïve assumption was justified; and he did succeed, after many false starts, in discovering three beautifully simple principles, by which the clumsy epicycles were finally done away with. He read astronomy at Tübingen, where he met Copernican ideas. Unlike Tycho, he adopted, and always afterwards defended, the central notion that the earth revolves with the other planets about the sun. But he was determined to eliminate the crude geometrical devices with which it was encumbered.

He first sought a rule governing the distances of the planets from the sun. Having found no simple numerical relation, he tried to solve the problem by geometrical constructions involving the regular polygons and regular solids. These attempts, which never led to anything better than a very rough approximation, were of no scientific value. They are interesting only because they illustrate the strange persistence of mathematical mysticism. Kepler was inordinately pleased with his final effort, which was as fantastic as any Pythagorean speculation. It consisted in fitting regular solids neatly into the gaps between the planetary spheres. Six planets were known in Kepler's time, so that there were five interplanetary gaps. It must have seemed providential that there were also five regular solids! But this construction did not impress the scientifically adult Tycho, who (like the Alexandrians) knew that a mature astronomy could not rest upon the superstitious admiration of geometrical figures.

It is not surprising that Kepler failed in this particular research; for there is no simple numerical or geometrical formula for the sizes of planetary orbits. The nearest thing to it (so far) is Bode's Law (so called), suggested by Titius of Wittemberg in 1766: 'Take the series 0, 3, 6, 12, 24, 48, 96, . . .; add 4 to each term; then divide by 10.' This gives the series 0·4, 0·7, 1·0, 1·6, 2·8, 5·2, 10·0, . . . If we take the distance of the earth from the sun as unit, the distances of Mercury, Venus, Mars, Jupiter and Saturn are in fact 0·39, 0·72, 1·52, 5·20 and 9·54. Thus, if we omit the 2·8 from Bode's series, the remaining figures correspond roughly to the distances of the first 6 planets from the sun. The figure 2·8 corresponds in a vague way to the crowd of minor planets between Mars and Jupiter. When Uranus was discovered, in 1781, the agreement was again close—Bode's distance 19·6; actual distance 19·18. But Neptune (38·8; 30·07) tilted the applecart, and Pluto (77·2; 39·5) upset it completely.

In suggesting that the earth moved, and was not at the centre of the universe, Copernicus challenged the authority of Aristotle and Ptolemy. But he had not altogether freed himself from the net of ancient ideas. He had Greek authority even for his most daring suggestions, and he never questioned the Greek prejudice in favour of uniform and circular motions. Kepler's early preoccupation with the regular solids suggests a still more conservative—not to say reactionary—outlook. It was, nevertheless, he who at last asserted the right of Western astronomers to absolute independence of thought. He introduced notions for which there was no ancient authority at all. It is perhaps he, rather than Copernicus, who should be regarded as the first genuinely modern astronomical theorist.

It was in trying to understand Mars that Kepler was at length forced to consider the possibility of motion that was neither uniform nor circular. Mars is easier to observe than Mercury or Venus, since, unlike them, it is visible for long periods at night. Its movements, also, had been more fully traced at this time than those of Jupiter or Saturn, because it completes its orbit more rapidly. Mars was therefore the best subject for a first investigation. Kepler's problem was to determine orbits and velocities for both Mars and the earth in such a way that the apparent motion of Mars, as noted by Tycho, should follow from them. He formed one hypothesis after another, concerning the dispositions of the orbits and the velocities of the planets. Each hypothesis was laboriously tested. The hypothetical behaviour of Mars was each time calculated in great detail, so that it could be compared with the observed behaviour. His early hypotheses still relied on the combination of uniform circular motions. It was only when he altogether broke with tradition, to introduce non-uniform and then non-circular motions, that he succeeded. In 1609, after years of work and disappointment, he announced two laws governing the motion of Mars:

(i) *The orbit is an ellipse with the sun at one focus.*

(ii) *The line joining Mars to the sun covers equal areas in equal times.*

Ten years later he applied these laws to the other planets.

It may be as well to explain the meaning of his statements in some detail. We have encountered the ellipse as cross-section of a cone. It may be obtained in other ways, of which we need consider only one. Let S and T (Fig. 35) be fixed points. If M moves, on the paper, so that the sum of the distances SM and TM is constant, then M will describe an ellipse. Thus the ellipse may be drawn by fixing pegs at S and T, placing a loop of string (represented by the dotted line) round these pegs and round the pencil M, and moving the pencil over the paper so that the string remains taut. S and T are called the foci. The ellipse is symmetrical about the line through S and T. If it meets this line at A and B, then AB is called the major axis. The point O, midway between A and B, is called the centre. The ellipse is also symmetrical about the line COD, perpendicular to AB. This line is called the minor axis. If OS is expressed as a fraction of OA, this fraction is called the eccentricity. When the eccentricity is small, the foci are near the centre, and the ellipse is nearly circular: if it is large, the foci are distant from the centre, and the ellipse is elongated. The planetary orbits have eccentricities varying from 0·007 (Venus) to 0·2 (Mercury), and do not differ greatly from circles.

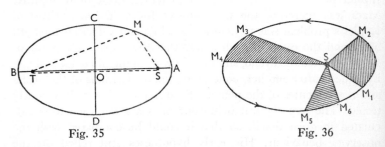

Fig. 35   Fig. 36

Fig. 36 represents the orbit of Mars, with the sun S at one focus. The points of the orbit nearest to and furthest from the sun —the opposite ends of the major axis—are called, respectively, the perihelion and aphelion. Together, they are called the apses. M_1, M_2, M_3, M_4, M_5, M_6 are successive positions of Mars. If it takes equal times to move from M_1 to M_2, from M_3 to M_4, and from M_5 to M_6, then, according to Kepler's second law, the shaded areas are equal. It is clear, therefore, that the planet moves faster when nearer the sun.

By 1619 Kepler was convinced that his two laws were obeyed by all the planets. He had discovered also a third law. This states that the squares of the periodic times of the planets are proportional to the cubes of their mean distances from the sun. The phrase 'periodic time' means the time taken by the planet to complete its orbit. 'Mean distance from the sun' is open to several interpretations. In this context it means half the sum of the greatest and least distances; i.e. half the length of the major axis of the orbit. If t is the periodic time and d is the mean distance from the sun, then t^2/d^3 is the same for all planets.

Thus, within 100 years, an encyclopaedic scholar, an incomparable observer and an imaginative mathematician, no two of whom could have succeeded without the third, had solved the problem set 2000 years earlier by the Greeks. The Ptolemaic System, with its fixed earth and crazy epicycles, was not yet generally disowned; but it could evidently not survive for long in face of the elegant heliocentric pattern which had now appeared. The intellectual unsettlement in Renaissance Italy had been followed by a new science in Western Europe as surely as the intellectual unsettlement in Athens was followed by a new science in Alexandria. The work of Copernicus, Tycho and Kepler was only the beginning of a period of science which more than bears comparison with that of the Museum. But, before noticing the other great steps in the Scientific Revolution, let us see how the heliocentric astronomy was preached, criticised and defended; and how it affected thought in general.

*   *   *

THE HELIOCENTRIC view was not readily adopted by the educated world. Its great virtue as a working hypothesis, after its modification by Kepler, was its striking mathematical simplicity. As originally put forward, however, it possessed this virtue in a very moderate degree. Its possibilities were at first foreseen only by a few men of exceptional insight. The notion of a fixed earth was natural to common sense. Men were not generally prepared to forgo it in return for the slight gain of simplicity which was all the new theory at first appeared to offer. There were, moreover, serious scientific and religious objections to reinforce those of common sense.

The first scientific objection was geometrical. We noticed it in connection with Aristarchus. The earth's motion about the sun should produce apparent changes in the relative positions of the fixed stars, unless they are at such a distance that the diameter of the earth's orbit is negligible by comparison. No such changes were detected, even by gifted observers like Hipparchus and Tycho. It was therefore necessary either to deny the orbital motion of the earth or admit that the stars were at a scarcely credible distance. Copernicus, like Aristarchus, underestimated the size of the earth's orbit. Even so, the least distance he could attribute to the stars, assuming the earth moved, must have seemed fantastic to most of his contemporaries. It was an act of great scientific faith to admit the possibility of such distances; but it was an act which had to be accomplished by all supporters of the Copernican theory for some 300 years. There was no direct evidence of these great stellar distances until the 19th century.

The other scientific objections were mechanical. If the earth moved, why could its motion not be felt? Why was there no rush of air? Why did falling bodies drop vertically, instead of being left behind in their flight by the moving earth? These were questions which existing mechanics could not answer. This science had to be rebuilt on fresh foundations before the mechanical problems set by the new astronomy could be solved. Kepler's suggestion of elliptic motion increased the mechanical difficulties. They *were* overcome, mainly by Galileo and Newton. But for the time being they formed a serious obstacle.

These scientific objections carried great weight with Tycho. He was the most distinguished scientific opponent of the heliocentric theory, although—ironically—he played an essential part in its perfection. The temporary scientific embarrassment of the Copernicans was, of course, remorselessly exploited by those who disapproved of the new astronomy for other than scientific reasons.

We may notice two obvious religious objections. Firstly, there are passages of Scripture which the heliocentric theory undoubtedly contradicts, if they are taken literally. Luther quoted Joshua 10:12. This says that Joshua commanded the sun to stand still: it implies, therefore, that (normally) the sun moves. The first verse of Psalm 93, quoted by Calvin, denies the motion of the earth: it says '... the world also is stablished, that it cannot be moved'. He might have used Psalm 104:5, with equal force. This kind of objection came naturally from leaders of the reformed churches, with their confidence in the final authority of the Bible.[1] The only valid answer, if the Copernican theory and the authority of the Bible are both to stand, is a figurative interpretation of the texts in question. But there were not many people in 16th- or 17th-century Europe willing to accept such an answer wholeheartedly.

Secondly, it was soon clear that the new astronomy, as it developed, disagreed more profoundly at every step with the Aristotelian and Ptolemaic science sponsored by the Roman Church. It challenged ecclesiastical, as well as biblical, authority. It was some time before Rome, with the Reformation already on its hands, realised the force of this new threat to its authority. Copernicus was himself a monk. He was also canon of Warmia, of which his uncle was Roman Catholic bishop and virtual ruler. He was a man of such integrity that he would either have left the Church or abandoned his new ideas if he had thought them irreconcilable with orthodoxy. He discussed his ideas freely with ecclesiastical superiors before publishing his work. There is no evidence that he had anything but encouragement from them. The first signs of religious opposition appeared in Protestant Wittemberg, in 1542, where Copernicus's friend Rheticus first sought a publisher for *De Revolutionibus*. The first edition in fact appeared at Nuremberg in 1543; but the editor, Osiander, thought it necessary to disarm criticism by rewriting the preface. The false preface suggested that the earth's motion might advantageously be taken as a hypothetical basis for calculation, but need not be regarded as a fact. Osiander struck out references to Aristarchus,[2]

[1] It is doubtful whether they would have approved the use made of Scripture by the Dominican friar, Caccini, in 1614. Opening the ecclesiastical attack on Galileo, he preached a sermon in the church of Santa Maria Novella, Florence (Plate 4b), in which he took his text from the Acts 1:11. This passage, which in our Authorised Version reads 'Ye men of Galilee, why stand ye gazing up into heaven?' lends itself to the translation 'Ye Galileans, etc.' We may admire Caccini's wit; but his sally was contemptible as a contribution to serious controversy—especially as one of the charges subsequently brought against Galileo was that of taking liberties with biblical texts!
[2] Thereby exposing Copernicus to unfair charges of dishonesty.

whose opinions he thought too daring. Passages remained in the book itself, however, which made it clear that Copernicus accepted the earth's motion as a fact; and there is no doubt that his 16th- and 17th-century followers did so. Thus the book, written by a sincere Catholic and dedicated to the Pope, was published with Papal approval in the face of Protestant opposition. Serious Catholic opposition came only after the Council of Trent. Its full fury fell upon those successors of Copernicus who popularised his ideas. During the 17th century, Catholic and Protestant leaders equally disliked Copernican ideas. But Protestant success in the Reformation was partly due to princes who wished to free themselves from ecclesiastical domination: and science was less persecuted in Protestant countries, where ecclesiastical power was less than in the Catholic countries.

The chief disseminators of Copernican ideas were Giordano Bruno, Kepler and Galileo. Augustus de Morgan says of Bruno: 'He was first a Dominican priest, then a Calvinist; and was roasted alive at Rome, in 1600, for as many heresies of opinion, religious and philosophical, as ever lit one fire.' Such a man was unable to support the opinions of Copernicus with moderation. He had to set them forth with a vehemence calculated to make Catholic hair stand on end. The speculations which he based on them clearly showed how dangerous to orthodoxy the new astronomy was likely to become. He laid emphasis on the great stellar distances, and boldly asserted that the physical universe was infinite. This was contrary to Aristotle; though the implied tribute to the majesty of God might perhaps serve to palliate the offence. He now went further; suggesting that there might be innumerable systems like that surrounding the sun, and innumerable inhabited planets like the earth. This made nonsense of the doctrine that the human race on earth enjoyed a uniquely privileged place in the universe and in the eye of God. Were there now to be as many Falls and as many Redemptions, as many Catholic Churches and rival popes, as there were planetary systems? It would be interesting to know whether St. John (10:16) was ever quoted in Bruno's defence on this point. Some of his other heresies were less respectable: and, although we may not believe in burning those who disagree with us, we must admit that Bruno went out of his way to fan the flames. He was the kind of advocate who does a cause more harm than good. His extensions of the Copernican thesis, however bold, were quite unscientific; and, by associating it with heresies that had nothing to do with it, he stirred up unnecessary animosity against it. But it was not until 1616, when the attack was in the abler hands of Galileo, that the Congregation of the Index banned *De Revolutionibus*. The book was released in 1620, with emendations on the lines of Osiander's preface.

While Kepler was engaged in the mathematical reformation of the new astronomy, Galileo (1564–1642, Plate 9b) was doing even more for it in other ways. He attacked Aristotelian science at all its vulnerable points. Thus, besides directly advocating Copernican astronomy, he did much to clear the way for it. He was the chief pioneer of the new mechanics, called Newtonian, for which we have already seen the need. This part of his work, probably the most important, is explained in the next chapter. At present we must consider his telescopic discoveries, which all testified against the systems of Aristotle and Ptolemy.

The possibility of a telescope was first shown by Hans Lippershey, an optician of Middleburg, in 1608. Galileo, hearing of it, soon constructed one. He made sensational discoveries with it in 1609 and 1610—within a year of the announcement of Kepler's first two laws. A new epoch in observational astronomy had begun. Tycho's observations were more accurate than those of the Alexandrians, but Galileo's were altogether different in kind.

He found that the lunar landscape was like that of a barren earth, and that there were dark spots on the face of the sun. Here was further evidence against Aristotle's belief in the immutability and unearthly perfection of the heavens. This belief had already been shaken by the appearance of bright new stars, observed in 1572 by Tycho and 1604 by Kepler. The Aristotelians tried to maintain that these stars were sublunary, but their case was feeble. Galileo also found that the Milky Way consisted of countless very faint stars. This disclosure made the vast extent, if not the infinity of the universe, more plausible.

The greatest stir was caused by his discovery that Jupiter had four satellites. This showed that there were bodies in the Solar System which did not revolve directly about the earth. Thus it seemed to lessen the probability that the earth was the centre of the universe. It was awkward for the Aristotelians in another way; since they held, without scientific reason, that there were only seven celestial bodies apart from the fixed stars. It is hard to believe or exaggerate the obstinate stupidity of the opposition met by Galileo concerning 'the circumjovial planets', as Kepler called them. Let us be content with part of a passage from Francesco Sizzi of Florence, quoted by Sir Oliver Lodge in *Pioneers of Science*.

> Moreover the satellites are invisible to the naked eye, and therefore can have no influence on the earth, and therefore would be useless, and therefore do not exist. Besides, the Jews and other ancient nations as well as modern Europeans have adopted the division of the week into seven days, and have named them from the seven planets: now if we increase the number of planets this whole system falls to the ground.

Jupiter's satellites soon turned out to have at least two uses (therefore they exist!). They are frequently eclipsed as they pass through Jupiter's shadow. As their periods of revolution are known, the times of future eclipses should be easily predictable. In 1675 the Danish astronomer Roemer noticed that the eclipses occurred before the expected time when Jupiter was at his least distance from the earth, and after it when he was at his greatest distance. Roemer explained this by supposing that light from the region of Jupiter takes longer to reach us when it has further to go. He thus confirmed the conjecture of Empedocles, that light has a finite velocity. Roemer was able, by comparing the observed and predicted times of the eclipses, to make the first rough estimate of this velocity.

Jupiter's moons also serve as a public clock, visible from all parts of the earth. The Greenwich times of the eclipses are known. Thus, wherever a man is, he can tell Greenwich time by observing them. He can then find his longitude by comparing Greenwich and local times, since these differ by 4 minutes for each degree of longitude. Such methods of finding Greenwich time (without going to Greenwich) were necessary to navigators before the introduction of accurate chronometers and radio time-signals.

The phases of Venus and the rings of Saturn complete the list of Galileo's main telescopic discoveries. According to Ptolemy, Venus and Mercury move as shown in Fig. 27. In this case their bright faces, which are turned towards the sun, will never be fully pre-

sented to the earth. If, on the other hand, they revolve about the
sun, as Copernicus maintained, they will have phases like the moon.
Fig. 37 illustrates this. When the planet is at A, we shall see it fully
illuminated. When it is at B, we shall still see it more than half

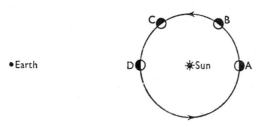

Fig. 37

illuminated. At C it will appear as a crescent. At D its bright face
will be turned right away from us, and we shall not see it at all.
Copernicus predicted such phases for Mercury and Venus.
Galileo saw them in the case of Venus. This showed that Ptolemy
was in one respect definitely mistaken. It did not show that the
Copernican theory was necessarily right. There are other theories,
such as that of Tycho, which account equally well for the phases of
Venus.

Saturn shook Galileo's faith in his own powers of observation.
He had announced that through his telescope it appeared to be a
triple planet—a large sphere with a smaller one in close attendance
on each side. Observing it some time later, he found it looking in-
nocently normal. He was, in fact, seeing Saturn's rings for the first
time; but he could not decide their nature correctly, because his
telescope was too feeble. They were first identified as rings by the
Dutch scientist Christian Huygens in 1655. Their aspect, as seen
from the earth, varies. They are prominent when seen as in
Plate 7. When looked at from the edge they can be seen only
with a very powerful telescope. This explains why Galileo saw
them on one occasion but not on another. It worried him. He seems
even to have thought, for a time, that all his beautiful discoveries
might be the result of hallucination. Such diffidence is characteristic of a first-class mind with a strong scientific case. The
arrogance of Galileo's opponents was that of very ordinary men
with no case beyond their own prejudice.

Galileo, like Bruno, was persecuted by the Inquisition. But his opinions, unlike Bruno's, were the product of sober scientific judgment, and related to purely scientific questions. The two cases were therefore different. Science proceeds by continuous, intelligent self-criticism. All scientific opinions are liable to doubt and change. But they are changed by reason, and the steady accumulation of evidence. Force, wielded by arbitrary authority, can only suppress them for a time. Galileo was compelled (outwardly) to deny his Copernican views. But his oppressors, in the long run, made themselves ridiculous without retarding the advance of science. It must be said that Galileo was treated courteously and, by the ecclesiastical standards of the day, leniently. He made the tactical mistake of commenting on biblical texts which he supposed to contradict Copernican astronomy. He would have been wiser to stick to his own subject, and leave this to the properly instructed theologians. He was often tactless and scornful in debate, thus unnecessarily aggravating the jealousy of his Aristotelian opponents in the universities and Church. Authority, however, had now no real chance of holding science back as in the past. Men like Galileo and Descartes were already writing in their native languages instead of Latin. Their ideas spread more rapidly and widely than those of their predecessors. Unorthodox thinkers could usually escape molestation, if not disapproval, in Protestant countries.

In England, as in Holland, men were free to hold whatever scientific opinions they chose. There was little or no persecution of science in Elizabethan times or during the 17th century. The Copernican system was accepted by several well-known Elizabethan scholars, of whom the most distinguished was William Gilbert, physician to Elizabeth and founder of the science of magnetism. The ideas of Copernicus, Kepler and Galileo steadily gained ground. By the latter part of the 17th century they were well established among early members of the Royal Society, such as Wallis, Wren, Hooke, Newton and Halley. It was among these men that the theory of universal gravitation, perhaps the most important achievement of the Scientific Revolution, took shape. Continental thought, meanwhile, was much influenced by Descartes, who, impressed by the misfortunes of Bruno and Galileo, preferred not to show any marked enthusiasm for the heliocentric view. Mathematics flourished under his influence; but astronomical theory, while advancing triumphantly in England, made little progress on the Continent.

Milton's references to the new astronomy are notable. They imply the spread of interest to those who were neither men of science nor supporters of ecclesiastical tradition. It was natural that a man of Milton's erudition should be aware of the revolution in thought that was going on outside his own sphere of letters.[1] And he would not have mentioned the subject without knowing what he was talking about. The interesting point is that he seems to expect a similar knowledge in his readers. In Book VIII of *Paradise Lost* there is a passage where Raphael, discussing the celestial motions with Adam, warns him not to study them too deeply. In this passage, Raphael asks

> What if the Sun
> Be Center to the World, and other Starrs
> By his attractive vertue and thir own
> Incited, dance about him various rounds?
> Thir wandering course now high, now low, then hid,
> Progressive, retrograde, or standing still,
> In six thou seest, and what if sev'nth to these
> The Planet Earth, so stedfast though she seem,
> Insensibly three different Motions move?

In the sixth and ninth lines Milton refers to the irregularities of apparent planetary behaviour, and the three motions—orbital, axial, precessional—with which Copernicus endows the earth in order to explain such irregularities. The reader who can see the point of these references must have more than a superficial knowledge of Copernicus. But this is not all that is expected of him. The third line, with its allusion to universal gravitation, presumes the general reader's acquaintance with a current scientific topic. For *Paradise Lost* appeared in 1667, when the notion of universal gravitation was still growing in the minds of Hooke and Newton. Newton's mathematical assault on the problem began in 1666; but the theory of gravitation was not well established until after the appearance of his *Principia* in 1687.

It is unlikely Milton would have made such allusions had he not

---

[1] He met Galileo in 1638.

felt sure they would be understood by at least some general readers. We may therefore suppose that science had begun to acquire an intelligent public in England.

*   *   *

ALTHOUGH PERSECUTION checked science for a time in some places, its total effect was negligible. It was no more successful in the 16th and 17th centuries against astronomy than in Roman times against Christianity. Its only permanent result is the preference still shown by astronomers for pagan names in the sky. Neither persecution nor argument could restrain the spread of Copernican ideas and the new outlook they implied. Anti-Copernicans, lay and clerical, were numerous for some time; and no doubt they still exist. The Roman Church maintained until 1822 that Copernican theory should be taught only as a mathematical device. There were universities, in Europe and America, which offered Ptolemaic and Copernican systems side by side during the 18th century.

The idea of absolute motion—i.e. motion of a body without reference to something else—is one which has never been successfully defined. The assertion that a body moves is meaningless, unless we say what other body it moves in relation to. The question 'Does the earth move?' which Copernicans and their opponents sometimes (erroneously) thought they were discussing, is pointless. If we ask whether the earth moves in relation to the fixed stars or the throne of God or the luminiferous ether, we may not discover the answer; but there is, at least, something to argue about. Thus, although the attachment of false prefaces to other people's books is not to be commended, Osiander saw the valid way out of trouble—in so far as the issue was simply the rest or motion of the earth. Let ecclesiastics, defending biblical authority, refer all motion to the earth. Let astronomers, predicting celestial events, refer motion to the sun, if they can thereby ease their calculations. Neither side then has any right to tell the other it is wrong.

But this was not the only point. Copernicans suggested a motion of the earth in relation to the fixed stars; a motion which was undetected because of the immense distance of the stars, but which might at any moment be detected. In this they were really open to contradiction. And, furthermore, their opponents had every reason to contradict them. For this undetected motion of the earth with reference to the stars, if it existed, had implications which, as we have seen, Bruno made embarrassingly plain. It was not so much the notion of a moving earth as the consequent notion of an almost limitless universe which enabled the new celestial geometry to threaten the foundations of established doctrine and cause a revolution in human outlook. The astronomical importance of the earth, and the unique cosmic importance of the human race, which so many men had complacently accepted since the appearance of Genesis, became at once open to grave doubt.

It is now fairly certain the Copernicans were right. All relevant observations since the 17th century have given evidence for the great size of the universe. A picture as awful as Bruno's wildest vision is now painted by calculating men of science whose whole training predisposes them to understatement. Those who began in the 17th century to see need for a radically new assessment of man's place in Creation have been fully justified. But the intense conflict of feeling that arose was mainly a conflict of science with orthodoxy, not of science with religion. The implications of the new astronomy, though they led many to question orthodox teaching in matters not purely religious, and though they suggested atheism to a few, were not essentially anti-religious. The universe now appeared vaster and more terrifying than Aristotle had supposed. This must have seemed to most men, in their newly discovered loneliness, to emphasise the need for belief in a protecting deity. Moreover, the new prospect of creation on a magnificent scale could hardly fail to promote worship of the Creator. Thoroughgoing Copernicanism was therefore quite compatible with an essentially religious outlook. There are, however, some matters in which men can rely indirectly on God, by using the senses and reason He has given them, and others which can be understood only through direct divine revelation. Resurgent science applied sense and reason to questions which the Churches still held within the sphere of revelation. The conflict was aggravated because a vested interest was at stake. Refusal to admit the final arbitration of the Churches, in whatever field, was ultimately an attack upon the power of priests. Many priests, despite their divine mission, were human enough to resent such an attack. Part of the opposition to science was no doubt the result of sincere, if sometimes mistaken, religious feeling. But the real clash was again between Reason and an essentially human Authority whose supporters, now as at the time of Constantine, had ulterior motives.

Reason this time gained the upper hand. It was more strongly represented by the vigorous new astronomy in the 17th century than by senile Greek philosophy and science in the 4th and 5th centuries. Authority was divided and weakened by the Reformation; and it made a bad tactical blunder by attacking science at the wrong point. It rashly challenged the validity of scientific conclusions. None of its supporters had the knowledge or intellect to win a battle of wits with Galileo on his own ground. They had to retire, looking foolish, and resort to force, which they could no longer use as ruthlessly as in the past. It is not suggested that scientific conclusions should be uncriticised. They are continuously and searchingly criticised by scientists themselves, who have the necessary knowledge and are adept in the appropriate modes of thought. The point is, simply, that Authority put itself at a disadvantage by trying to use the very weapon in which its enemy's superiority was greatest. It failed, meanwhile, to make any effective use of the strongest argument against science. This argument appears in the third chapter of Genesis and in the Greek myth of Prometheus. It does not deny the validity of science; it suggests that scientific knowledge is inimical to human happiness. It is as forceful now as ever. Are the comforts of modern medicine, transport, engineering and agriculture worthwhile if they go with poison gas, atomic bombs and truth drugs? Should a highland glen be spoilt for the sake of hydro-electric power? Do you prefer the peace of mind that accompanies simple faith, or would you rather have the intense intellectual satisfaction of discovery? Is ignorance, perhaps, really bliss? Our answers to questions of this sort depend on judgments of value. The verdict may at any time turn against science. Without taking sides, we can see that a debate on these lines might be nicely balanced. It is unwise to argue with an astronomer about the distance of the stars or the existence of Jupiter's moons. He is probably right, and can probably maintain his case successfully before an impartial audience. But his moral and aesthetic judgments are likely to be no sounder than your own. You have a good chance of defeating him if you assert that his occupation is pernicious because men are not so happy now as when they thought the stars were nearer. It is easier to persuade people that the scientist's work is harmful than to convince them that his results are false.

* * *

SUCH 18th- and 19th-century work as initiates new lines of thought will be considered later. But much of the work of these two centuries is so directly founded on the ideas of the Scientific Revolution that it is best studied in immediate relation to its 16th- and 17th-century beginnings. In the last section of this chapter, therefore, we consider how the new notions of celestial geometry have been extended in more recent times.

The 18th century saw rapid improvements in astronomical instruments and methods of observation, associated chiefly with the names of James Bradley (1693–1762) and Sir William Herschel (1738–1822). Bradley confirmed Roemer's discovery of the velocity of light. The known extent of the Solar System was greatly increased by Herschel's discovery of Uranus in 1781. This caused a great sensation; but the less spectacular and more important discoveries were being made outside the Solar System. Herschel, who came to England from Hanover as a musician, became the founder of modern stellar astronomy. He made his own telescopes, the best of his day; and he used them diligently to scan the whole northern sky. His study of the distribution of the stars convinced him that the sun was one of a great cloud of stars, the Galaxy or Galactic System, having roughly the shape of a rather flat bun.[1] This conclusion has been amply confirmed; but his belief that the sun was near the centre of the system has been modified. If we suppose the bun cut and buttered, then the butter serves as an image of what is called the Galactic Plane. The sun is nearly in this central plane, but is now thought to be some way from the centre of the system. The irregular band of faint light, visible across the sky on a clear night, which is called the Milky Way, is what we see when we look edgeways, towards the circumference of the Galaxy, through a great depth of stars. Some parts of the Milky Way are brighter than others. It is reasonable to suppose that these are the parts we see when we look towards the Galactic centre. If the sun were near the centre, we might expect to see a fairly uniform density of stars all round. Herschel realised that the earth's

[1] This simile is due to Sir James Jeans.

11

orbit was infinitesimal compared with the distance of even the nearest stars. He knew, therefore, that the Galaxy must be very large; though he could not estimate its diameter.

Herschel also discovered many of those faint cloud-like objects called nebulae (Plate 8). These vary in apparent size, and are mostly far from the neighbourhood of the Milky Way. The German philosopher Kant suggested, in his *Natural History of the Heavens*, that they might be star systems, similar to the Galaxy, at very great distances. This conjecture, like most of Kant's astronomical suggestions, had no serious scientific foundation; but it is now known in many cases to be correct. Most of these extra-Galactic systems appear very small. If their sizes are comparable with that of the Galaxy, as would seem likely, their distance must be immense. But nothing more precise than this could be said in Herschel's time.

The first reliable estimate of the distance of a star was made in 1838 by F. W. Bessel, director of the Prussian Observatory at Königsberg. The simple principle is shown in Fig. 38. Let F be a very distant star, and S a comparatively near one. Let α be the

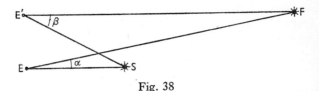

Fig. 38

angular separation of S and F, as measured from the earth E. Six months later, when the earth is at E′ on the other side of its orbit, the angular separation of S and F will have a different value, β. Since F is very distant, EF and E′F are nearly parallel. Hence the difference between β and α is due almost entirely to the difference in direction of the lines ES and E′S. This difference in direction is the angle ESE′, subtended at S by the earth's orbit. This angle now being known, it is easy to compute the distance of S trigonometrically.

The practical difficulties were great. The difference between α and β is minute—never more than a fraction of a second of arc. Now a second of arc, which is 1/3600 of a degree, is the angle sub-

tended by an ordinary pin at a distance of about 7 miles. It is therefore evident that great skill in observation and measurement was
necessary. A fair share of the credit should go to the optician,
Fraunhofer of Munich, who made Bessel's instruments.

Secondly, it is necessary, before making any measurements, to
select two stars of which one is much nearer than the other. Good
judgment and some luck are needed here. The obvious plan is to
choose one very bright star and one very faint one, the presump-
tion being that the faint star is more distant. Bessel did not do
this. The near star, 61 Cygni, whose distance he measured, is not
very bright. He chose it because its position in relation to other
stars had been known for some time to be changing rather quickly.
Its movement in 100 years is about one-third of the moon's apparent diameter. This may not sound much; but it is exceptional
for a 'fixed' star. The improved instruments of Halley, Bradley and
Herschel had shown that the fixed stars do move slightly in relation to one another, though their movements are negligible by
planetary standards. The pattern of the constellations is changing;
but the change is so slow that it was not noticed by the Alexandrians, or even Tycho. The proximity of 61 Cygni was suggested
by the fact that, for a star, it appeared to move so fast.[1] Bessel's
success was largely due to his fortunate choice of this star for the
first attempt. He detected the slight backward and forward motion
which appears to be superimposed on its steady motion by the
earth's annual changes of position.

Bessel's importance is obvious. He may be compared to Aristarchus. The early Copernican vision of an almost limitless
universe was bound to create a temporary sensation; but, had it
remained a vision, it could not have had a profound permanent influence on thought. Herschel gave the vision a more definite form,
when he began to see a pattern in the Galaxy and among the distant
nebulae. Bessel, by initiating actual measurement among the stars,
showed how firm a foundation in fact the vision might really have.
He found the distance of 61 Cygni was about 640 000 times that of
the sun.[2] This was the distance of one of the closest stars. It was

---

[1] It is a fact of daily experience that the motion of a nearby object is more
obvious than that of one farther away.

[2] Recent measurements give 680 000.

evident that, whether the universe was infinite or not, men had to face an alarming cosmic isolation.

The measurement of stellar distances has led to the introduction of successively greater units. The mean distance of the earth from the sun, about 93 000 000 miles, is called the astronomical unit. This is suitable for measurement within the Solar System; especially as Kepler's 3rd Law relates the earth's orbit very simply to the other planetary orbits. Even Pluto, the farthest known planet, is within 40 astronomical units of the sun. But the astronomical unit is inconveniently small when the distances of stars are in question. The light-year and the parsec are then used. Light travels about 186 000 miles a second. The light-year is the distance light travels in a year. It is about 63 000 astronomical units; so the distance of 61 Cygni is nearly 11 light-years. The parallax of a star is the angle subtended at the star by the mean radius of the earth's orbit. Thus the parallax of star S (Fig. 38) is half the angle ESE'. If the parallax of a star is 1 second of arc, then its distance is 1 parsec. The parsec is about 3·26 light-years.

Bessel's method has revealed the distances of many of the nearer stars. But it cannot be extended to the extra-galactic nebulae, or even to the remoter parts of the Galaxy. The distances of these have since been estimated by the study of a special class of stars called Cepheid Variables.[1] These are not the only stars of variable brightness, but their mode of variation is distinctive. A rapid increase of brightness is followed by a rather slower decline, the rise and fall being regularly repeated. The graph of light from a typical Cepheid has the form shown in Fig. 39. The period, from peak to

Fig. 39

peak, may be as short as 1 day or as long as 2 months. It is remarkably constant for any given Cepheid. In some cases the rise is much steeper than the fall, in others only slightly steeper. But the general pattern is the same for all Cepheids, and enables them to be distinguished from other variable stars. The pattern, like a tune, can remain recognisable despite considerable modification.

[1] First discovered in the constellation of Cepheus.

There are many Cepheids in the Lesser Magellanic Cloud, an isolated swarm of stars in the southern sky. Since the size of this swarm is negligible compared with its distance, the stars in it may be regarded as all at approximately the same distance. It has been found that, among Cepheids in the Cloud, those of the same period have the same apparent brightness. As they are all about equally distant, their apparent brightness is an indication of their absolute brightness (or luminosity). Thus, at least within the Magellanic Cloud, it seems that Cepheids of equal period are equally luminous. The same relation of period to luminosity is found among Cepheids in other distant star clusters. It may therefore reasonably be supposed that the relation holds for all Cepheids. Thus, if the luminosity of any one Cepheid can be independently determined, that of any other can be inferred from its period alone. The distances of some of the nearest Cepheids have been estimated by methods akin to that of Bessel. The amounts of light we receive from them can be measured. Hence their luminosities can be computed. The luminosity of any Cepheid can therefore now be found from its period alone, in virtue of the period-luminosity relation. We can then find its distance by comparing its known luminosity with its measurable apparent brightness.

Cepheids have been found in a few extra-galactic nebulae. The distances of these nebulae can therefore be determined. The two nearest are about three-quarters of a million light-years away. Most nebulae are so far away that individual stars cannot be picked out in them. But, if we assume them comparable in total brightness with those nearer to us, we can judge their distances by the amounts of light we receive from them. The most remote nebulae yet observed are at distances between 100 and 200 million light-years. The actual size of a nebula whose distance is known can be estimated from its apparent size. The Andromeda Nebula, the most conspicuous of external galaxies, is about 60 000 light-years in diameter. The Galaxy, to which the sun belongs, is thought to be somewhat larger than this. But its remoter parts are hidden by clouds of inter-stellar dust; so that accurate measurement of its size seems impossible.

Millions of external galaxies can be observed with modern telescopes (Plate 8). They appear to be receding from us, with velocities which become greater as their distances increase. The evidence for this recessive motion is considered later. The recession is an important element of present day celestial geometry.

* * *

THE NOTION of a comfortable central earth, circled by kindly lights, has altogether lost its plausibility. This is a direct result of the original Copernican suggestion that the earth moves.

6

CELESTIAL MECHANICS

THE MECHANICAL problems set by the new astronomy could not be solved by the mechanics of Aristotle. The Aristotelians saw in this an argument against the new astronomy; but Galileo and Newton demolished their objections with a new and adequate science of mechanics. This was founded on the revival of a long-neglected suggestion of the Greek atomists, who maintained that atoms, once in motion, continued to move uniformly, without assistance, unless interfered with by other atoms. This idea is far from obvious. We need not wonder at its being ignored for nearly 2000 years. Everyday experience overwhelmingly favours the belief that bodies move only so long as there is something to move them. The idea that they go on indefinitely of their own accord, unless something stops them, is not a common-sense idea; it can appeal, even as a hypothesis, only to those who have given some thought to the problems of motion. The natural idea—No force, no motion—became the basis of Aristotelian mechanics. It had the combined support of orthodoxy and common sense throughout the Middle Ages. It was not altogether unchallenged, for, despite its plausibility, there were objections to it which were not easily overcome. The most serious of these is put by the question 'Why does the arrow continue to move after leaving the bow?' According to Aristotle, the arrow should stop when the driving force is removed. The reply was that, as the arrow moved, the air rushed in behind it to fill the space that would otherwise have been left empty. This rush of air continued to propel the arrow. This is a lame answer: the air rushes in because the arrow moves; and the arrow moves because the air rushes in. But, even if the argument were not circular, it would only offer new difficulties for old. It is now not clear why the arrow should ever stop; and it would seem that the arrow cannot move in a vacuum. This last difficulty did not worry the Aristotelians, who denied the possibility of a vacuum. But they could not justify this denial; and it was not easy to maintain—especially after the invention of the air pump in the mid-17th century. But, despite such difficulties, the view that motion could not exist without driving force was not easily discredited.

The Law of Inertia, which underlies the new mechanics, was partially understood by Galileo. It is, however, rightly called Newton's 1st Law of Motion. It asserts that every body continues in a state of rest, or of uniform motion in a straight line, unless acted upon by some force. Thus the formula 'No force, no motion' has become 'No force, no *change* of motion'. The additional words make a vital difference. Aristotle, in effect, defined force as the cause of motion; Newton redefines it as the cause of changes in motion. A change of motion may be an acceleration, a retardation or a change of direction. Any of these, according to Newton, requires a force to produce it. But, in the absence of resistance, no force is needed to maintain steady motion in a straight line.

A forward force accelerates the body, a backward force retards it, and a force across its line of motion alters its course. If the force acts obliquely to the line of motion, there will be changes of both speed and direction. Suppose a body P is moving along the line AB (Fig. 40). Let a force F begin to act on it as shown. This force acts partly backwards and partly sideways; so that P will move in a

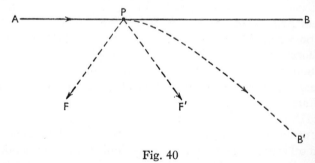

Fig. 40

curve PB' with reduced speed. Under the force F', P will move in a curve with increasing speed. But, in the absence of force, P will continue in the line AB without change of speed.

Let us see how this idea eliminates the more obvious objections to the earth's motion. Why should a stone fall vertically, despite the movement of the earth? An analogy, considered by the 17th-century scientists themselves, may make this clear. Suppose a stone is dropped from the mast of a moving ship: where will it hit the deck? The Aristotelian argument is this:

> While the stone is held by the man on the mast, it is physically connected to the ship: and the ship provides a driving force to maintain the stone's horizontal motion across the sea. When the man lets go, this force is removed, and the stone at once loses its horizontal motion. It falls towards the earth because of its instinctive urge to regain its proper sphere. But, while it falls, the ship continues to move forward. Hence the stone hits the deck behind the mast.

But the reasoning based on the Law of Inertia is this:

> The stone in the man's hand is moving horizontally with the ship. When he lets go, it falls with an acceleration caused by gravity. While falling, it retains its horizontal motion, since there is no horizontal force to interfere with this motion. As it falls, therefore, it keeps pace horizontally with the ship. It will thus land at the foot of the mast.

We need not go to sea to make sure that the second argument is the one that gives the correct result. Anyone can perform the experiment on a small scale, by dropping things to the floor of a steadily moving railway carriage. Just as the motion of the ship does not prevent the stone from falling at the foot of the mast, so that of the earth does not prevent a stone from landing immediately below the point it is dropped from.

The second awkward question is how the earth can move without a rush of air. This question is only partly answered by the Law of Inertia. It is connected with another question; namely, whether a vacuum is possible. Assuming that a vacuum *is* possible, and that interplanetary space is empty, there is no great difficulty. The earth's atmosphere is then only a layer of gas, covering its surface to a depth of some few miles. If we suppose that the earth and its atmosphere were originally set in motion together, then the atmosphere will keep pace with the earth, just as the falling stone keeps pace with the ship. There is no reason why the earth should leave its atmosphere behind, because there is no force to hold the atmosphere back. But if a vacuum is impossible, and if there is consequently an atmosphere of some sort throughout space, then it is indeed difficult to see how the earth can move without our feeling the draught. To overcome this second objection to the earth's motion, therefore, we must refute a second Aristotelian principle— the belief that Nature abhors a vacuum. The Law of Inertia, as before, enters into the explanation. But it can do so only when the possibility of empty space between the planets is admitted. This problem of the vacuum belongs to the science of pneumatics, which was much in evidence during the 17th century. We can see at this point how pneumatics, often treated as a thing apart, comes right into the main current of thought, and makes its peculiar contribution to that total overthrow of Aristotelian science which was necessary before the new astronomy could be firmly established. Let us therefore interrupt the main argument with a short account of 17th century pneumatic discoveries.

*   *   *

IT IS not unusual for a scientific idea to be at first derided, then tolerated, and finally taken too much for granted. Empedocles had shown that air is a substance, which can occupy space and exclude water. Vessels which are usually described as empty are really not so. This notion must have been regarded as a paradox when new. But, as it became familiar, it grew among the Greeks into the dogmatic belief that there was no such thing as empty space: a vacuum

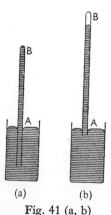

was impossible; space was a *plenum*, everywhere full. This dogma was part of the Aristotelian physics which held the field for so long. It was bound to be questioned by supporters of Copernican astronomy.

Galileo was struck by the observation that water could not be lifted more than 32 feet, by what was then supposed to be suction, from above. His pupil Torricelli made the crucial experiment in 1643. Torricelli filled a glass tube, closed at one end, with mercury. He held this vertically, with its open end beneath the surface of mercury in a trough. He found that if the distance AB was less than about 30 inches (Fig. 41a), the tube remained full of mercury. This could be explained by the Aristotelian principle: the mercury had to remain in the tube, because Nature would not allow a vacuum at

(a)   (b)

Fig. 41 (a, b)

the top. But when the tube was raised (Fig. 41b) so that AB was more than 30 inches, the mercury rose to a height of 30 inches only. A space appeared at the top: and this was presumably quite empty, as there was no way for anything to enter it. Here, then, was a vacuum that Nature refused to fill. Some cause, other than the supposed impossibility of a vacuum, was needed to explain how the mercury was supported in the tube.

Torricelli concluded that the mercury was kept in the tube by the weight of the atmosphere, pressing down the mercury in the trough. In order that mercury might run out of the tube, the level of mercury in the trough would have to rise. This was prevented by the pressure of the air. Water will rise about 32 feet before the vacuum appears. According to Torricelli's theory this is to be expected; because a 32-foot column of water and a 30-inch column of mercury, having the same cross-section, are equally heavy, and therefore need the same amount of support.

This apparatus of Torricelli is the barometer. The height of the mercury column was found to fluctuate; and the practical value of the barometer, as a storm glass, was quickly recognised. But the most interesting fact, from a scientific point of view, was that the barometer fell steadily as its height above sea-level increased. This suggested that the atmosphere extended to only a limited distance from the earth's surface. When the barometer was on a hill, there was less pressure on the mercury in the trough, because there was less air above it to be supported. Thus Torricelli's invention did more than demonstrate the vacuum at the top of the tube. It supported the belief that the atmosphere is only a thin layer surrounding the earth, and that outer space is empty.

The air pump was invented, about 1654, by Otto von Guericke. It was improved by Boyle and Hooke soon afterwards. Aristotelian embarrassment was thus increased by the appearance of better and better vacua. Guericke demonstrated the pressure of the atmosphere with the Magdeburg hemispheres. These were of copper, with edges made to fit accurately. They were placed together to form a hollow sphere, from which the air was exhausted. Two teams, of 15 horses each, were unable to separate them until the air was readmitted. Boyle showed that combustion depended on the presence of air. Newton later experimented with falling bodies in a vacuum.

*   *   *

It WAS necessary for Copernicans thus to overcome the mechanical objections to the earth's motion. But the new astronomy could not be firmly established by mere destruction of the arguments against it. Something more positive was needed; namely an explanation, in mechanical terms, of why the planets should behave as Copernicus and Kepler said they behaved. The crystal spheres of Aristotle were incompatible with anything but plain circular motion. In any case, Tycho's observations indicated that comets could cross the planetary orbits unhindered. This further discouraged belief in the crystal spheres. A more subtle explanation seemed necessary, to account for the order which undoubtedly prevailed in the heavens. Such an explanation, founded on the mechanical ideas of Galileo, was evolved in England during the second half of the 17th century, chiefly by Newton. But a solution of the problem was attempted before this, in Aristotelian terms, by Descartes. His opinions were accepted for some time on the Continent in preference to Newton's. Their influence, if not their adequacy, makes them worth notice.

Descartes (1596–1650, Plate 9c), a younger contemporary of Galileo and Kepler, was a figure of great significance in the Scientific Revolution. He was chiefly distinguished in mathematics and philosophy; but for the moment we consider only his explanation of the planetary motions. He was naturally inclined to believe in a fixed sun and moving earth; but he was willing to abandon this belief when he learnt, to his surprise, that the Catholic Church condemned it as impious. He was educated by the Jesuits of La Flèche; but this was before the Roman authorities had finally decided against Copernican astronomy. *De Revolutionibus* was not put on the Index until 1616, when Descartes was 20. In creating his planetary theory, as a young man, he took the heliocentric view without suspicion of its orthodoxy. He refrained from publishing his work, when he found it might lead him into trouble with the Church; but it became influential after his death. He believed, like some of the ancients, that he could discover the whole secret of the universe for himself, without the aid of other minds. He therefore thought it unnecessary to be well read; and he was ignorant, among other things, of Kepler's Laws. His Theory of Vortices was the one big attempt to reconcile the new astronomy with the old mechanics and physics.

The Aristotelian law of motion supposes that, as well as something to guide the planets, there must also be something to urge them forward. This idea goes back to Greek mythology, which furnished Apollo[1] with a chariot and horses. It was taken up by Christian mythology, which preferred the motive power of angels to that of horses. Descartes adopts it, together with the view that space is nowhere empty; but he does without the horses and the angels. Each planet, he maintains, is at the centre of a vortex, or whirlwind, in the space-filling fluid by which it is surrounded. The rotation of this vortex, which is most rapid near the centre, gives the planet its axial rotation. The outer parts of the vortex carry round any satellites the planet has. The local planetary vortices are set in a larger vortex, with the sun at centre, which carries them— each with its own planet—continually round the sun. The arrangement is shown in Fig. 42. The currents of the main solar vortex are represented by unbroken lines; those of the local vortices, surrounding the planets P and Q, by dotted lines.

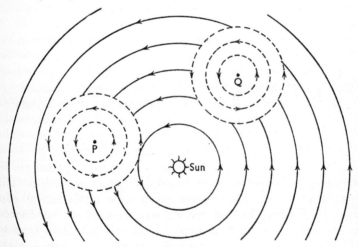

Fig. 42

This theory is ingenious, and at first sight attractive. Vortices turn about the regions of low pressure in a fluid. The most familiar terrestrial vortices are those which occur when the water runs out of a bath. One may cite, also, the cyclonic winds which circle a

[1] The sun.

depression. Anyone who watches the emptying bath will notice that the rotation, if allowed to occur naturally, is always in the same direction.[1] The rate of rotation increases towards the centre of the vortex. If the vortices in the space-filling fluid have similar properties, then Descartes' theory shows why all the planets revolve in one direction round the sun, and why those nearer the sun move more quickly. According to the theory, also, the axial rotation of the planets, and the revolutions of their satellites about them, should again be in the same direction. The observations of Descartes' time suggested that this was the case: certain satellites of Jupiter and Saturn, however, are now known to disobey the general rule. The vortex theory has two other merits. Firstly: if the earth is carried round by its own local vortex, there is no reason why its motion should entail a rush of air. The turmoil of conflicting currents will occur only at the outer boundary of the earth's vortex, and we shall be untroubled by it. Secondly: we know that small objects tend to move towards the centre of a vortex. If the earth really is at such a centre, we have at least a superficial explanation of gravity.

A hypothesis must be judged by the accuracy of its predictions. The weakness of Descartes' hypothesis was that it could not be developed mathematically, and could not therefore be adequately tested. The problems of fluid motion were beyond the mathematics of the 17th century. It was possible to predict, from Descartes' hypothesis, that the planets nearer the sun would move more quickly; but it was not possible to predict the precise relation that should hold between their distances and periodic times. Nor was it possible to predict the shape of the orbit which a planet would describe when swept about in a complex system of vortices. The laws of planetary motion were given with mathematical precision by Kepler. The least that was now required of a satisfactory mechanical theory was that Kepler's Laws should follow from it. Theories agreeing only with the main features of planetary motion, in a vague, qualitative way, were no longer wanted. They had had their day. The demand was for a theory whose *measurable* consequences could be calculated, and their agreement with minute observation tested. Descartes' over-confidence in his own powers,

[1] Always clockwise in the southern hemisphere; always counter-clockwise in the northern—according to Ferrel's Law.

and his consequent disregard of the work of others, led him to much waste of time in this matter. He set about explaining the heavens without properly understanding what had to be explained. Vortices, nevertheless, had an important place in 17th-century thought; and the comparison of Descartes with Newton (Plate 9d) may help us to understand the nature and growth of the modern scientific method which was about to reach maturity.

*   *   *

IF WE assume that planets move in empty space and obey the Law of Inertia, a different kind of theory is required to explain their behaviour. A planet left to itself would move uniformly in a straight line. We know in fact that it moves in an ellipse with the sun at one focus, and that its speed is greater when it is nearer the sun. In Fig. 43, S represents the sun. P_1, P_2, P_3, P_4, P_5, P_6 are successive positions of the planet. It is easy to see, by comparing this diagram with Fig. 40, that a force always pulling the planet towards the sun will account roughly for its behaviour. When the

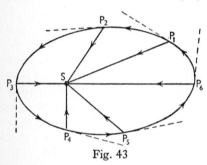

Fig. 43

planet is at P_1 or P_2, the force acts partly across its line of motion and partly forwards. The planet will therefore gain speed, while its path will deviate from the straight towards the sun. At P_3 the force acts at right-angles to the path. The planet will therefore no longer be gaining speed; but

its path will still be bent towards the sun. At P_4 and P_5 the planet will be losing speed, since the force now acts partly backwards. When P_6 is reached, the speed will be at its least, and will then begin to increase again. If at any time the force towards the sun should cease, the planet would thereafter move, with whatever speed it then had, along the tangent to its orbit at the point where it then was.

All this suffers, as it stands, from that vagueness which we noted as a fault in the theory of vortices. Several difficult questions arise. Can a force towards the sun, *alone*, account for motion according to

Kepler's Laws? Should it be a constant force; and, if not, how should it vary? Is the hypothesis of such a force the only reasonable one, or are there others which will account for the observed facts just as well? If such a force exists, then what is its nature? It was Newton who first gave convincing answers to these questions. The fundamental physical ideas on which his answers depended were not his own. De Morgan, using two anagrams of Newton's name, says he *went on* with what was *not new*. This must be true in the main of any genius, however great. Important advances, in whatever field, are made only by those who study and appreciate their predecessors. The achievements for which Newton is justly celebrated are: that he gave precision to ideas which previously lacked it; that he saw the connection between ideas which previously seemed unconnected; that he overcame, with apparent ease, mathematical difficulties which defeated others. His was a tremendous feat of correlation and development, which he could hardly have accomplished had he lived 50 years earlier.

*   *   *

NEWTON'S BASIC concepts were those of space, time and mass, all of which are measurable and can be handled mathematically. He had no use, in physical science, for concepts which did not admit of such treatment. Modern physics follows him in excluding them from its apparatus of ideas. 'Abhorrence' and 'natural desire' were among the concepts by which Aristotle attempted to describe the physical world. Such notions are no longer thought appropriate in the exact sciences. This does not mean, as sentimentalists would have us think, that the scientist is without a soul, uninterested in love or hate or beauty or justice. But he does not use these ideas in his effort to understand the behaviour of inanimate things.

Motion can be defined in terms of space and time. Thus velocity is change of position per unit of time, while acceleration is change of velocity per unit of time.

Matter has the essential properties of extension (in space) and duration (in time). It has a third characteristic property, mass, which is not so easily understood. Newton does not give a satisfactory definition of mass; though his understanding of the concept is clear from the way he uses it. He says that the mass of a body is its volume multiplied by its density; but this leads us no-where, unless we can define density without reference to mass. There is another definition, still given uncritically in some text-books, which is no better. It says that the mass is the quantity of matter in the body. This tacitly assumes that all kinds of matter, despite their superficial differences, are fundamentally alike. We may grant this. But, even so, the definition is of little use; since it gives no hint of how in practice we should estimate the quantity of fundamental stuff in any given body. If we assume the modern electrical theory of matter, we may give the definition an appear-ance of precision, by saying that the quantity of matter in a body is determined by the number of ultimate particles—protons, elec-trons and so on—it contains. But the practical futility of the idea is still obvious. It is easier to number the hosts of Midian than the ultimate particles of a single stone.

The Newtonian concept of mass, never explained by Newton, but nevertheless permeating his work, is clearly expressed by Clerk Maxwell, the most original of the distinguished mathematical physicists of Victorian Cambridge. Bodies have equal masses, Maxwell says, if, in similar circumstances, they suffer equal changes of motion in a given time. That is; similar circumstances produce equal accelerations in equal masses. If the accelerations are different, then the body having the greater acceleration has the smaller mass. The ratio of the masses is defined as the inverse ratio of the accelerations. Let bodies A and A', whose masses are m and m', be found to have accelerations f and f' in similar circumstances. Then $m:m' = f':f$. Here is a criterion by which the relative masses of two bodies can be theoretically and practically decided; for we can observe and measure their changes of motion. There is an ele-ment of doubt, because we may err in judging the circumstances similar. Maxwell, as an example of what he means, supposes the bodies pulled in turn with a given piece of elastic stretched to a predetermined extent. But he points out that we have to assume the properties of the rubber remain unchanged.[1] It is possible that some change of circumstances may escape our notice. But science, relying always on human judgment at some point, can never give us certainty. If, however, in comparing masses, we find that several

[1] *Matter and Motion*, Section 45.

12

different attempts give the same result, we may reasonably attribute some significance to this result.

The measurement of any mass consists in comparing it with a standard mass. The ultimate British standard is a lump of platinum, marked P.S., 1844, 1 lb. If A has a mass of 20 lb, then its acceleration will be 1/20 of that which the standard lump of platinum has in similar circumstances. The standard now used for scientific purposes is the gram.

Mass should be distinguished carefully from weight. The weight of a body is the force with which the earth attracts it; and this varies from place to place. Thus a body removed to some distance from the earth will weigh less than before; but its mass will not be altered by its change of position. It will be easier to lift, because the earth attracts it less, but no easier to accelerate. Bodies of equal weight balance one another in the scales. There is no logical reason why bodies of equal mass should have the same weight; just as there is no logical reason why things of the same colour should have the same smell. Careful experiments have, however, shown that masses judged equal by Maxwell's criterion do in fact balance one another in the scales. Our everyday method of comparing masses relies on this experimental fact. But it is important to remember that we know this fact *only* from experience; just as we know only from experience that men live longer on boiled beef than cyanide. To sum up, let us say that the mass of a body measures the resistance it offers to any effort we make to change its speed or direction of travel. The words 'inertia' and 'mass', as used by scientists, are synonyms.

The Laws of Motion give precise form to the concept of force. The First Law, the Law of Inertia, gives a qualitative definition of force, as the cause of a change of motion. The Second Law decides how force is to be measured: it gives a quantitative definition. Let us first define the momentum of a body as its mass multiplied by its velocity. (Newton called this 'the quantity of motion'.) Then the Second Law may be stated thus:

The force acting on a body is proportional to the change of momentum it produces in a given time; and the direction of the force is that in which the change of momentum takes place.

Thus the direction and magnitude of a force are to be estimated from its observed effect on the body to which it is applied. A given force, acting for a given time, always produces the same change of momentum. This change of momentum may take the form of a small change of velocity in a large mass or a large change of velocity in a small mass.

The Third Law states that action and reaction are always equal and opposite. This means that, whenever A exerts a force on B, then B automatically exerts an equal and opposite force on A. If the momentum of B is increased by the influence of A, then that of A must be equally decreased by the influence of B. If A imparts to B a certain momentum in one direction, B must impart to A an equal momentum in the opposite direction.

Let us suppose (e.g.) that a truck A, of mass 2 tons, overtakes and bumps into a truck B, of mass 4 tons. Suppose that, as a result, the speed of B is increased by 2 miles an hour. The forward push given to B by A has thus increased the momentum of B by 8 units. Then, according to the Third Law, the backward push, automatically given to A by B, will *reduce* A's momentum by 8 units. As A's mass is 2 tons, its velocity must be reduced by 4 miles an hour.

In trying to understand the Newtonian concept of force, we must attend as much to what the Law of Reaction implies as to what it explicitly states. It implies that there can be a force only when there is a body to exert it, as well as a body to respond to it. Force is essentially the influence of one *body* on another; not an independently existing thing, able to affect matter when it meets it. The Law also implies that forces always occur in pairs. A magnet cannot attract iron without the iron attracting the magnet; the earth cannot pull a stone downwards without the stone pulling the earth upwards. When there is a great disparity of mass, the change of velocity in the greater mass may, of course, be so small that it cannot be observed.

The Third Law, although it deals with the interaction of material bodies, does not involve the Aristotelian belief that one body can influence another only by contact with it. The new mechanics is not indeed concerned with the mechanism (if any) by which bodies affect one another's motion. It is content to accept the fact that they do influence one another, and to provide means of predicting the extent of the effect in any given case. It is essentially modern, in that its object is the interrelation and precise description, not the ultimate explanation, of certain natural phenomena. It represents a step towards the separation of science from metaphysics. Such separation is of great significance; for scientists have certainly achieved the more by coming to know and mind their own business. This is an important fact, even if not a good thing.

These general mechanical principles express opinions founded, after due reflection, on experience. But they cannot be confirmed by direct experiment. The First Law at once presents an insuperable difficulty. In order to verify it, we must have a body acted on by no force—i.e. out of reach of the influence of any other body. This is impossible, as we must ourselves be present to see what happens.[1]

The system must stand or fall as a whole. Like other systems of physical principles, it has the indirect support of experience. Instead of verifying the principles themselves, we can verify their logical consequences. We have faith in them because observation confirms what we infer from them. Even so, we should not regard them as 'true' in any absolute sense. They provide us with an adequate starting point from which to calculate the motion of material bodies; but we have no right to make any higher claim for them.

*   *   *

THUS NEWTON approached the problems of planetary motion equipped with precise ideas of velocity, acceleration, momentum and force, derived from more fundamental concepts of measurable space, time and mass. He was not alone in the possession of these general physical ideas, though perhaps his feeling for them was more sensitive than that of others. But in one respect he had no living equal. His mathematical power was comparable with that of Archimedes; and this was the main reason for his success where others failed. Contemporaries, themselves important figures in the history of mathematics, admitted his superiority with little of the usual hesitation. Isaac Barrow resigned the Lucasian Chair of Mathematics, so that Newton might take it at the age of 26. Even when, as Master of the Mint in later life, Newton no longer devoted himself seriously to mathematics, he solved in a few hours the

---

[1] This Law of Inertia, although it cannot be *proved* experimentally, was *suggested* to Galileo by an observation—namely, that when a body, after rolling down a slope, is allowed to continue on the level, it ceases to gain speed, and thereafter moves almost uniformly.

famous problem of the brachistochrone,[1] which had occupied his chief continental rival, Leibniz, for six months.

Newton's planetary theory was not published until his *Principia* came out in 1687; but he began serious work on it in 1666. The questions he had to answer were these: (i) Can a force towards the sun, alone, account for motion according to Kepler's Laws? (ii) Should it be a constant force; and, if not, how should it vary? (iii) Is the hypothesis of such a force the only reasonable one? (iv) What is the nature of the force if it exists? Let us first consider Newton's answers in a logical rather than a chronological order.

Taking the Laws of Motion as premises, he proved, by purely mathematical reasoning, without any further physical assumption, that a planet will obey Kepler's 2nd Law if, *and only if*, the force acting on it is directed towards the sun. Thus the law of equal areas implies a force towards the sun; and a force towards the sun implies the law of equal areas.

He next proved that, if the planet also obeys Kepler's 1st Law, then the force, F, acting towards the sun, must vary inversely as the square of the planet's distance, r, from the sun. That is $F = k/r^2$, where k is a constant. Thus motion in an ellipse with the sun at one focus implies the Inverse Square Law of force. The Inverse Square Law does not, however, necessarily imply motion in an ellipse. It implies, as Newton showed, motion in a conic. Although the planets in fact move in ellipses, it is possible for a body, moving under the sun's influence, to describe a conic of some other kind—which kind depends upon how and where the body was originally set in motion.

Kepler's 3rd Law does not come into the picture until we compare the motion of one planet with that of another. For the motion of a single planet, questions (i), (ii) and (iii) can now be answered as follows. Granting the validity of the Laws of Motion, which we have no particular reason to doubt, a force towards the sun, varying inversely as the square of the distance, is alone sufficient to account for observed planetary behaviour according to Kepler's first two laws. No other kind of force will produce or permit such behaviour.

It is now important to remember what was said in Chapter 1

[1] The path by which a body, under gravity, descends most quickly from a given point to another given point at lower level.

about the scientific validity of mathematical conclusions. There is no doubt that the conclusions follow from the premises; but the conclusions themselves, as statements of physical fact, are no more reliable than the premises. Newton does not *prove* the existence of a force pulling the planets towards the sun according to the Law of Inverse Squares. What he does prove is that we are logically bound to believe in such a force so long as we admit the Laws of Motion and the empirical statements of Kepler. Belief is not certain knowledge. Belief in something consists, merely, in feeling sure enough about it to act as if it were the case. We may, in this sense, believe general statements about the physical world: but such belief, however strong, should never be unshakable. The evidence for a scientific belief is often partly mathematical. The mathematical link in the chain then has a certainty which the other links have not; and this is apt to lend a false air of certainty to the evidence as a whole. The danger is greatest when, as in the case of Newton's planetary theory, the mathematical investigation is particularly interesting and brilliant. It is easy to be so carried away by the ingenuity and force of the deductive reasoning that one forgets the vulnerability of the hypothesis on which it rests.

Question (iv), though logically last, was the one which Newton attended to first. This was in 1665 and 1666, when he was still an undergraduate. He made several of his most important discoveries at this time, while living at his home at Woolsthorpe in Lincolnshire to escape the plague. He had not then calculated the precise effects of a force towards the sun, varying as the inverse square of the distance. But he already suspected that such a force would account fully for observed planetary motions. Acting upon this suspicion, he considered what the nature of the force might be. He became convinced that it was the same as the force that makes things fall to the ground.

The circumstances in which it became desirable to face the question were also those in which it became possible, and indeed natural, to give Newton's simple and satisfying answer. The need for a force towards the sun became apparent as soon as the attempt was made to correlate the new astronomy and the new mechanics. They had risen like the two sides of an arch: and, in order that the sides of an arch may rest upon each other, a keystone is necessary. The keystone, in this case, was a force attracting planets to the sun, and satellites to the planets. Only let such a force be found, and the whole new structure of scientific ideas would at once become self-supporting. Gravity as conceived by Aristotle could not serve the purpose. But gravity as newly conceived, by those who took the heliocentric view, was just what was needed. So long as the earth was thought to occupy a privileged place at the centre of the universe, it was natural to believe that gravity was associated with the earth, and with the earth alone. All solid bodies were supposed to seek the centre of the earth because, being the centre of the universe, it was the place ordained for them in the cosmic scheme— they had a natural disposition to return to it when removed from it. This was the orthodox Aristotelian doctrine. It altogether ceased to make sense in a Copernican universe. For the earth, in such a universe, was no longer privileged: it was only one of several heavenly bodies which were similar and had the same status. Since objects near the earth were attracted to the earth, it now seemed reasonable to suppose that objects near Jupiter would be attracted to Jupiter, those near the sun to the sun, and so on. Gravitation thus came to be regarded, not as the attribute of a supposed Universal Centre, but as the attribute of any large material body.

Newton took over this new idea in its most general form, supposing that every particle of matter attracted every other particle. Thus he attributed the power of attraction to all bodies, of whatever size; not only to large bodies. And he supposed that the attraction of a body might have effect at any distance, however great—though, of course, its strength would diminish with increasing distance. The attraction exerted by a large body, being the sum of the attractions exerted by its many particles, was naturally greater than that of a smaller body composed of fewer particles.

In giving precise mathematical form to this idea, Newton made two assumptions. He assumed the attraction between two bodies was proportional to the product of their masses. This is strongly suggested by the fact that the weights of bodies near the earth are known experimentally to be proportional to their masses. He assumed also that the attraction was inversely proportional to the square of the distance. He had not yet shown that this was the law compatible with elliptic orbits. But it was a natural assumption; and he was not the only man of his time to make it. It is a reasonable hypothesis concerning any influence which is supposed to radiate in all directions from a point. At a distance of 1 unit from the point, the influence is spread over the surface of an imaginary sphere of unit radius. At a distance of 2 units, it is spread over a sphere of radius 2 units—i.e. spread over 4 times the previous area. In this second case, therefore, the influence may be expected to have $\frac{1}{4}$ of its previous intensity. For this geometrical reason the Inverse Square Law comes readily to mind when such phenomena as gravitation, electrical attraction and the diffusion of light are in question. But, although it wears this air of probability, it can be properly established only by experiment and observation in each case.

Newton thus arrived tentatively at what later became famous as the Law of Universal Gravitation:

> Any two material particles, P and P′, having masses m and m', attract each other with a force F, given by the formula $F = Gmm'/d^2$, where d is their distance apart.

G is a constant—the same everywhere, for all kinds of matter—called the Constant of Gravitation. It is very small; so that the attraction is noticeable only when at least one of the masses is considerable. The value of G was first reliably measured by Henry Cavendish in 1797–8. Kepler's 3rd Law, as Newton was able to show, is the geometrical consequence of the constancy of G throughout the Solar System.

Universal Gravitation certainly provides the forces necessary to keep the planets and satellites in their orbits. But this is not all it does. It presents us with the complex problem of a Solar System in which everything attracts everything else. We cannot accurately predict the behaviour of Mars by considering merely the force exerted on it by the sun; we must allow also for the influences of other planets and of satellites. It is, however, the case, as Newton saw, that the *dominant* influence on the course of any planet is that of the sun, because the sun is so much more massive than other bodies of the Solar System. We may, therefore, calculate a good approximation to the planet's motion by considering the sun's effect alone.

Newton first began to test his hypothesis of universal gravitation in 1666, by supposing that the earth's pull extended to the moon. The unbroken line AB (Fig. 44) represents as much of the moon's orbit as it traverses in one second. The dotted line is the tangent to the orbit at A. If the moon were left to itself it would, in one second, move along this tangent to B'. In the course of one second, therefore, it is pulled sideways through a distance BB'. This distance can easily be calculated from the moon's time of revolution and the size of its orbit. Let us now compare the moon's motion with that of a stone near the earth's surface. The moon's distance from the centre of the earth is about 60 times that of the stone. Thus, if the intensity of the earth's gravitation varies as the in-

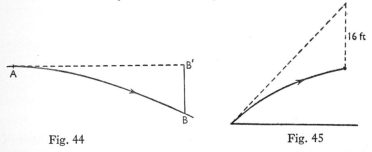

Fig. 44   Fig. 45

verse square of the distance, its effect on the stone will be about 3600 times its effect on the moon. Now a stone, thrown near the earth's surface, falls away 16 feet from its original line of motion in the first second (Fig. 45). If, therefore, we find that BB' is about 1/3600 of 16 feet, then we have good reason to think that the force which holds the moon in its orbit is of the same nature as that which makes the stone fall.

The earth and moon are in such close company (by astronomical standards) that they are effectively equidistant from the sun. Thus the sun influences them both to practically the same extent. Any change of motion which the sun produces in the earth is accompanied by a nearly equal change of motion in the moon. The motion of the earth-moon system, as a whole, in relation to the rest of the universe, is governed by the sun; but the motion of the moon in relation to the earth is much the same as it would be if the sun did not exist. They are like partners waltzing in a ship's ballroom, whose motions in relation to each other are determined by the forces they exert upon each other, while their motion together over the sea is controlled by the ship. That is why Newton, in this particular calculation, was free to ignore the sun's influence.

The agreement of theory with fact, in this case of the moon, was not close enough to warrant any definite conclusion. Newton therefore set aside his calculation of 1666. But this temporary disappointment did not upset his faith in the universal influence of gravitation. There were three likely explanations of the discrepancy: (i) There might be some other force at work, besides gravitation—perhaps an effect of the vortices imagined by Descartes. Newton at first favoured this explanation. (ii) He assumed, in his calculation, that a large body, like the earth, would behave (gravitationally) as if its whole mass were concentrated at its centre. This assumption is in fact valid for a spherical body; but in 1666 it was still questionable. (iii) The values he had taken for the distance of the moon and the radius of the earth might be inaccurate. This turned out to be the true explanation; but it seems not to have occurred to him at the time.

Thus, although the moon did not behave exactly as the new hypothesis suggested it *should* behave, there was not on this account sufficient reason to reject the notion of universal gravitation out of hand. But Newton took little further notice of the subject until 1679, when he was recalled to it by a letter from Robert Hooke. This letter, as well as showing Newton he was not alone in the field, mentioned a re-estimate of the earth's radius—made in 1672 by the French astronomer Jean Picard—of which Newton was unaware. With this new datum, Newton repeated his calculation. The agreement was now so close as to leave little room for doubt. He must have realised at once that a mechanical explanation of planetary motions was at last within his reach.

He therefore began to work out the mathematical consequences of his Principle of Universal Gravitation in detail, discovering that Kepler's Laws could be deduced from it. He refrained from publishing his results, though he mentioned some of them in his Cambridge lectures. Rumours of his success reached Hooke, Wren, Halley and others in the Royal Society, who were thinking on the same lines but could not manage the mathematics. They decided to approach Newton; and Halley went to Cambridge in 1684 to sound him. He returned with the news that Newton had already calculated the effects of a force towards the sun, varying inversely as the square of the distance. He obtained Newton's promise to complete and publish his work, if the Society would pay for the printing. Newton had a morbid dislike of controversy and contradiction. This first appeared in an acrimonious dispute with Hooke, who had dared, some years before, to criticise Newton's early optical discoveries. Persuading Newton to reveal his thoughts was like getting blood out of a stone; and Halley was enjoined by the Society to 'keep Mr. Newton in mind of his promise'. The appearance of the *Principia*[1] (1685–7) was largely due to Halley's tact and generosity. He humoured and encouraged the moody Newton, and himself paid for the printing when the Society failed in its undertaking to do so.

*   *   *

THE *Principia* formally states the Laws of Motion and that of Universal Gravitation. It shows how the motions of bodies governed by these principles can be predicted. The results are then applied to the Solar System. It is shown that, if the small perturbing forces exerted by planets on one another are neglected, then Kepler's Laws will be obeyed exactly. Even this was beyond the power of Newton's contemporaries. He would have been an outstanding figure had he done no more. But he goes on, with astonishing virtuosity, to calculate many of the small deviations from exact conformity with Kepler's Laws. He shows, further, that the gravitation of sun and moon can sufficiently account for the tides and the precession of the earth's axis.

There was one difficulty which held Newton up for some time. This difficulty will be understood from Fig. 46. O is the centre of a planet. A is a small body near the planet. According to the Law of Universal Gravitation, the various particles (P_1, P_2, P_3, etc.), of which the planet is composed, will attract A with various forces in various directions. What is the combined effect of these innumerable separate pulls? This is not an easy question. One may suppose (without being too far from the truth) that the planet is spherical,

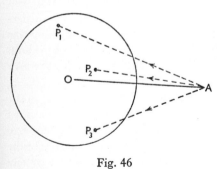

Fig. 46

[1] The full title is *Philosophiae Naturalis Principia Mathematica*.

and that its density is the same at all points at a given depth below its surface. Newton made these assumptions. He then proved that the effective force on A was the same as if the whole mass of the planet were concentrated at O. It is clear that this is approximately true when the distance OA is so great that the diameter of the planet is negligible in comparison; for the lines AP_1, AP_2, AP_3, etc., are then nearly parallel, and their differences in length are relatively small. It is most remarkable that the theorem should remain *exactly* true even when A is actually at the surface of the planet.

The beautiful simplicity of this result must have seemed almost too good to be true. It meant that his deductions from the Law of Gravitation, instead of being only fair approximations, were almost exact. He had always, from necessity, treated the sun and planets, in his calculations, as point masses. He now knew that, in doing so, he had introduced no appreciable error. In particular, his original comparison of the lunar motion with that of a stone now seemed altogether convincing. For it was in the case of the stone (because of its closeness to the earth) that any error likely to arise from treating the earth's mass as concentrated at its centre would have been most serious.

The whole *Principia* was written in about 18 months (1685–6). Competent critics agree that it surpasses all other scientific works in originality and power. It is not easy to suggest any other human creation, in whatever field, to rival it. Much of the material for the earlier part—the general mechanical and gravitational theory—was already in Newton's mind before he began to write. But even this had to be revised, completed and shaped into a coherent narrative. In the later part of the book the behaviour of the Solar System is worked out in detail by reasoning from the general principles. As to this section, it is likely that most of the creative thought was undertaken simultaneously with the writing.

The book also deals with the motion of fluids, in order to show that Descartes' Theory of Vortices is inconsistent with Kepler's Laws. It was necessary to clear the ground in this way, because the ingenious and plausible Cartesian theory was held in high esteem.

The Herculean labour of the 18 months was increased by the difficulty of making the work intelligible. Many of Newton's results were obtained by his new method of fluxions, now called the differential and integral calculus. His contemporaries—except Leibniz, who independently discovered something similar—were unacquainted with this powerful method, which had not been published. In order that the *Principia* might be generally understood Newton had to recast his proofs in the classic geometrical form familiar to readers of Euclid or Archimedes. The ingenuity with which he did this was astonishing. His early readers, who knew nothing of the methods of analysis by which his results were first reached, must have wondered whether they were dealing with a man or a magician. The effect on English mathematics was depressing, since the understandable hero-worship of Newton led to an excessive reverence for the geometrical methods he used in his *published* work. English mathematicians clung to these archaic methods throughout the 18th century, while the continentals, influenced by Leibniz, were using the new Calculus with great success. Newton's pioneer work opened a vast field of research in mathematical physics. The opportunities were exploited in Germany, Switzerland and (pre-eminently) France, while Newton's countrymen were handicapped by their insular conservatism. A benevolent but shortsighted government meanwhile rewarded Newton by appointing him to the Royal Mint, diverting his energies from science while he was still at the summit of his powers.

The last British mathematicians of distinction in the 18th century were Maclaurin (1698–1746) and Simpson (1710–61). The sterile period which followed them persisted until continental methods were introduced by the Cambridge Analytical Society early in the 19th century. Victorian Cambridge, in Kelvin, Stokes, Maxwell, Rayleigh and J. J. Thomson, produced a line of mathematical physicists equal to any in Europe.

* * *

IN RECOGNISING Newton's genius, we must not overlook his debt to others. His reputation rests mainly on the precise solution of certain great celestial problems. The very existence of these problems, in the form in which he solved them, would have remained unsuspected but for the painfully won success of Copernicus, Tycho, Kepler, Galileo and Bruno in propagating heliocentric astronomy. These men *created* for Newton the whole field of research in which he most distinguished himself. But it was not only in the creation of the problems that others helped him. All the main ideas underlying the solutions were at least partly developed before he began work. He derived the general mechanical principles from Galileo. The first attack on the difficult mathematics of curvilinear motion was made by Huygens, who, however, considered only the simple case of motion in a circle. Huygens' results were not published until 1673; but he probably possessed them by 1660. It is likely that Newton heard of them before making his first crude calculation of 1666, in which the moon's motion was treated as circular. It is worth noting that Huygens visited England, and was elected F.R.S., in 1663.

The concept of universal gravitation had already occurred in many minds in various forms. There were good reasons for this. The first was the waning of belief in the earth's central position. Now that the earth's standing among the planets had ceased to appear privileged, it no longer seemed reasonable to suppose that gravitation was exclusively terrestrial. The second reason was the new interest in 'action at a distance', excited by Gilbert's work on electricity and magnetism.[1] This science was not thoroughly developed until the 19th century: but its beginnings, like those of pneumatics, make their small and significant contribution to the main current of thought in the Scientific Revolution. Aristotelians (not unnaturally) believed that one body could exert a force on another only by contact with it. They did not think of gravitation as a pull exerted by the earth; but rather as a natural desire of heavy bodies to *move themselves* towards their proper sphere. The idea that one body should move another, from a distance, without the intervention of any apparent mechanism, seemed absurd. But the study of magnets, which attract and repel each other without contact, did much to overcome the prejudice against action at a distance. Such action might be puzzling; but it now seemed undoubtedly to exist. Why should there not be some similar action between the earth and the falling stone, or between sun and planets?

Copernicus supposed that all heavenly bodies had the power of gravitation, but he did not suggest that they thereby affected one another's action. Gilbert and Kepler thought gravitation was a

[1] Published in *De Magnete*, 1600.

magnetic manifestation. Kepler believed the sun's gravitation was one of the forces controlling the planets: but he was unacquainted with the new mechanics; and, though he saw that the sun's pull might explain the *curvature* of the orbits, he retained the Aristotelian belief that there must also be some tangential force to keep the planets moving. He suggested that the tides were caused by the moon. Galileo, on this account, mistakenly reproached him for listening to old wives' tales. Alfonso Borelli (1608–79) agreed with Kepler in believing that the planets were held in their orbits by the sun's attraction. He maintained that, if this attraction ceased, they would move in straight lines out of the Solar System, like stones released from a sling. The idea that gravitation was exerted by every particle of matter, and not only by large bodies like the sun and earth, originated with G. P. Roberval (1602–75).

Huygens, Wren, Hooke and Halley—familiar with one another's views through membership of the Royal Society—were convinced that the pull of the sun varied as the inverse square of the distance. Regarding the planetary orbits (for purposes of rough calculation) as circular, they showed that Kepler's 3rd Law implied such an attraction. But they could not show that it would account for the 1st and 2nd Laws; nor did they offer any reason for supposing the attraction was of the same kind as that which makes a stone fall. Hooke, indeed, foresaw the main outlines of the Newtonian synthesis; but only qualitatively. He felt sure that solar gravitation could maintain motion according to Kepler's Laws; and he knew that the full solution of the problem would be complicated by the small disturbing forces the planets exert on one another. But he could not do the mathematics. His temper was jealous; and, while the *Principia* was being written, he laid prior claim to some of Newton's discoveries. This upset Newton, whom Halley soothed; but the claim was never taken seriously by other scientists. Hooke was shrewd enough to see what had to be done: but Newton did it.

*　　*　　*

NEWTON'S HEALTH was affected by the strain of writing the *Principia*. After his recovery much of his attention was given to the responsibilities of public office, in Parliament and later at the Mint. In any case, he never thought of science as the main employment of a lifetime, but rather as a recreation when there was nothing more important to do; and he tended to prefer theology. It is clear, from incidents like that of the brachistochrone, that his ability was undiminished. The progress of science might have been advanced by 50 years if he had given the rest of his life to it. In the event, however, the development of gravitational astronomy, beyond the point reached in the *Principia*, was carried out by others. Halley maintained that even the wayward comets kept the Law. This was a point in which superstition died hard. Evelyn, Secretary of the Royal Society, who must have heard the views of the most advanced scientists of his time, nevertheless writes as if very unwilling to relinquish old beliefs (*Diary*, 12th Dec., 1680):

> We have had of late several comets, which though I believe appear from natural causes, and of themselves operate not, yet I cannot despise them. They may be warnings from God, as they commonly are forerunners of his animadversions.

The prediction of the moon's motion was a difficult problem, important for navigation, which Newton only began. It was tackled by the Swiss Euler, working in the Academies of St. Petersburg and Berlin, and by the Frenchman Clairaut (1713–65). Clairaut was the last distinguished continental mathematician to use Newtonian methods. The limit of what could be done by these methods had been reached. Further progress depended on the new analytical methods, begun by Leibniz and developed with tremendous vigour by Euler and his contemporaries. These were brilliantly exploited by Lagrange and Laplace, the ablest mathematicians of the 18th century, who found ways of calculating in detail the perturbations of one planet by another. Their conclusions were outlined by Laplace in his *Système du Monde*, and expounded more fully in his *Mécanique Céleste*. Perturbation causes gradual changes in the eccentricities and positions of planetary orbits. Newton, who knew of these changes but did not investigate them thoroughly, supposed that in time they might so confound the order of the System that divine intervention would be necessary to restore it. But Lagrange and Laplace showed that, provided the Solar System is a collection of rigid bodies influenced only by mutual gravitation, the changes must be periodic and can never be great. Each dimension of the System fluctuates regularly about a mean value, from which it departs first on one side and then on the other but never far. Thus an increase in the eccentricity of an orbit will be followed, before it has any catastrophic result, by a decrease re-establishing the *status quo*. This is what is meant by saying that the Solar System is dynamically stable. The need of divine intervention, to prevent the return of chaos, now seemed less likely than Newton supposed. Laplace probably had this in mind when he made his famous reply to Napoleon, who asked why God was unmentioned in the *Mécanique Céleste: 'Je n'avais pas besoin de cette hypothèse-là'*. He can hardly have meant there was no need of God as a *creator*. The stability of the Solar System may be upset by some cause, such as tidal action, of which the potency was not suspected in the 18th century. But the mathematics created by Lagrange and Laplace in their attacks on the problem will have permanent value.

The study of perturbations led to the discovery of Neptune. It was found that, even after allowing for the disturbances caused by Jupiter and Saturn, the calculated positions of Uranus differed from his observed positions. He was sometimes ahead of the calculated place and sometimes behind it. The discrepancies, though small, could not be ignored. It was supposed either that the Law of Gravitation was inexact at great distances from the sun, or that Uranus was influenced by an unknown planet. The second explanation seemed the more likely; and Bessel thought of trying to deduce the position of such a planet from the observed effects on Uranus. He died before attempting the calculation, and it was done independently by Adams in England and Leverrier in France. Adams sent his results to the Astronomer Royal, Sir G. B. Airy, on 21 October 1845—giving the place of Neptune, as we now know, to within a few degrees. Airy, accustomed like all eminent scientists to the importunities of cranks, was sceptical and asked for further details. Adams neglected to reply; and the search for Neptune was delayed until 29 July 1846, when it was begun by Prof. Challis in Cambridge. Leverrier, unaware of what was happening in England, obtained a similar result, which he sent to J. G. Galle, of Berlin, on 23 September 1846.

The detection of a faint planet depends on noticing its motion among the contiguous stars. Successive small regions of the sky, in the crucial neighbourhood, are charted night after night, in the hope of finding some object which has moved in relation to the rest.

13

This tedious process is much eased if one already has a reliable star-chart of the region. The planet was probably elsewhere when the chart was made: it is therefore only necessary to find an object which does not appear on the chart. Challis had no such chart. Galle, who had, found Neptune the night after reading Leverrier's letter.

Leverrier knew what he was doing when he sent his forecast to a German observatory. A handsome dividend was paid by the Teutonic thoroughness which had the charts ready. The Babylonian discovery of the Saros, and the discovery of the precession by Hipparchus, are similar examples of what may unexpectedly reward patient routine work. Modern photographic methods make the detection of planets comparatively simple. The telescope, with camera mounted at its eyehole, is turned by clockwork so as to follow the stars across the sky. The plate is developed after an exposure of some hours. The fixed stars produce point images, while the planet, which has moved among them, traces a bright line (Plate 10).

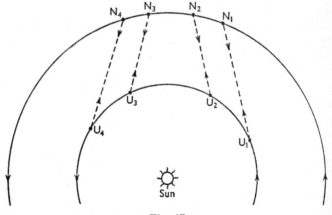

Fig. 47

Fig. 47 shows how Neptune will sometimes accelerate and sometimes retard Uranus. Other planetary perturbations are similar. Neptune takes positions N_1, N_2, N_3, N_4 while Uranus, moving more rapidly, takes corresponding positions U_1, U_2, U_3, U_4. At first U is pulled forward and N back; but after U has overtaken N, the state of things is reversed. It is also clear that the mutual attraction will tend to increase the radius of U's orbit and reduce that of N's.

The discovery of Neptune has been praised from time to time with some lack of perspective. It was a brilliant episode, but not comparable in scientific importance with the discoveries of Copernicus, Galileo and Newton, or even those of Lagrange and Laplace. It was self-contained and opened no great new field. It is considered at some length here because it illustrates the general nature of perturbation. It excited immense popular interest. It advertised the success of mechanistic science, perhaps more than any other single incident, thus contributing much to the growing self-confidence of 19th-century materialism. In considering the *influence* of science, therefore, we must give this incident more attention than it would otherwise deserve.

7

CHANGES OF OUTLOOK AND METHOD

ROBERT BOYLE observed that, until Copernicus began to reveal the extent of the visible universe, Man had been like a spider in a palace interested only in her own web. This was not true of the Alexandrians, but it was true of the Middle Ages. The first important extra-scientific consequence of the new astronomy was to revive the spider's notice of the palace. Men began to have again the vision of an immense creation in which they themselves seemed insignificant. This affected them variously, according to their characters and avocations.

Exponents of traditional philosophy and theology resisted the new ideas with an obstinacy which, in extreme cases, involved even a refusal to examine the evidence. They were sometimes ready to use dishonest argument or persecution to maintain their influence and power. Some few, like Bruno and Galileo, saw the opportunity for an unimagined adventure of discovery. The gusto with which they turned to an unexplored universe was like that with which the early Greeks turned to an unexplored earth. But the general psychological effect was one of bewilderment, rather than anger or excitement. Men were disturbed by the suggestion that, instead of living at the centre of a system whose amenities existed for their comfort, they were adrift in a small boat in an apparently boundless ocean of space. Uncertainty and humiliation began to replace confidence and complacency. The old belief, in Man's central importance, was supposed to rest on Divine Revelation: could it, perhaps, be only the outcome of wishful thinking? The atmosphere in which such a question could arise was one of insecurity and indecision. It lessened the self-confidence which men had begun to regain with the Renaissance, and shook their reappearing belief that they could look after themselves.

Thus the new celestial geometry, giving men an unwonted sense of isolation, and reducing their sense of importance in relation to their environment, had a depressing influence. The consequent celestial mechanics, however, had the opposite effect. It accepted the newly revealed state of things as a challenge to action rather than a ground for despair. It showed how, despite their insignificance, men might learn to predict the strange environment which so impressed them with its complexity and vastness. The power of prediction can bring with it a valuable, if limited, power of control over Nature. Even when it does not, it may enable men, by planning ahead, to take more advantage of favourable circumstances or a better guard against coming disaster. Men began to see that by applying their own intelligence they might make for themselves an oracle wiser and less capricious than that of Delphi, and so command their fate more fully than ever before. Such feelings of impotence and frustration as the Scientific Revolution created in its first stages were thus overwhelmed by stronger feelings of mastery and elation. The apprehension excited by the immensity of Creation was tempered by the growing conviction that the world functioned according to invariable laws, whose discovery would lead to its subjection. The line of thought which led to the triumph of Newton created an atmosphere of scientific optimism which persisted, despite occasional moderating protests, throughout the 18th and 19th centuries.

The power of prediction, which helps to bring the physical world under control, depends upon a special kind of knowledge— knowledge of the uniformities of Nature. Some of these uniformities are so obvious that they must be noticed. We cannot fail to know that vivid lightning is always followed by thunder; that rubbing things together makes them warm; or that drinking destroys the sensation of thirst. Others are elusive. No amount of everyday experience is likely to reveal the fact that equal masses (in the same place) always have equal weights; or that planets always move in ellipses. The reliability of our predictions increases with the subtlety of our knowledge of natural uniformities. A superficial uniformity was discovered by the Babylonians in the Saros. This enabled them to forecast eclipses, with luck, to within a few days. Eclipses many years ahead can now be forecast with virtual certainty to within a few seconds. This is because we now appreciate the more general underlying uniformity expressed in the Law of Gravitation.

The knowledge of natural uniformities is a rather superficial kind of knowledge. It cannot satisfy metaphysicians; for it says nothing about the ultimate nature or final purpose of Creation. But, no doubt *because* of its superficiality, it is a kind of knowledge that human faculties are well fitted to discover and apply. It may excite contempt among aspiring philosophers. But there is no denying that scientists have had some success in the search for it. The success of philosophers in their higher quest—judging by the disagreement of one with another—seems very dubious. The hunt for absolute metaphysical knowledge has ended time and again in heroic failure. May not human ability be more wisely devoted to a less ambitious pursuit, in which it has been shown to have good chances of success? 'Man's reach should exceed his grasp'; but it is useless reaching for the stars.

The attitude of intelligent men to this question was profoundly affected by late-17th-century science. The impression made by Newton, in particular, helped to alter the whole trend of intellectual endeavour. Although his discoveries *were* important for their own sake, they were not *in themselves* epoch-making. Their real importance—and this cannot be exaggerated—is that they demonstrated the vast possibilities of an essentially new pattern of thought. As the nature of Newton's work, and the reasons for his success, became widely understood, men of first-rate intellect increasingly followed his example. More of them began to find scope for their talents in the discovery of natural uniformities by the scientific method he perfected. The fresh approach, which Newton sponsored, now made the field of science as attractive to able minds in Western Europe as the fresh approach of Aristotle made it in Alexandria. There was a marked decline in speculation, and a rapid growth of knowledge concerning the regular behaviour—as opposed to the final purpose and essential nature—of the physical world. This change of direction in the main current of thought, creating a new intellectual climate, was in itself significant enough. But it was not all. The reliable if comparatively shallow knowledge, which rapidly accumulated, was of just the kind that can be applied to practical purposes. The ways of men of action were as much changed as those of men of thought.

This substitution of lower aims for higher may at first sight seem a step back. But there is much to be said for it. The human mind has so often failed in its search for knowledge of ultimate reality that we may doubt whether it is constitutionally able, in its present state of development, to attain such knowledge. As an instrument for the discovery of natural uniformities, however, it is not to be despised. Its diversion from speculative philosophy to physical science would thus seem to be the diversion of a tool from an unsuitable to a suitable use. This may well be thought a sign of progress.

In a sense, too, the new intellectual outlook was less arrogant. There is a certain presumptuousness in the man who offers confident opinions about the inner secrets of Creation without first diligently examining its surface. Those who, with more humility, have paid scientific attention to this surface have still not penetrated far beneath it. Yet they have found more than enough to excite their wonder and satisfy their passion for inquiry. The complexities and difficulties met, even in the superficial examination of Nature by the scientific method, have forcibly suggested the prematurity of immediate attempts to go deeper. The extent of the unknown becomes increasingly evident. Followers of science for its own sake have generally had a deep reverence for the Creator, and a refreshing readiness to admit their own ignorance. Newton says : 'I do not know what I may appear to the world; but to myself I seem to have been only like a boy, playing on the seashore, and diverting myself, in now and then finding a smoother pebble, or a prettier shell than ordinary, whilst the great ocean of truth lay all undiscovered before me.' This seems a modest claim, if set beside the optimistic and ambitious programmes of great imaginative system-builders like Plato, Aristotle and Descartes. The efforts of individuals to explain everything out of their own heads did not entirely cease after Newton. But there was a tendency to abandon this occupation; and those who still practised it found the educated world less willing to be impressed. It is possible that human minds may in time understand ultimate realities. But, if they ever do, it seems more likely to be by scientific perseverance than by any single flight of the imagination.

The intellectual humility which came from the study of pure science was tempered by the pride of subsequent achievement in applied science. Men now boast less of what they know, and more of what they can do. They can see and speak to people hundreds of miles away; they can breakfast in London and dine in New York on the same day; they can destroy cities in a few seconds; they can painlessly remove, repair and replace one another's insides. Such are the practical results of the new pattern of thought devised in the 17th century. We may doubt whether these accomplishments make life happier or more worth while: the pros and cons can be discussed indefinitely from moral or aesthetic standpoints. But we are now concerned with facts. There is no doubt that a radical change in ways of thought—inevitably followed in time by an equally radical change in ways of daily life—occurred in the 17th century. We should, therefore, examine the character and implications of the new scientific method, first fully developed for the purpose of astronomy, whose subsequent *general* application brought about such far-reaching changes.

*   *   *

IT IS often said that Newton *explained* planetary motion. This is true only if 'explain' is used in a limited scientific sense. What Newton really did was to leave us with only one puzzling question where there were two before. He did not discover *why* stones fall, or *why* planets obey Kepler's Laws. He *did* show that the descent of the stone and the elliptic motion of the planet are phenomena of the same kind. Calculation from a certain set of hypotheses—the Laws of Motion and Universal Gravitation—can predict them both equally well. When (if ever) we know what makes the stone fall, then we shall also know what makes the planets move as they do.

When the notion of the crystal spheres was abandoned, and the planets were conceived to move, unattached, in empty space, their regular movement became a source of great wonder. They were evidently subject to a rule; but how was it enforced, if there were no controlling spheres? The falling stone, although equally detached from its surroundings and equally constant in behaviour, is too familiar to excite wonder, except in those who have considered it with due reflection. Newton showed that the behaviour of planets deserves as much wonder as that of stones, and *no more*. Both are manifestations of a single natural fact—the constant tendency (called gravitation) of any two particles of matter to approach each other with an acceleration determined by their masses and their distance apart. Newton offered no reason for the existence of such a tendency. He admitted ignorance of the mechanism, if any, by which it is produced. He simply pointed to it as a fact, which the stone's fall and the planet's orbit *equally* exemplify.

When the motion of the planet and the fall of the stone were regarded separately, the one seemed miraculous because unfamiliar, and the other natural because observed daily. But when the movements of the planet and the stone were found to be calculable by the same rules, the planet's movement ceased to *seem* miraculous, and was *to that extent only* explained.

Scientific explanation is always of this kind. It reveals the connection of events that are surprising or terrifying with such as, being familiar, cause no surprise or alarm. It consists in seeing uniformities where they were unnoticed before. It may show that apparently diverse events are really of the same kind. It may enable us to predict or control events of one kind in virtue of their resemblance to those of a more familiar kind. But it never claims to give the ultimate reason for anything. We say the rainbow is 'explained' when we understand that its nature is that of the spectrum we can make with a prism. We no longer think of it as the supernatural symbol of God's promise, because we know that a not unlikely combination of meteorological conditions will invariably produce it. We say Franklin 'explained' the lightning when he compared it with the electrical discharge of a Leyden jar. We no longer associate it with the wrath of Zeus or the hammer of Thor. We say the motion of Mars is 'explained', because it is shown to resemble that of a falling stone. We have no further need of crystal spheres actuated by a Prime Mover. But, although we have enough superficial knowledge of light, electricity and gravitation to predict or control some of the events dependent on them, we are yet almost totally ignorant of their underlying natures. The explanations we give in terms of them only push our difficulties back a little: they account for miracles only in terms of other miracles to which we are so accustomed that we fail to recognise them as such.

Thus, by relating phenomena to one another, science can make our *descriptions* of the world more coherent and concise. It can help us to control events, by showing how some depend on others. But it can *explain* nothing in any deep sense. All it offers by way of explanation is a hint that the unfamiliar is just another aspect of the familiar. We may then fancy we understand the unfamiliar, in virtue of its connection with the familiar. But the illusion vanishes when we critically examine the foundations of our supposed understanding of the familiar.

Such opposition as there was to Newtonian ideas arose mainly from failure to understand this difference between the aims of the new science and those of traditional metaphysics. It was objected that the notion of an attractive force, between bodies not materially linked, was absurd; or that the notion was valueless so long as the mechanism by which the attraction operated was undisclosed. Newton's failure to propose any such mechanism does indeed invalidate his theory as a source of metaphysical explanation. But metaphysical explanation was not his purpose. His purpose was to show that the motions of planets could be calculated by the same rules as those of terrestrial objects. This he well succeeded in doing. Those who underestimated his achievement did so because they still hankered after the complete and final understanding optimistically promised, though never convincingly given, by speculative philosophy. The theory of vortices, although it proved useless as a basis for precise mathematical deductions, and although there was no solid evidence to support Descartes' fancy, still made an insidious appeal. The belief in a whirling fluid, controlling the planets by actual contact with them, suited the metaphysical habit of mind, because it purported to reveal the substantial cause beneath appearances. Men accustomed to this habit of mind still supposed the goal of science was the discovery of underlying substantial causes. They underrated the importance of scrupulous attention to detail. They were better pleased with the vague far-reaching claims of Descartes than the closely reasoned, strictly limited, generalisation of Newton. Newton disappointed them, because he could only refer one phenomenon to another, without referring anything to an ultimate cause.

Great self-restraint appears in Newton's refusal to consider what the cause of gravitation might be. He maintained a studied reserve, concerning any matter of natural philosophy, unless very sure of his ground. His famous remark, '*Hypotheses non fingo*', expresses the resolve never to guess where he cannot confirm. The hypotheses he refers to are speculative hypotheses—i.e. guesses incapable of direct or indirect experimental verification. He was not opposed to hypotheses in the logical sense. The Law of Gravitation is itself a hypothesis in this sense. It is the starting point of a system of mathematical deductions, leading to theses which can be observed to agree or disagree with sensible fact. It is to be accepted with increasing (though never absolute) confidence as more of its implications are confirmed. But it must be rejected if there is ever reason to deny a single one of its logical consequences. Few of Newton's contemporaries would submit to such a degree of intellectual asceticism. But his severely correct attitude is now habitual among scientists. It has had, through them, a subtly astringent influence on ways of thought in general.

The preference for Descartes naturally lasted longer on the Continent than in England.[1] But even there the Newtonian outlook rapidly gained ground, especially through the influence of Locke and Voltaire. It was gradually realised that the aims of science, though limited and superficial, were attainable and useful; while those of speculative philosophy, though deeper and more desirable, were at present out of reach.

We cannot finally decide whether this change of outlook was for the good or not. There is no doubt that it was largely due to the success of the new celestial mechanics, and that it deeply affected intellectual, religious, material and social conditions. The scientific search for natural uniformities, like the speculative search for ultimate reality, was (and often still is) inspired by intellectual curiosity. It did not begin with any conscious desire for technical advance. But technical advances inevitably followed.

*   *   *

A NEW method was evolved during the 17th century, and brought to maturity by Newton, to serve the new purpose with which science was infecting thought. This Scientific Method was not the creation of any single man. Francis Bacon (1561–1626, Plate 11b) has sometimes been given too much of the credit for it. He certainly advocated, with all the force of his authority, the view that knowledge of the physical world could come only by experience: systematic observation must be the source of it. No doubt this needed emphasising in his time; and he did science a great service by pointing

---

[1] In his *History of the Theories of Aether and Electricity* Sir E. Whittaker remarks: 'It is curious to speculate on the impression which would have been produced had the spirality of the nebulae been discovered before the overthrow of the Cartesian theory of vortices.'

it out in his *Novum Organum* (1620). But it was not a new idea. Aristotle made it the basis of his method in biology. The Alexandrians applied it in astronomy and physics. Roger Bacon courageously repeated it before a hostile audience in the 13th century. Copernicus, Kepler, Tycho, Gilbert, Galileo and Harvey were fully alive to it, and founded lives of discovery on it, before the *Novum Organum* was published. It was, nevertheless, still important that an eminent man of the world, with the prestige of a Lord Chancellor, should openly prefer observation to speculative thought as a means of getting to know Nature. Observation was still often despised (*à la* Plato) outside scientific circles. It was regarded as an occupation unfit for anyone of finer intellectual mettle than an alchemist. Bacon gave it tone.

There is more in Scientific Method than the mere appeal to observation. The formation of guiding hypotheses and the discreet use of mathematics are essential to it. Bacon failed to realise the importance of these. He supposed that the accumulation of empirical data must in time lead automatically to the discovery of such natural uniformities as science sought. The business of scientists should be to pile experiment upon experiment, and record results. Theorising was waste of time, at least in the early stages. General truths would emerge, of their own accord, when a large enough assembly of particular facts had been made. The less obvious and more important uniformities in Nature have *not* generally appeared in this way; and Bacon did not foresee the subtleties of the method by which science would eventually reveal them. The strength of his reputation as a pioneer in science—especially on the Continent—is illustrated by a remark of Rousseau:[1] 'The greatest orator in the world was Consul of Rome, and perhaps the greatest of philosophers Lord Chancellor of England.' Although he dares to rank Bacon with Descartes and Newton, Rousseau himself suggests a reason for the inflated reputations of both Cicero and Bacon: 'Can it be conceived that, if the former had only been a professor at some University, and the latter a pensioner of some Academy, their works would not have suffered from their situation?'

The proper use of Scientific Method always demands a touch of genius. Bacon was wrong in supposing it could be effective in the

[1] *A Discourse on the Moral Effects of the Arts and Sciences* (trans. G. D. H. Cole).

hands of any competent experimenter. Its characteristics are well illustrated in the establishment of Universal Gravitation. The secret lies in the suggestion, early on, of a fruitful hypothesis; and in the perfect relevance, rather than the great number, of the observations taken into account.

Scientific discoveries do not usually arise from the analysis of a great mass of facts. The first stage is nearly always the outcome of reflective thought set going in a penetrating mind by the impact of *a few very striking facts*. This leads to an hypothesis—a shrewd imaginative guess—concerning the nature of the uniformity (if any) underlying the few facts in question. It is next necessary to work out the logical consequences of the hypothesis. At this stage mathematics usually plays an important part. The few original facts *must* be among the logical consequences of the hypothesis. It has been deliberately framed so that they *shall* be. But there will be other known facts, of a kindred nature, which were not in the investigator's mind when he framed the hypothesis. These also must be shown to follow logically from it; and it must be relinquished if any of them can be shown not to do so. When it has been shown to imply all the relevant facts, the hypothesis acquires the standing of a theory. It has yet to survive another ordeal. The systematic calculation of its consequences will no doubt reveal some which have never been observed. Mathematicians, using it as a premise, can predict the outcome of experiments not previously thought of. These experiments will be performed, and the predictions tested. The theory will become more firmly established with each successful prediction. At the same time scientists will secure empirical knowledge of phenomena which would otherwise have passed unnoticed.

Thus a double purpose is accomplished. The experimental search for particular items of empirical knowledge is directed, by the theory, so that it is much more likely to reveal significant facts than if the experiments were made at random or at the whim of the experimenter. Secondly: the probability that there is some element of *general* truth in the theory itself is meanwhile steadily strengthened. The theory assumes a uniformity, underlying many particular phenomena. Belief in the approximate validity of this assumption, though never absolute, can become very confident as deductions are experimentally verified in increasing numbers.

Such reasoned confidence in the approximate validity of far-reaching theoretical assumptions may be an imperfect substitute for certain knowledge of general truths. But it is attainable; and it is all science has to offer.

The subtle blend of observation, hypothesis, mathematics and planned experiment in the Scientific Method is a more effective procedure than that of Bacon, who would have us collect facts in plenty *before* we begin to theorise. It is difficult to abstract any but the most obvious uniformities from a jumble of miscellaneous facts, all presented at once. The chance of success is greater if we adopt a hypothesis at an early stage. The experimentation is then restricted to the search for such empirical knowledge as has a bearing on the validity of the hypothesis: instead of being vaguely hopeful, it is organised and purposeful. Wrong hypotheses may often be adopted. But their falsehood will soon be detected; so that they can be modified or recast. It is, in any case, quite clear from the history of science that experiments directed, even by a false hypothesis, are more valuable than those directed by no hypothesis at all. An hypothesis need not be correct in order to be useful.

Users of Scientific Method agree with Bacon that the evidence for scientific beliefs must ultimately be empirical. The accepted guarantee of good faith among scientists is the publication of experimental results in such detail that they can be confirmed by repetition. The spread of the empirical outlook was encouraged by Bacon's writings. But he was not its sole, or even its chief, originator.

The qualities needed for successful use of Scientific Method are so various that they are hardly ever all found in one man. They are: (i) Deep understanding of previous science, its virtues and short-comings.[1] (ii) Alertness, acute power of observation, and the flair for spotting connections between apparently disconnected facts. (iii) Imagination in forming the hypothesis, and instinct for the kind of hypothesis likely to be fruitful. (iv) The mathematical ability to develop the hypothesis. (v) Experimental ingenuity, and the mechanical skill to implement it. Archimedes and Newton had these gifts in abundance. Faraday, the electrician, had all but the fourth. Maxwell, who developed Faraday's ideas mathematically,

---

[1] Bacon and Descartes are examples of men whose work suffered from their inadequate appreciation of the past.

lacked only the fifth. But men as talented as these are rare. A scientific theory seldom grows up in the care of one man: the various abilities of many are nearly always needed.

The discovery of Universal Gravitation exhibits all the features of that new pattern in scientific thought which has since become so familiar. It begins with the association, in Newton's alert mind, of the moon's behaviour with that of the falling stone. There is no delay, on Baconian lines, while a host of facts is assembled. The initial hypothesis, that the earth's pull extends to the moon and obeys the Inverse Square Law, is immediately set up. Its only foundations are a geometrical intuition, and the likeness perceived by genius in two superficially unrelated phenomena. Newton sees that the moon's path may be bent towards the earth for the same reason that the path of the flying stone is bent—i.e. because the earth attracts it. Geometry suggests the Inverse Square Law. His first limited hypothesis is then tested by a calculation which only half confirms it. But this shred of evidence is encouraging enough to lead at once to a much more general hypothesis, that every particle of matter exerts a calculable attraction on every other. A mathematical *tour de force*, occupying even Newton for some years, enables him to show that all the known celestial motions are implied by this hypothesis. Universal Gravitation becomes an established theory. The final triumphs—of prediction—come spectacularly with the return of Halley's comet and the discovery of Neptune. By the end of the 19th century, after surviving every test for 200 years, Universal Gravitation commanded more general consent than any other scientific theory. The evidence for it seemed overpowering. Yet early in the 20th century it had to be modified drastically. Eternal Principles have no place in science.

*   *   *

APART FROM Bacon, the men of letters most deeply implicated in the Scientific Revolution were John Locke (1632–1704) and Voltaire (1694–1778). Locke's part in the affair was mainly creative. He saw that philosophy could no longer ignore science; and he tried to reform it on scientific lines. Voltaire, whose talents were well suited to the purpose, was mainly concerned with the destruction of the enemy. We must go back a little, to understand how these two fit into the general scheme.

The struggle between Reason and Authority went in favour of Authority in the 4th and 5th centuries, but turned in favour of Reason in the 16th and 17th. There was, however, a second struggle at the same time, within the ranks of Reason, between empiricists, who believed knowledge of the World could come only from experience, and upholders of the *a priori* method, who believed such knowledge could be obtained by pure thought based on intuitively known general principles. We must return to this subsidiary conflict, noticed in Chapter 4. It was already apparent among the Greeks. The Alexandrian tradition, represented by Hipparchus and Archimedes, was empirical: that of Athens, represented by Plato (with his contempt for stargazers), was the opposite. Aristotle was an empiricist in subjects, like zoology, which really interested him. He was content with *a priori* speculation in astronomy and mechanics, which he took less seriously. The different outlooks were associated with two different attitudes to mathematics. Those who were impressed by the success of mathematics, but who failed to understand its true nature, tended to favour the *a priori* method. They supposed that, if geometry could give spatial knowledge of the world by the process of pure thought, then its deductive methods could also give other kinds of physical knowledge. They forgot, or did not realise, that the axioms of geometry, though seemingly self-evident, were in fact generalisations from experience. Empiricism flourished either among those (like Aristotle) who knew little about mathematics, or those (like Archimedes) who understood mathematics deeply enough to know its limitations.

This subsidiary conflict, as to method, was renewed, along with the deeper conflict between Reason and Authority, after the Renaissance. Apriority then had the support of a number of influential philosophers. The most distinguished were Descartes, Leibniz and Spinoza. These men agreed in attaching little weight to the evidence of the senses. They regarded introspection and intuition, followed by deductive development, as surer sources of knowledge. We find among them, as among their ancient prototypes, a naïve over-confidence in mathematical methods. D. and L. were themselves eminent mathematicians, whereas S. was not. But an indiscreet respect for mathematics is as evident in all three as it is in Plato; and it has the same effect. Descartes, in his *Discourse on Method*, having decided to reject the teaching of the past and begin

(a) Kepler

(b) Galileo

(c) Descartes

(d) Newton

PLATE 9

Minor planet trails

PLATE 10

again for himself, remarks as follows concerning the method he
intends to use:

> The long chains of simple and easy reasonings by means of which
> geometers are accustomed to reach the conclusions of their most
> difficult demonstrations, had led me to imagine that all things, to the
> knowledge of which man is competent, are mutually connected in the
> same way.

Spinoza is equally ready to extend the application of geometrical
methods. His *Ethics* is set out in the manner of Euclid's *Elements*.
It begins with a list of definitions and supposedly self-evident
axioms, which is followed by a series of numbered propositions.
Each proposition is formally proved, with reference to the earlier
propositions on which it depends. Each proof ends with the formula 'Q.E.D.' In political thought, a similar infatuation for the
methods of geometry is shown by Hobbes.

Empiricism was meanwhile represented by the great scientists,
with the literary support of Bacon, Locke and Voltaire. It was
suited to the temper of late-17th-century and early-18th-century
England, but it took longer to make headway on the Continent. Its
spread beyond the domain of the natural sciences, for which Locke
was pre-eminently responsible, was one of the most far-reaching
intellectual consequences of the Scientific Revolution—hardly less
important than the victory of Reason over Authority.

*   *   *

LOCKE (Plate 11a) wrote influentially on government and education; but his most important book of general philosophy is *An
Essay Concerning Human Understanding* (1690). This proposes a
kind of philosophy whose purpose is not so much to seek knowledge
as to analyse and correlate the methods and results of the special
sciences. The acquisition of knowledge is the business of physics,
anatomy, astronomy, theology, history and the rest. Philosophy is
to preside over them; to restrain them; to examine their foundations and the validity of their claims; to assess and reconcile their
conclusions. Its first need, therefore, is to understand the powers
and limitations of the human mind, on which all the sciences depend. Thus Locke was interested in psychology and the theory of
knowledge. It is clear, from *The Epistle to the Reader* with which

14

the *Essay* begins, that his opinion concerning the proper methods and purposes of thought is influenced by his admiration for 17th-century science:

> The commonwealth of learning is not at this time without master-builders, ... : but every one must not hope to be a Boyle or a Sydenham; and in an age that produces such masters as the great Huygenius and the incomparable Mr. Newton, ... it is ambition enough to be employed as an under-labourer in clearing the ground a little. ...

Locke became much more than an under-labourer. He was not the *intellectual* equal of the incomparable Mr. Newton; but as an *influence* in the history of thought, he was hardly less important.

He states clearly, in the *Essay*, his belief that all knowledge is ultimately empirical. The only knowledge we have is knowledge about the ideas in our minds. These are either directly presented to us by our senses; or they are combinations, imagined by us, of simpler ideas which have been so presented in the past. Thus sweetness and redness are ideas we get directly from our senses. We do not get ideas like that of a centaur from direct experience: but even this idea depends on experience for its existence. We form it by putting together two simpler ideas, 'horse's body' and 'man's head', which we have already acquired sensually. An abstract idea, such as beauty, is equally dependent on the senses, since we cannot form it without first *experiencing* beautiful things.

Thought consists in contemplating ideas, classifying them, memorising them, uniting them to form more complex ideas, analysing them into simpler ideas, noticing the relations between them. There can be no knowledge without thought, no thought without ideas, no ideas without the senses. Even the principles of logic would be unknown to us without the help of our senses. It is often supposed (Locke says) that we are born with these principles stamped on our minds. This is not so. Inference consists in discovering the connection between one idea, A, and another, Z. We may perceive the connection immediately, or we may have to make use of intervening ideas to discover it. We directly perceive a connection between A and P, another between P and Q, a third between Q and Z. We thus indirectly recognise a connection between A and Z.

A man needs two faculties in order to make inferences. He must have direct perception, in certain cases, of the connection between one idea and another. When he lacks this, he must be able to find just those intervening ideas by means of which he can construct the necessary chain of such direct perceptions. Anyone who has these faculties can reason effectively. There is no need for him to be acquainted with the formal rules of logic, such as the syllogism 'If every A is B, and no B is C, then no A is C.' Formulae of this kind do not in fact represent innate principles which we *must* already have in our minds before we can *begin* to reason. They are mere useful records of the forms which *experience* has shown to underly successful practical inference in the past. Thus successful reasoning is necessarily prior to the formulation of logical principles, since these principles are *derived* from the study of successful reasoning. The belief that successful reasoning depends on the pre-conception of logical principles is false.

It may be argued that logical principles are valid only in virtue of the meanings we attach to certain words. They are simply consequences of the way in which we agree to use language. They are correct only because we understand such words as 'if', 'every', 'is', 'not' and 'no' in a particular sense. This is a reasonable comment, not only on the principles of logic, but also on the theorems of mathematics. It does not, however, save them from dependence on experience. We learn the meanings of words by *observing* the circumstances in which we *hear* them used, or from dictionary definitions in terms of other words whose meanings we have already acquired in this way.

The belief that men enter the world endowed with innate principles is thus as unacceptable as the belief that they enter it endowed with innate ideas. The mind begins as a blank tablet, which is furnished with impressions only as they come into it through the senses.

In Book I of his *Essay*, Locke first attempts to destroy all the common arguments in favour of innate ideas and principles. His criticism of these arguments is, on the whole, effective. He is certainly himself convinced by it. Having, as he supposes, destroyed the arguments in favour, he proceeds to give his arguments against. His main contention appears in the following extract (Bk. I, Chap. II):

It is an established opinion amongst some men that there are in the understanding certain innate principles . . . . It would be sufficient to convince unprejudiced readers of the falseness of this supposition, if I should only show . . . how men, barely by the use of their natural faculties, may attain to all the knowledge they have, without the help of any innate impressions . . . For I imagine anyone will easily grant that it would be impertinent to suppose the ideas of colours innate in a creature to whom God hath given sight, . . .

The core of his argument is that, since God has given us faculties which enable us to get knowledge for ourselves, it is impertinent to suppose He should take the further trouble of giving us that same knowledge in the form of innate ideas. He has not even given us an innate idea of Himself, but has left us to infer His existence and quality from our own nature and that of the world we inhabit.

Locke seems to assume that God's predilection for economy of means is like his own. If he had considered the prodigality of Nature in some other matters,[1] he might have seen the doubtfulness of this assumption. Even if Locke succeeds (as he hopes he will) in showing that all our knowledge *can* be obtained by reason operating on material supplied to it by sense, it hardly follows that every unprejudiced reader should therefore be convinced that all our knowledge actually *does* come in this way.

Yet, despite the weakness of this initial argument, Locke does in the end present a strong case for his empiricism. Its strength lies in the thoroughness and good sense, rather than the irrefutable logic, with which he develops his theme in detail in the later books. There may be inconsistencies and questionable statements here and there; but it seems unlikely anyone could read through the *Essay*, with even a modicum of good will, and still retain an altogether unshaken faith in innate ideas and principles. The book, as a whole, must leave most people with a strong bias towards empiricism.

* * *

LOCKE IS diametrically opposed to Plato in all this. Plato's belief, that every man has certain ideas and principles already in his mind at birth, is to be read between the lines in almost everything he wrote. His most arresting outright statement of it is perhaps that in

[1] E.g. in the vast number of eggs that have to be laid to ensure the production of a single adult herring.

the dialogue called the *Meno*, which is one of the most delightful passages in the literature of thought. The overt purpose of the dialogue is to decide whether or not virtue can be taught. But, as is not unusual in Plato's dialogues, a side issue is so developed as to overshadow the original question. The most important part of the *Meno* is a central portion in which Plato (using Socrates as mouthpiece) tries to convince us that 'inquiry and learning is reminiscence all'.[1] A man's soul, having existed before entering his body, is fully endowed with knowledge before he is born. All he need do is recall this knowledge, of which he is merely unconscious for the time being. The process which we call learning is in fact no more than a systematic effort of recollection.

To show this, Socrates calls a servant boy, who, Meno assures him, has never been taught geometry. The boy, being asked how to draw a square having twice the area of a given square, makes two false starts. Socrates, by asking questions, makes him see and admit his errors. He then sketches the diagram shown in Fig. 48, and asks a series of questions about it. The boy, in answering, tells him: (i) that square AXYT is 4 times as great as the given square ABCD; (ii) that each of the thick lines cuts one of the small squares in half; (iii) that square BUWD, made by these lines, is therefore half as big as AXYT; (iv) that BUWD is twice as big as ABCD. Thus the square on the diagonal of a given square has twice the area of the given square.

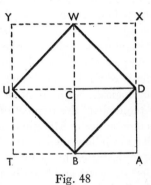

Fig. 48

Socrates points out that he has told the boy nothing. He has merely asked him questions; thereby bringing to light the knowledge latent in the soul which, though it now inhabits the boy's body, existed before the boy was born. Two conclusions are drawn: that the soul is immortal; and that knowledge is to be sought by a man within himself—by introspection, not by looking outwards at the world.

If the truth of things therefore is always in the soul, the soul should be immortal. So that whatever you happen not now to know, that is,

[1] *Meno*; trans. Floyer Sydenham, 1773.

not now to remember, you ought to undertake with confidence to seek within yourself. . . .

This extract makes the essential point of Plato's theory of knowledge absolutely clear, and shows how radically it differs from that of Locke. The same kind of thing is said again and again. Let us be content with only one quotation from another dialogue, which denies the value of the senses as it praises that of inward thought:

> And surely the soul reasons best when none of these things disturb it, neither hearing, nor sight, nor pain, nor pleasure of any kind, but it retires as much as possible within itself, taking leave of the body, and, as far as it can, not communicating or being in contact with it, it aims at the discovery of that which is.[1]

But the argument of the *Meno*, though cunning and most elegantly put, involves two fallacies. It is unlikely the boy would have solved the problem unless the questions had been asked by someone who already knew the answer. Socrates provides just the right figure, and asks all the pertinent questions. The whole scene would have been more convincing if he had summoned *two* untaught boys, and set one to interrogate the other. But, even if we let this pass, there is a still more serious objection. The trick could never have worked if the knowledge sought had not been mathematical or logical. No amount of questioning could have made the boy 'remember' the population of Athens or the name of the Persian commander at Marathon, unless he had actually been taught them by his fellow men in this life. Socrates, having (very dubiously) demonstrated his point in the special case of *mathematical* knowledge, tacitly and blandly assumes its general validity. Meno takes it all like a lamb. As in many other dialogues, the path of Socrates is made too easy. It would be refreshing, sometimes, to find him up against a harder-hitting opponent. This is a common weakness of the dialogue as a vehicle for philosophical opinions. The character through whom the author speaks is so much more gifted than the others that he is never fully extended. Galileo's Simplicius is no match for Salviati; nor can Berkeley's Hylas give Philonous a real run for his money.

* * *

Phaedo; trans. Henry Cary, 1848.

THUS LOCKE and Plato disagree completely about the method by which knowledge is to be obtained. One looks to sense and experience, abetted by reason; the other to a process of pure thought, based on the exhumation of innate notions buried somewhere in the soul. But *method* is not the only point of difference. They also have conflicting views about the *purpose* to which human intellect should be devoted.

They agree that the world of sense is not everything. Our sight, hearing and touch reveal only a façade; and behind it is an ultimate reality with which our senses never bring us directly into contact. This opinion is expressed by Plato, early in Book VII of the *Republic*, in the famous simile of the cave. He imagines men chained in a cave, with their backs to the light, facing a wall at the back of the cave. They can see only shadows, cast on this wall by events taking place behind them. They take these shadows for reality. If one of them escapes into the light, he is at first dazzled. But, when his eyes become accustomed to the brightness, he begins to perceive the truth, of which the shadows give a quite inadequate picture. When he returns, the others laugh at his account of what he has seen, and resume their futile contemplation of the shadows.

Locke similarly holds that there is a hidden reality behind appearances. We find that certain phenomena always occur together. A particular colour, softness, taste and smell appear to be so linked that we never experience one without the others. The constant association of these qualities leads us to suppose that there must, behind the scenes, be something in which they all reside. Locke uses the word 'substance' for this underlying thing, whatever it may be, which is supposed to hold the associated qualities together by virtue of their common residence in it. He does not use the word, as we now do, to mean only something material. He uses it, in the original sense, to mean that which subsists or stands beneath or supports. He supposes spiritual substances underlying spiritual phenomena, just as physical substances underly physical phenomena. We do not *perceive* a substance. We *infer* its existence, because it offers the most natural and satisfying explanation of the observed fact that certain qualities always go together. The colour, softness, taste and smell, mentioned above, forcibly suggest, by their invariable appearance together, the existence of a substance we call cheese. We perceive only the co-existing qualities; but we believe in the subsisting cheese, because we can imagine no other reason for the *regular* co-existence of the qualities. They might *occasionally* come together by pure chance—but hardly as often as in fact they do.

Here the agreement ends. Both philosophers suppose there is something behind appearances, which (to distinguish it from appearances) we may call reality. But they have different views as to what our attitude to this underlying reality should be. Plato believes that, by a supreme and purely intellectual effort, we can have access to reality; and that such access is the only achievement really worth striving for. The intellectual effort is symbolised by the painful struggle of the man in the cave to break his chains and accustom his eyes to the light. The false standards (of sense) accepted by most men are suggested by the preference shown for 'the magic shadow show' by others in the cave.

Locke, on the other hand, believes our faculties can tell us nothing about the fundamental nature of substances. We can infer their *existence* with some confidence; but that is all. We may be sure there is *something* behind the scenes, but we seek in vain to know what. He says (Bk. II, Chap. XXIII):

> ... it seems probable to me, that the simple ideas we receive from sensation and reflection are the boundaries of our thoughts; beyond which the mind, whatever efforts it would make, is not able to advance one jot; nor can it make any discoveries, when it would pry into the nature or hidden causes of those ideas.

We should assess our powers of understanding, and set our aims within them; being content 'to sit down in quiet ignorance of those things which, upon examination, are found to be beyond the reach of our capacities'. We need not be dissatisfied with our faculties because they cannot make us omniscient. There are many pursuits to which they are well adapted and to which we can usefully apply them:

> It is of great use to the sailor to know the length of his line, though he cannot with it fathom all the depths of the ocean. It is well he knows that it is long enough to reach the bottom, at such places as are necessary to direct his voyage. ...

This attitude of Locke's is very like what we now call scientific agnosticism—the frank admission of ignorance, except where we

can rely on the application of reason to the data supplied by sense.
It is an attitude which, even today, is sometimes thought slightly
disreputable. Most of us have a sneaking sympathy for the man
who dares the impossible. We admire his 'high-mindedness' or
'other-worldliness', without being clear what we mean by such
phrases. Anyone who suggests he is wasting his time is apt to be
thought ungracious. Robert Bridges, having praised the sceptic's
virtues, remarks that even he cannot always resist the urge to seek
the knowledge he believes unobtainable:

> But from his sleepy castle he will be tempted forth
> If ever a hunting-horn echo in the woods around,
> For he loveth the chase, and, like a good sportsman,
> His hounds and his weapons as he loveth the prey.

Locke, who recognises this partly sanctimonious and partly sport-
ing instinct in his fellow men, tries to justify himself by a cunning
theological argument. A benevolent Creator has given us certain
powers, which, in virtue of His perfect wisdom, are necessarily all
we need. The attempt to do what is beyond them is therefore not
only futile but impious.

Thus Plato believes we can and should approach absolute knowledge; and because such knowledge is really hidden within us, our
approach to it should be purely intellectual. Locke believes we cannot approach it; and we are better occupied seeking such shallower
knowledge as we can gain by the joint use of intellect and sense.
The outlook of one is metaphysical; that of the other scientific.

If Plato's views seem odd to us now, it is largely due to Locke's
influence. It seems absurd today that anyone should ever advise
students of astronomy to 'leave the starry heavens alone'. But we
must not judge Plato without remembering Collingwood's advice,
mentioned in connection with Thales. We should enquire what
Plato was trying to do. He was just not interested in the kind of
knowledge the senses give: he scarcely, even, regarded it as knowledge. Knowledge, for him, meant a grasp on the inward essence of
a thing—the everlasting 'Idea' behind it. Speaking of such essences
in the *Phaedo*, Socrates asks: 'Now then: have you seen anything of
this kind with your eyes? . . . Did you ever lay hold of them by any
other bodily sense?' Given his purpose, it was natural that Plato
should despise empiricism.

*   *   *

THE CHALLENGE, thrown down in 1690 to Plato and his intellectual heirs (who were numerous after the Renaissance), was important for the future. European philosophy did not immediately and wholeheartedly follow Locke. Since his time, however, it has been divided. One main stream, predominantly British, developed the empiricism of its patriarch Locke. This line includes Berkeley, Hume, Mill and Russell. These men, despite their differences, agree in thinking that our intellectual business is to analyse experience and decide what we can validly infer from it. The other stream, predominantly German, continued to believe in the possibility of *a priori* knowledge outside, as well as within, the domains of logic and mathematics. Men like Kant, Hegel and Nietzsche have, in this respect, maintained the tradition of Plato, Descartes, Spinoza and Leibniz. There is something very Platonic about Hegel's announcement, on philosophic grounds, that there could not be more than seven planets—an announcement which unfortunately coincided with Piazzi's discovery of Ceres in 1801.

The introduction of empiricism into philosophy was significant in several ways. It influenced the methods of some philosophers. They began to imitate the scientists, by concentrating on one limited objective at a time. It also provided the new science with a philosophical background and support. And, although science could already stand fairly well on its own feet, its hand was still further strengthened.

But a much more important fact was that, once the empiricism pioneered by scientists won a foothold among philosophers, the general outlook associated with it was bound to spread to other fields. Philosophy is linked with thought of all kinds. Political thought was particularly affected. A system of government in which policy is decided by reasoning from general principles, pre-established and held inviolable, is likely to be intolerant, rigid and ultimately unsuccessful. A system whose guiding principles are gradually evolved, from tentative experiments in policy, is less liable to these faults: for principles evolved in this way are subject to modification in the light of further experience, and are never looked upon as permanent. The *a priori* thinker, whose opinions depend on his principles, is necessarily jealous of those principles. If they are destroyed, the whole foundation of his life and conduct is removed. He has therefore some reason to be intolerant of those who disagree with him. But the empiricist derives his principles from experience. They simply epitomise such experience as he has so far had. He expects them to suffer change.[1] Having no principles which he desires to maintain permanently, he has less motive for intolerance. He can tolerate anything but intolerance itself.

Thus empiricism, as its influence spread, fostered political and (concurrently) religious toleration. It also gave the strength of flexibility to political systems founded on it. Science owes its strength to the fact that its principles are never fixed: the system adapts itself to change, here and there, instead of breaking down as a whole. A political system with empirical foundations can similarly yield to circumstances without snapping. Such a system can, like science, be used by men to serve their ends. It may not always work perfectly; but, when it goes wrong, the damage is limited. With a system based on pre-established principles, it is easy for men to become enslaved by the system that should be serving them. It is then difficult for them to free themselves without catastrophe.

Locke's influence had much to do with the growth of flexible and liberal institutions in many parts of the world; and his political thought was founded on a general philosophy which owed much to the influence of science. The totalitarian systems, on the other hand, which we have seen in our own time, have been much devoted to fixed, non-empirical, principles. They have in many ways been apt, if bitter, caricatures of Plato's republic, emphasising its faults and lacking its virtues. The sacrifice of individuals to the power of the State; the carefully indoctrinated ruling class; the privileged military caste; the lying propaganda; the state-organised eugenics; the political censorship of arts and sciences; the ruler who is unquestioned interpreter of an official philosophy: all these had some part in the *Republic*.

* * *

AFTER *De Revolutionibus* and the *Principia*, Locke's *Essay* is perhaps the most important book of the Scientific Revolution. It is certainly one of the most illuminating for those who wish to understand the effect of science on thought. Although not a scientist,

---

[1] If, where the rules not far enough extend,
(Since rules were made but to promote their end)
Some lucky licence answer to the full
Th'intent proposed, that licence is a rule. (Pope: *Essay on Criticism*.)

Locke shrewdly senses the virtues and the limitations of science. He fully understands the danger of attaching overmuch importance to the methods of mathematics. In pointing out the futility of trying to obtain scientific knowledge by deduction from general principles (which are, as he maintains, the *conclusions* rather than the *foundations* of science), he says:

> One thing which might probably give an occasion to this way of proceeding in other sciences, was (I suppose) the good success it seemed to have in *mathematics*, . . . (Bk. IV, Chap. XII).

He realises that the objects of mathematical thought are ideal; so that mathematics has no *direct* connection with physical fact:

> The mathematician considers the truth and properties belonging to a rectangle or circle only as they are an idea in his mind. (Bk. IV, Chap. IV.)

There could be no clearer recognition of the mistake made by so many *a priori* thinkers.

Locke, unlike Bacon, appreciates the value of hypotheses; though he knows that no amount of indirect confirmation can give them the status of certain knowledge. Like the Greek atomists, he has an eye for the kind of hypothesis likely to be useful to science. There are many passages in the *Essay* which show that he foresees lines of development in the next 200 years. Although he denies our ability to *know* the nature of substances, he is a thorough-going mechanist. He clearly believes that, if we could penetrate behind the scenes, we should find all physical phenomena explained in terms of matter and motion. The qualities of bodies depend entirely on 'bulk, figure and motion of parts'. Scientists have only recently begun to abandon this assumption, which served them splendidly as a scaffolding throughout the 18th and 19th centuries. The most striking instance of Locke's intuition is found in his prophetic statement of the kinetic theory of heat:

> Thus, observing that the bare rubbing of two bodies violently one upon another produces heat, . . . we have reason to think, that what we call *heat* and *fire* consists in a violent agitation of the imperceptible minute parts of the burning matter. (Bk. IV, Chap. XVI.)

*　　*　　*

THE DISTINCTION between empirical and *a priori* theories of knowledge is so significant, and Locke's championship of the former had such far-reaching effects, that we may well pass on at once to a related 19th-century development—the invention of non-Euclidean geometry. We have seen how the early success of geometry encouraged those who believed in *a priori* knowledge of the external world. Geometry remained their great stronghold against advancing empiricism during the 18th century. It was difficult to refute their contention that, where spatial relations were concerned, pure thought gave certain knowledge of physical truth. If this was the case with one kind of knowledge, why should it not be the case with others? There were those who had their doubts; but it was not easy to establish such doubts. Geometers themselves, in the end, did what was necessary to offset the past damage done by misplaced faith in the general applicability of mathematical methods.

The crucial question was, how Euclid's axioms, if in fact true, were *known* to be true. Nobody seriously doubted that the rest of his geometry followed from them. It seemed possible the axioms might be generalisations from experience; but this supposition could hardly be reconciled with the great strength of conviction they carried. Nobody had ever thought it necessary to subject them to the test of microscopic measurement; yet everyone instinctively *felt* they were exactly and absolutely true. Their apparent certainty argued against their empirical origin. But it was difficult to see what other origin they could have.

The German philosopher Kant (1724–1804) tries to avoid this paradox by suggesting that space and time are not constituents of the outer world. We have *sensations* of space and time; but these arise from the efforts of our own minds to arrange the material presented to them by our senses. Our faculties are such that we cannot take in everything at once. We have to *order* our acts of attention; and, by so doing, we *create* space and time for ourselves. Sensations of space and time are *consequences* of the way in which our own limitations force us to use such intellect as we have.

A parallel may help to make this clear. An office cannot be efficient if the papers are in a muddle. For a limited intellect to control the business, there must be a filing cabinet or system of pigeonholes. Space and time are analogous to a filing system. We cannot help knowing something about them, because they are part of the functional office furniture within our minds.

This seems to be what Kant means by calling space and time 'forms of intuition'. If it is admitted, it can (perhaps) resolve the paradox. The axioms of geometry, since they deal with space, are not statements about the external world, but inevitable consequences of our own mental constitutions. We *must* therefore be aware of them with complete certainty and without appeal to our senses. They are psychological, not physical truths. They tell us something, not about the world, but about the way we apprehend it.

Kant's opinion cannot be logically refuted. The main objection to it may be found in the success of physical science, which does undeniably enable us to predict and control our environment. Now physical science depends on the assumption that space and time have some sort of objective existence; or (at least) that there is *something* in the outside world which corresponds, and gives rise, to our sensations of space and time. This assumption is quite as plausible as Kant's and much more convenient. Thus Kant's position, though perhaps defensible, is not readily acceptable.

But if Kant's solution of the difficulty is rejected, what shall take its place? The answer came from mathematicians themselves, who had begun, early in the 19th century, to reach an explicit understanding of the real nature of their own subject. Agnosticism reared its head where it was least expected. Instead of trying to explain how Euclid's axioms were known to be true, the mathematicians attacked the problem from another angle; boldly asserting that the axioms were *not* known to be true, and might (as statements of physical fact) very well be false. The logical reasoning of geometry could ensure only that the theorems followed from the axioms, and that the axioms did not conflict with one another. Mathematics was not concerned with the *truth* of the propositions whose inter-relation it studied, but only with their mutual agreement. The truth or falsehood of an axiom must be decided, if at all, on non-mathematical grounds: mathematics itself offered no means of forming an opinion. The only propositions of which mathematics could legitimately assert the truth or falsehood were logical propositions about other propositions. There was *a priori* knowledge to be had in mathematics; but it was logical, not physical, knowledge. Thus a mathematician might (with strict professional propriety) assert that proposition p was incompatible with the joint truth of propositions q and r: but he had nothing whatever to say (as a mathematician) about the truth or falsehood of p, q and r individually.

This unwonted display of mathematical modesty took the wind out of *a priori* sails. Those who have believed that thought alone can reveal the nature of the external world have, it seems, often been inclined to confuse truth with freedom from contradiction. They have overlooked the fact that, although contradiction implies falsehood, absence of contradiction does not guarantee truth. They have supposed, therefore, that if they could once imagine a system in which everything was satisfactorily interlocked, then this system must be that of the actual world. They have hoped to derive all knowledge from the principle that no two items of knowledge can be logically incompatible.[1]

Any such hope was bound to be severely shaken by an open admission that the mere self-consistency of geometry had no connection with its physical truth. But the most telling blow came with the actual construction of geometries which rested on sets of axioms other than Euclid's. Each of these different systems of non-Euclidean geometry was self-contained and free from contradiction. Each was therefore logically possible. But, starting from different sets of axioms, they reached different conclusions. It had previously been thought that any set of axioms other than Euclid's must, in the course of its development, eventually lead to contradictory consequences, and so prove itself inadmissible. Gauss, Bolyai, Lobatschewsky and Riemann, the creators of the new geometries, showed that this was not the case.

The different systems of geometry have the same mathematical status. They are all interesting and logically possible; their truth or falsehood is not the mathematician's business.[2] But the natural scientist, who uses geometry as an aid to understanding his

---

[1] It is significant that Themistius, representing the Aristotelians in Boyle's dialogue *The Sceptical Chymist*, offers the following as his *main* argument for Aristotle: 'For that great man, in his vast and comprehensive intellect, so framed each of his notions, that being curiously adapted into one systeme, they need not each of them any other defence than that which their mutual coherence gives them.'

[2] The words 'truth' and 'falsehood' do not enter his professional vocabulary; he recognises only 'agreement' and 'disagreement' (with whatever set of axioms he happens to be using).

environment, must adopt the system whose predictions are confirmed by measurement. In recent years, in certain fields, this has turned out to be non-Euclidean. From the scientist's point of view, the different systems of geometry are so many hypotheses, to be selected or rejected according as they do or do not stand the experimental test.

The place of mathematics in the scientific scheme is now established beyond doubt. It is indispensable for extracting the latent information from such empirical data as we have; but by itself it can give us no physical knowledge. It can help us to analyse and make the most of what we find out by observation; but it cannot enable us to do without observation. This was recognised in practice by the Alexandrians and the great scientists of 17th-century Europe. But the long-standing opinion, that (whatever the empiricists might say about other modes of thought) *geometry* offered *a priori* knowledge of the physical world, survived in some quarters for a long time. While its influence lasted, much thought followed what must now be taken for a false scent. Non-Euclidean geometry invalidated this opinion, and finally destroyed the case against scientific empiricism. It was therefore an important landmark, not only in the history of science, but in that of thought as a whole. W. K. Clifford suggests that Gauss, Bolyai and the others have begun a revolution as radical as that of Copernicus.[1] This may be the exaggeration of an enthusiast; but it is also the remark of an intelligent and far-seeing man. It emphasises the importance of a development which has had less attention than it deserves. Perhaps the only comparable intellectual event in the 19th century was the establishment of Evolution. Yet, for every 100 people who know something of Darwin and Huxley, there is probably not one who has even heard of Gauss or Riemann.

* * *

VOLTAIRE (Plate 11d), like Descartes, was educated by Jesuits. He was an elegant and witty writer, an occasionally unreliable historian, and a devastating propagandist. One can only guess which (if any) of these qualities he owed to his education. He represented

[1] Clifford (1845–79) was fellow of Trinity College, Cambridge, from 1868 until 1871, when he became professor of applied mathematics at University College, London. He was one of the first to appreciate the wide and deep implications of non-Euclidean geometry, and he drew attention to it in his public lectures.

(a) Locke   (b) Bacon

(c) Berkeley   (d) Voltaire

PLATE II

(b) The 100-in. reflector at Mount Wilson Observatory

PLATE 12

(a) Newton's reflecting telescope

an intelligent middle class, professional and mercantile, which was then more numerous and more respected in England than in France. His aggressive independence of opinion and character led to his being twice imprisoned in the Bastille. His sympathies were all with Reason against Authority, and with empiricism against apriority. His contact with England began when he met the exiled Lord Bolingbroke in 1721; but it was made mainly during a three-year visit, when he was in his early thirties. He published his *Lettres Philosophiques sur les Anglais* two years after his return to France. It will be convenient to refer to these simply as the *Letters*.

He found an intellectual, political and religious freedom in England which was not apparent in his own country. 'An Englishman,' he says, 'as one to whom liberty is natural, may go to heaven in his own way.' He made no secret of his admiration for English institutions and thought. He became the chief continental missionary of empiricism—the experimental philosophy, as he calls it.[1] The *Letters* do not all deal with this subject. The important ones from our point of view are those on Bacon, Locke and Newton, his special heroes. In his letter on the Lord Bacon he says:

> . . . if true greatness consists in having received from heaven a mighty genius, and in having employed it to enlighten our own mind and that of others, a man like Sir Isaac Newton, whose equal is hardly found in a thousand years, is the truly great man.

Voltaire points to Bacon as a staunch supporter of experimental methods; but, like Rousseau, he overdoes his praise. He is astonished to find in Bacon a mention of 'the new attraction, the invention of which is ascribed to Sir Isaac Newton'. He offers this as evidence of Bacon's originality. He was unaware that *many* of Newton's predecessors had the vague general idea of gravitation. Nor does he appreciate the difference between merely having the general idea and actually calculating the detailed consequences. He credits Bacon with a similar anticipation of Torricelli. These exaggerations are perhaps pardonable in a man of letters who was not deeply read in science and whose main purpose was the advocacy

---

[1] As an instance of the empirical spirit he admires in the English and misses in the French, he mentions experiments—introduced from Turkey by Lady Mary Wortley Montagu—which led to the inoculation of children against smallpox.

15

of a genuine belief in empiricism. But his remark that 'no one before the Lord Bacon was acquainted with the experimental philosophy' is plainly silly.

The *Letter* on Mr. Locke begins with a mock review of past philosophers, and the learned stuff they wrote about the soul. Voltaire's wit, at its best, is turned against his transcendental enemies. Descartes is particularly scolded. Voltaire's purpose, as well as spreading Locke's philosophy on the Continent, was to hasten the success of Newtonian astronomy. The Cartesian Vortices were a serious obstacle to this, especially in France. By attacking Descartes in one field, Voltaire can help to discredit him in another:

> Our Descartes, born to discover the errors of antiquity, and at the same time to substitute his own, and hurried away by that systematic spirit which throws a cloud over the minds of the greatest men, thought he had demonstrated that the soul is the same thing as thought, in the same manner as matter, in his opinion, is the same as extension. He asserted, that man thinks eternally, and that the soul, at its coming into the body, is informed with the whole series of metaphysical notions: knowing God, infinite space, possessing all abstract ideas—in a word, completely endued with the most sublime lights, which it unhappily forgets at its issuing from the womb.

He then sketches Locke's philosophy, and recommends his modesty and good sense:

> Such a multitude of reasoners having written the romance of the soul, a sage at last arose, who gave, with an air of the greatest modesty, the history of it. Mr. Locke has displayed the human soul in the same manner as an excellent anatomist explains the springs of the human body. He everywhere takes the light of physics as his guide. He sometimes speaks affirmatively, but then he presumes also to doubt.

Voltaire further attacks the metaphysical method in his novel *Candide*. Candide is taken up by the philosopher Pangloss,[1] who maintains, *a priori*, that all is for the best in this best of all possible worlds. The empirical evidence for this proposition, collected by Candide and Pangloss in their travels, consists of hangings, burnings, robberies, floggings, galley-slaving, treachery, mutilation and other such experiences. As they enter Lisbon harbour, an Ana-

[1] A caricature of Leibniz.

baptist, in saving the life of a sailor who has struck him, falls into the sea. The sailor leaves him to drown. Candide wants to help, but is prevented by Pangloss, who points out that Lisbon Harbour was made on purpose for this particular Anabaptist to drown in. Voltaire drily remarks that 'Whilst he was proving this from first principles, the ship split in two and all perished except Pangloss, Candide, and the brutal sailor.'

Candide tries manfully to live up to the principles of his tutor, who sticks to them through thick and thin. 'I still hold my original views', says Pangloss after many misfortunes, 'for I am still a philosopher. It would not be proper for me to recant, especially as Leibniz cannot be wrong; and besides the *pre-established harmony*, together with the *plenum* and the *materia subtilis*, is the most beautiful thing in the world.' In the end Candide is disillusioned by observing the happiness of a Turkish farmer. He decides to forget Pangloss and work industriously in the garden.

The most pertinent of the *Letters* are those in which the astronomical theories of Descartes and Newton are compared. Voltaire assessed their merits shrewdly. He understood that Descartes' most valuable achievement was not his metaphysics, or his Theory of Vortices, but his less spectacular invention of analytical geometry. He justly complained that, in England, Descartes was not given proper credit for this. Descartes is fairly praised for his share in destroying the errors of the past. Voltaire also points to Newton's better fortune in place and time of birth. Late-17th-century England was more liberal and tolerant than early-17th-century France; and, while Descartes was forced from place to place to avoid persecution, Newton was honoured in his own country in his lifetime. But the inferiority of Descartes as a natural philosopher is asserted without compromise:

> I indeed believe that very few will presume to compare his philosophy with that of Sir Isaac Newton. The former is an essay, the latter a masterpiece.

Voltaire was not content with mere polemics: he did his best to explain Newtonian ideas in France. It is clear from Letter XV, on 'Attraction', that his understanding of Universal Gravitation was remarkable for one whose main business lay outside science. He loses touch only when he tries to follow Newton's purely

93918

mathematical work on fluxions and infinite series. His mistress, Madame du Châtelet, translated the *Principia* into French. They wrote together an account of the Newtonian system. It may seem strange to us that a man of letters should be so well up in current science. But, even in Voltaire's time, the division of interests was much less marked than now. We should be surprised today to find an able controversial defence of Relativity written by (e.g.) Mr. Evelyn Waugh. Yet the parallel would be fairly close. Relativity has been about as long established now as Universal Gravitation was when Voltaire wrote: and there is surely a literary kinship between *Candide* and *Decline and Fall*, in each of which the misfortunes of an innocent make material for satire on a false world.

   Voltaire foresees the objection likely to be raised against Newton by those whose minds have still a metaphysical bent: namely, that Universal Gravitation is unacceptable unless we can understand the means by which it operates. How can we believe in this attraction between bodies, far apart in a vacuum, when we are not told *how* one so influences another at a distance? Voltaire's answer is modern in spirit. We misconstrue the purpose of science, which does not seek the ultimate causes we thoughtlessly demand. Newton clearly shows that celestial motions and those of falling bodies have the *same* cause: we should not blame him for failing to say what that cause is. He has done, superbly, what is within the province of science. He shows humility and wisdom in refusing to speculate on matters outside that province. Descartes, with his *plenum* and vortices, offers a pretentious 'explanation', which panders to our metaphysical instincts. His account, in terms of the *push* exerted by a space-filling fluid, persuades our small minds that they can understand. But he offers no evidence. We must not be deceived by his sublime (but idle) speculations, while we despise the less ambitious (but undoubtedly solid) achievements of Newton, who (like Candide) prefers to work quietly in the garden. Newton successfully and scrupulously minds his own business; Descartes burns his fingers by meddling with that of God.

   Vortices may be called an occult quality, because their existence was never proved. Attraction, on the contrary, is a real thing, because its effects are demonstrated, and the proportions of it are calculated. The cause of this cause is among the *Arcana* of the Almighty.

Thus Voltaire recommends to science the agnostic motto *Procedes huc, et non amplius.*

*   *   *

THE INSTINCTIVE desire for explanations is very strong; and the metaphysical attitude did not at once pass out of science. Neither the reserve of Newton nor the ridicule of Voltaire altogether silenced its exponents. The passage of heat and light, through apparently empty space, was as puzzling as the action at a distance involved in gravitation. The ether theories put forward to account for these phenomena were very much in the Cartesian vein. Space was filled with a subtle medium, to which, at various times, the oddest qualities were attributed. It required some of the properties of an elastic solid, to transmit the supposed waves of heat and light; yet it had to be so refined as to offer no resistance to the moving planets. Maxwell, who was less mechanical in outlook than most 18th- and 19th-century scientists, proposed an ether with electric and magnetic, rather than elastic, properties. But all the ether theories, to some extent, made space resemble a Cartesian *plenum*, pervaded by a *materia subtilis*. Some, especially those produced by men with engineering propensities, were as fanciful as any Ionian speculation. Lord Kelvin, who boasted that he could never understand a thing unless he could make a model of it, suggested an ether which was not a simple fluid, but a fluid everywhere contorted into minute vortex rings.[1] He maintained that such an ether could transmit the vibrations of heat and light, and yet allow the passage of solid bodies without resistance.

But the most bizarre of all ether theories was offered by Osborne Reynolds, at the 1885 meeting of the British Association. Reynolds tried to explain the universe by turning it inside out. He suggested that what we take for empty space is really packed with tiny, hard granules. Particles of what we take for solid matter, on the other hand, are rifts in this otherwise continuous granular medium. Heat, light and gravitation, which we so naïvely suppose to pass from matter to matter through space, are really influences passing from space to space through matter!

Ether theories often played the proper part of scientific

---

[1] I.e. structures similar to smoke rings.

hypotheses: they acted as the foundations of mathematical deductions that could be experimentally checked. But the authors of some of them were, at least partly, prompted by the old metaphysical desire for explanation. Osborne Reynolds, after lecturing on the properties of granular media, such as sea sand, went on to say:

> this places a hitherto unknown *mechanical contrivance* at the command of those who would *explain* the *fundamental* arrangement of the universe.

(These words are quoted by Sir Oliver Lodge in Chapter IV of his book *Advancing Science*. The italics are mine.)

In the 20th century, science has given up trying to explain things metaphysically. Explanation is attempted only in the sense of linking the unfamiliar with the commonplace. There will always be some things of which we must frankly admit that we know they happen but not why. What science does, by interrelating phenomena, is to reduce the number of separate confessions of ignorance we have to make. Before Newton, men had to admit (separately) that they did not know why a stone falls, or why Jupiter moves in an ellipse, or why the law of equal areas is obeyed. After Newton, they had only to admit that they did not know why material particles attract each other according to the Inverse Square Law. One item of ignorance took the place of several. But *where men remained ignorant*, their ignorance was as profound as ever.

Another example of this appears in Maxwell's Electro-magnetic Theory of Light (1864), which made optics depend on electromagnetism. Once this theory was established, light was explained in terms of something else; and two fundamental problems became one. Maxwell, like Newton, suggested a connection which others overlooked. By assuming this connection he predicted the possibility and behaviour of radio signals, akin to light in their mode of transmission. These were produced in the laboratory by Hertz (1887). The practical achievements of Marconi and his successors, all based on Maxwell's theory, have had incalculable effects on social life, politics, industry and war. The indirect evidence for the connection between electricity and optics is thus very strong. But nobody yet knows what electricity is.

8

OTHER DEVELOPMENTS IN THE
16TH AND 17TH CENTURIES

THIS CHAPTER deals with important steps in sciences other than
mechanics and astronomy. These were not of such immediate significance as the advances in mechanics and astronomy; but they all
contributed to the fundamental change of outlook, and many of
them were the seeds of later flourishing growths. We shall follow
them into the 18th and 19th centuries whenever it seems natural to
do so.

Mathematics, as in Alexandria, kept pace with astronomy. To
understand how it developed we must turn back to the Renaissance
and the (often clandestine) contacts of the West with Islam. As a
result of these contacts—especially through Moorish centres of
learning in Spain—Greek mathematics, in Arabic translation, with
Arabian commentaries and some Oriental additions, gradually became known in the West. First came the copy of Euclid's *Elements*
brought from Cordova by Adelhard of Bath early in the 12th century. This was followed by Ptolemy's *Almagest*, translated from
Arabic into Latin by Gerard of Cremona, who obtained it in
Toledo. At the beginning of the 13th century Leonardo Fibonacci,
of Pisa, having studied in North Africa, published his *Liber Abaci*,
founded on the work of Alkarismi. This expounded the algebra
which had been developed by the Arabs from Greek and Oriental
sources. It also spread the knowledge—previously confined to a few
Italian merchants, trading with the East—of Arabic numeration
and the modern system of arithmetic, known as algorism, which
went with it. The Emperor Frederick II (1194–1250), who cultivated the society of learned Jews and Mussulmans, caused many
Greco-Arabic writings to be translated. By the end of the 13th century European scholars were partly and indirectly acquainted with
Archimedes and Apollonius, as well as Euclid, Ptolemy, Diophantus

and the Oriental arithmeticians. The knowledge of ancient mathematics was much more complete after the Greek originals became available in the 15th and 16th centuries; but for some time before that it was far from negligible.

The Renaissance, at first, was not so much distinguished by original thought as by enthusiastic study of the rediscovered past. Creative work at this time consisted mainly in the exuberant exploitation of ancient methods and forms. The search for fresh lines of advance did not begin in earnest until later. Thus, until early in the 17th century, the course of European mathematics was almost entirely determined by the character of the ancient learning on which it was based.

Now Greek geometry had a completeness and finality that made it incapable of much further development. Everything that could conveniently be done by its methods had already been thoroughly and gracefully done by its inventors. It was admirable and eminently worth learning, but not suggestive. There were no obvious ways of modifying or extending it. But arithmetic and algebra, despite Arabian and Hindu efforts to improve them, were still rudimentary. They presented many unsatisfactory methods and unsolved problems. They could be developed as they stood, without any *fundamental* change. It was therefore natural that the creative energy of Renaissance mathematicians should at first be devoted mainly to these subjects. The great advances in geometry came later, when the spell of the past was broken and tradition altogether set aside.

We have seen that algebra first arose in the attempt to solve the inverse problems of arithmetic—those in which we have to find an unknown number such that certain operations performed on it shall lead to a predetermined result. The reasoning in such problems was at first conducted in ordinary language. The algebra, at this stage, is called rhetorical. This procedure was so laborious that symbols other than words were introduced for the purpose of abbreviation. These symbols were *no more* than abbreviations applied to what was still essentially literary language. The ordinary rules of syntax were observed; but constantly recurring words were replaced by concise special symbols. The result was a kind of algebra which is called syncopated. Syncopation was valuable, in that it reduced the labour of writing and reading long passages of argument.[1] But it did not facilitate the reasoning processes themselves. The mere shortening of words, or replacing them by signs and letters, was not enough. A clean break with linguistic tradition was necessary. Real progress depended, not upon a more convenient vocabulary, but upon drastic modification of the way in which the words were put together. It was only when algebra developed a *syntax* of its own, devoid of such irregularities and idioms as occur in common speech, that it began to reach maturity. Modern algebra, in which the special syntax is so devised that each variation of the verbal structure corresponds to one and only one mode of thought, so that mechanical manipulation of the language can actually assist or carry out the reasoning, is called symbolic.

The evolution of symbolic algebra, from the rhetorical algebra of Diophantus, the Hindus and the Arabs, was the joint work of many competent Renaissance mathematicians, mostly Italian. The most eminent of them, whose names are quoted for the sake of reference, were Regiomontanus, Paccioli, Stifel, Tartaglia, Cardan, Record, Ferrari, Bombelli, Stevinus and Vieta. Their lives cover the years 1436–1620. They were not the individual equals of the great mathematicians of the 17th century; but, between them, they made a supremely important contribution to scientific progress. Modern mathematics would be quite impossible without its extensive and beautifully adapted symbolism. The firm foundations of this symbolism were laid by the Renaissance algebraists. We may date the beginning of modern mathematics from Descartes. But he and his immediate successors could hardly have taken the bold strides they took, if they had not found an elementary algebra, essentially similar to that we still use, already prepared for them.

The end of the Renaissance period saw the invention of logarithms. This was hardly as significant as the creation of symbolic algebra; but, as an advance in arithmetic, it was second only to the introduction of Arabic numerals.[2] The calculations of astronomers

---

[1] 'Syncopated' means 'contracted by having parts cut away'. The early algebraists often just omitted letters from the words they required most frequently. Thus Diophantus abbreviated the word κύβος, for the cube of the unknown number, to κ^v: Paccioli, in the late 15th century, wrote $\bar{p}$ and $\bar{m}$ for plus and minus.

[2] There has been a comparable advance recently, with the development of electronic calculators.

and navigators were now so cumbersome that it was absolutely necessary to ease the burden of multiplication and division.

The first published table of logarithms, the work of John Napier of Merchiston, appeared in 1614. Rouse Ball in his *Short Account of the History of Mathematics* says of Napier: 'the business of his life was to show that the Pope was Antichrist, but his favourite amusement was the study of mathematics and science'. If this was so, then Napier must rank among the most distinguished of great amateurs. A somewhat similar set of tables was independently published by the Swiss mathematician Jobst Burgi in 1620. As Napier outlined his idea to Tycho in 1594, and as Tycho was in touch with nearly all the scientific men of Europe, it is likely that Burgi, before beginning work, had a hint of Napier's approach to the problem. The idea was taken up by Kepler, who had an urgent personal interest in the simplification of arithmetic, and by Henry Briggs of Cambridge, later Savilian Professor of Geometry at Oxford. Briggs spent much of his life constructing tables more convenient and extensive than those of Napier and Burgi. It was largely due to him that logarithms were in use throughout Western Europe by about 1630.

*   *   *

THE MECHANICS and astronomy of Kepler, Galileo and Newton drew attention to two very far-reaching mathematical problems— the study of continuous but non-uniform motion, and the geometry of curves other than the circle. 17th-century mathematicians devised methods by which these problems (and, incidentally, many others) could be attacked. Such, particularly, were the methods of analytical geometry and the infinitesimal calculus. The importance of Descartes and Leibniz, perhaps over-celebrated as philosophers, and certainly not at their best as natural scientists, now becomes apparent.

The period of comparative neglect suffered by geometry after the rediscovery of the Greek writings on it, in the end did it more good than harm. It could not progress far in its stiff Greek dress; and its new lease of freedom in the 17th century was, oddly enough, made possible by the preference of Renaissance mathematicians for another field of research. For the powerful new method, created by Descartes and Fermat, depended on the fusion of geometry with algebra. This could not have taken place without the prior development of algebra: and the rapid growth of algebra between 1450 and 1600 was no doubt largely due to temporary disregard for the rival claims of geometry.

The fundamental idea in Cartesian geometry is the use of co-ordinates. We may define the position of a point P, in a plane, by giving its distances from two fixed perpendicular axes, X'OX and Y'OY (Fig. 49). The distance of P from Y'OY is called x; its distance from X'OX is called y. We take x to be positive or negative according as P is to the right or left of Y'OY; and y to be positive or negative according as P is above or below X'OX. The numbers x and y are called the co-ordinates of P, and P is called the point (x, y). The co-ordinate system can be extended to space of three dimensions; but we need not consider the extension here.

It is clear that, if x and y are allowed to vary freely, P can move anywhere in the plane of the axes. But this is no longer the case if x and y are related by an equation, so that the value of one is determined by that of the other. The wanderings of P are then, in general, restricted to some particular straight or curved line (called its locus). If $x^2+y^2=4$, P is restricted to a circle, of radius 2 units,

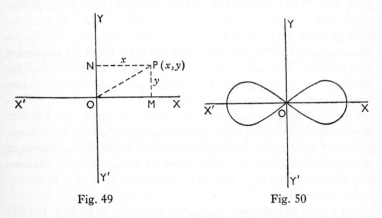

Fig. 49   Fig. 50

with O as centre. It can be anywhere on this circle, but nowhere else. Thus the equation $x^2+y^2=4$ may be said to *represent* the circle. In the same way, the equation $y=2x$ represents a certain straight line through O; and $(x^2+y^2)^2=x^2-y^2$ represents a lemniscate (Fig. 50). Indeed, every line or curve, constructed

according to a precise geometrical rule, is represented by an equation
of its own, different from that corresponding to any other line or
curve. The geometrical properties of a curve can be discovered by
examining the algebraic behaviour of its representative equation.
The relations between curves—where they meet or whether
they touch each other, for instance—can be predicted from the
algebraic relations between their equations. Thus, once the
characteristic equation of a curve is derived from its geometrical
definition, the discovery of its other geometrical properties is a
mere matter of algebraic calculation. The power of the symbolic
machine, originally designed for the arithmetician, is now also at
the disposal of the geometer.

Such is the method of co-ordinate (or analytical) geometry. Its
virtue is that it enables geometrical results to be sought by a systematic procedure which, if properly applied, can hardly fail. The
discovery of individual new theorems, which with Greek methods
always depended on the flash of insight or the stroke of luck, is
brought within the sphere of ordinary professional competence.
The advance of geometry, essential to that of science, is less romantic but much more rapid than it was. Analytical geometry has
probably affected human life more thoroughly, though less obtru-
sively, than the steam engine or the aeroplane. It was an essential
part of that revolution in thought and outlook of which the
steam-engine and the aeroplane are not even the most important
by-products. The conception of new general methods is of far
greater significance than the discovery of particular items of knowledge, however interesting or useful.

Gerard Desargues, contemporary with Descartes and Fermat,
was meanwhile developing projective geometry. He saw the possibilities of yet another far-reaching general method. The germs of
this are discernible in the early Greek treatment of conic sections,
but it grew mainly from the effort of Renaissance artists to understand perspective.

Let a geometrical figure be drawn on a flat glass plate p. Let the
shadow of this figure be cast, by a light L, on a flat screen P, not
necessarily parallel to p. The figure and its shadow will be (generally) different in both size and shape. But there must evidently be
a predictable relation between them, depending for its exact nature
on the relative positions of L, p and P. In virtue of this relation, the

geometrical properties of the shadow can be inferred from those of the original figure. In particular: the shadow of a circle will be a conic. The properties of conics can thus be deduced from the known properties of circles.

This projective method was exploited by several contemporary mathematicians, notably Pascal.[1] But, because of the general pre-occupation with Cartesian methods, it received less attention than it deserved. It was revived early in the 19th century, and has since thriven. Any systematic procedure by which two figures are re-lated in such a way that the properties of one can be inferred from those of the other, is called a transformation. Projection is only one of many such procedures; and projective geometry has really justi-fied itself by leading to the general study of transformations. Transformations have been invaluable to modern geometers, as, for instance, in the theory of map-making. A transformation need not be accomplished by a geometrical construction, such as that of projection. It may consist in an algebraic relation between the co-ordinates of a point in one figure and those of the corresponding point in the other. The essential notion of Desargues (that of transformation) is thus united with the essential notion of Descartes (that of co-ordinates).

* * *

THE INFINITESIMAL calculus has two branches, differential and integral. The differential calculus, which is concerned with rates of change, arose in the attempt to solve two apparently diverse prob-lems—both urgent for 17th-century science—which are in fact closely related. One was that of non-uniform motion; the other that of finding the precise direction of the tangent at any point on any curve. If we first consider the problem of motion, it will soon be clear why the two problems are essentially the same.

The behaviour of a moving body can be represented on a graph, showing its distance from its starting-point at any time (Fig. 51). If the motion is uniform, so that equal increases of distance always correspond to equal increases of time, this graph will be a straight line. Otherwise it will be a curve. The speed of the body is the rate

---

[1] Who, with Fermat, invented the mathematical theory of probability—now of great scientific importance. They were directed to this subject by a gambler's question.

at which the distance is increasing. It is clear that this is shown by
the steepness of the graph. Where the graph slopes up steeply, a
large increase of distance corresponds to a small increase of time.

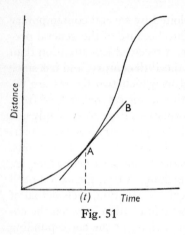

Fig. 51

Where it slopes less steeply, a
smaller increase of distance corresponds to the same small increase
of time. Hence the problem of
calculating the velocity is that
of calculating the steepness (or
gradient) of the graph. If we require the velocity at a particular
time (t), we must find the gradient
at the point A which corresponds
to the time t. Now the gradient
of a curve is that of its tangent.
Hence our problem is to find the
gradient (i.e. the precise direction)
of the tangent AB. Thus a fund-
amental mechanical problem is, in essence, identical with an
equally fundamental geometrical problem.

The tangent problem was solved by the ancients in many
special cases. But Newton and Leibniz, the main authors of the
differential calculus, invented a general method (called differentiation) by which it could always be solved. We need not discuss the
details: what concerns us is the importance of the method. Physical
laws are concerned with the relations between variable quantities.
When one variable (y) depends on another (x), then y is said to be a
function of x. Thus the distance of a moving body from its starting-
point is a function of the time; the attraction between two magnets
is a function of their distance apart; the tension of a spring is a
function of its length. We frequently wish to compare the rates of
change of two functionally related variables. The problem is
always equivalent, as in the case of distance and time, to that of
finding the direction of the tangent to a curve. For this reason, the
tangent problem is of much more than purely geometrical interest.
In early days the differential calculus was often called 'the method
of tangents'.

The integral calculus arose in the attempt to calculate lengths of
curves, areas bounded by curves, and volumes bounded by curved

surfaces. It is perhaps easiest to understand, in principle, with reference to the length of a curve. LM is the arc whose length is required. L is linked to M by a chain of chords (Fig. 52). The total length of these chords is less than that of the arc. But, if the number of chords is in-definitely increased, while their individual lengths are indefinitely reduced, their total length will approach a limiting value. This limit-ing value will be the length of the arc. Thus the process of calculating the length of LM may be graphically (if loosely) described as 'adding up an infinite number of infinitely short chords'.

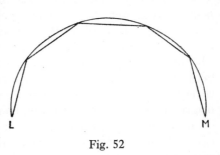

Fig. 52

The calculation of such a limiting sum is called integration. It is essentially the same as the process by which Eudoxus found the volume of a pyramid and Archimedes the circumference of a circle. Thus, in its root idea, the integral calculus is nothing more than the Greek method of exhaustions. But the crucial 17th-century discovery, which converted the method of exhaustions into the far superior integral calculus, was, that the ancient process of integration could be related to the recently invented process of differentiation. Differentiation gives the direction of the tangent, at any point, to a curve whose equation is known. The inverse process gives the equation of a curve when the direction of the tangent at every point is known. This inverse process, often easily performed, turned out to be mathematically equivalent to the apparently un-related process of integration. A general method of integration was thus available. The Greeks had to invent an *ad hoc* method on each occasion. Such bringing together of previously unrelated ideas is a constant feature of scientific progress. For obvious reasons, the integral calculus was at first called 'the inverse method of tangents'. It has many applications in physics as well as geo-metry. Newton's problem, of summing the attractive forces exerted by the numberless particles of a spherical planet, is a classic instance.

*   *   *

LEIBNIZ AND NEWTON, egged on by supporters who made the matter one of national pride, became involved in an undignified quarrel. The question at issue was that of priority in the invention of infinitesimal calculus. Such quarrels were common at the time. The scientific periodicals, by which discoveries are now generally made known, were not then in regular circulation.[1] New ideas were often put forward for the first time in university lectures, or in letters. Printed evidence might not appear for years. It was possible for scientists in one country to work in ignorance of what had been done in another; and there was considerable chance of a discovery being made by two men independently. In such conditions plagiarism was easy and not uncommon. There was an atmosphere of suspicion, and results were sometimes concealed in anagram or cipher. Thus Hooke's well-known formula for the extension of a spring under load was stated in the form *ceiiinosssttuv*, which, after rearrangement, becomes *ut tensio sic vis*.

The issue between Leibniz and Newton was complicated by Newton's sensitive unwillingness to publish, and by the fact that both owed much to predecessors such as Barrow, Wallis, Cavalieri and Fermat. The affair is mentioned only for the light it throws on conditions of research. Newton first used his method of fluxions in 1665–6, during that astonishing period of retirement at Woolsthorpe in which he began his work on gravitation. But, although his ideas gradually became known among his friends, it was not until 1687 that the first printed reference to fluxions appeared as a lemma in the *Principia*. A fuller account, in two letters from Newton to Wallis, was printed with a work of the latter in 1693; and another with Newton's *Opticks* in 1704. Leibniz's independent invention was made between 1675 and 1677. But, although Newton was first with the idea, Leibniz was first to publish it generally (1684). The seeds of controversy are obvious in the situation, but we need not follow its course.

The symbolism of Leibniz was far superior to that of Newton. For this reason, most of the credit for making infinitesimal calculus available, as a convenient tool, to later mathematicians is due to Leibniz. The symbolism, as De Morgan points out,[2] was the only

[1] Some had been started. The *Philosophical Transactions* of the Royal Society first appeared in 1664. The *Acta Eruditorum* of Leipzig began in 1682. But access to them was not easy for scientists in other countries.

[2] *Essays on the Life and Work of Newton.*

important part of mathematics to which Newton made no valuable contribution—perhaps because his wonderful powers enabled him to do so much without symbolic aid. But most mathematicians depend for their success on the use of adequate symbols. Mathematics is the most important of all scientific instruments, since it extends the power of intellect. An intellect equipped with a good mathematical technique—a technique involving a well-adjusted symbolism—can accomplish feats of thought which would otherwise be quite beyond it.

*　　*　　*

WHILE CALCULUS and analytical geometry were being developed as new intellectual instruments of science, the 17th century also saw the invention of many valuable physical instruments, able to sharpen the power of the senses and widen the field of observation. Without underrating the thermometer (Galileo?), the barometer (Torricelli), the air pump (Guericke) and the pendulum clock (Huygens), one must give pride of place to the optical instruments. Optics made more progress in the 17th century than any other branch of physics except mechanics. It revealed new worlds with the microscope and telescope. Dutch spectacle makers, early in the century, experimenting with combinations of lenses, inevitably came across the principles of telescope and microscope. The production of high-quality lenses in Holland was stimulated by Snell's discovery of the correct law of refraction in 1628. This led to better understanding of the theory, and hence to improvement in the design of lenses. The fact that the telescope and microscope, from being interesting novelties, so soon became practical scientific instruments was largely due to the skill of Dutch glass-polishers. Spinoza, while in Holland to escape persecution, lived by polishing lenses. Glass dust is not good for the lungs; and a man whose life was devoted to *a priori* thought thus ruined his health in the service of empiricism.

Refracting telescopes were improved by men like Galileo and Huygens; but they had a fault which could not be overcome at the time. This was chromatic aberration, which produced a fringe of colour to spoil the image seen in the telescope. For this reason, reflecting telescopes, in which curved mirrors took the place of lenses, were designed by James Gregory and Newton (Plate 12).

16

The immediate difficulty was thus avoided; but the important general problem of colour was not brought nearer solution. This problem was, however, studied by Newton, who laid firm foundations for subsequent work on it.

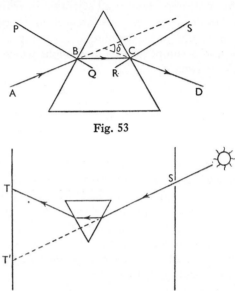

Fig. 53

Fig. 54

A ray of light ABCD, passing through a glass prism (Fig. 53), is bent towards the normal PQ as it enters the glass at B, and away from the normal RS as it leaves the glass at C, according to Snell's law. The angle δ, between the incident ray AB and the emergent ray CD, is called the deviation.

Newton let a sunbeam into a darkened room through a horizontal slit S, so that it should pass through a prism and illuminate the opposite wall at T (Fig. 54). In the absence of the prism, the parallel rays would pass directly across the room, producing an image of the slit at T'. The prism might be expected to deviate the light, and produce an image at T instead of T'. Newton found this was not the case. There was no clear-cut image; but a band of light, varying in colour from red at the bottom, through orange, yellow, green and blue, to violet at the top. The order of colours was that which occurs in the rainbow.

The explanation, as Newton saw, is that the apparently white light of the sun consists of many different coloured lights in combination, and some colours are more sharply refracted than others.

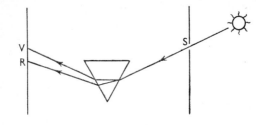

Fig. 55

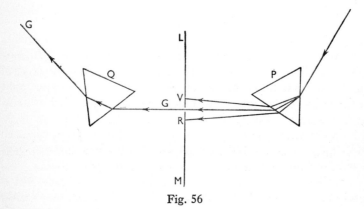

Fig. 56

The red light, which suffers least deviation, arrives at R (Fig. 55); while the violet, which suffers most, arrives at V. The other colours suffer intermediate deviations, and appear, in the well-known order, at points between R and V. This phenomenon is called dispersion, and the resulting band of colour is called a spectrum.

Newton checked his conclusion in two ways. It was possible that the colours were not, as he supposed, the separated constituents of the original white light: they might be somehow added to it in its passage through the prism. Beyond his first prism P, therefore, he put a screen LM and a second prism Q, as in Fig. 56. In LM he made a narrow slit, through which light of only one colour—green, say—might pass. He found that the green ray, passing through Q, was neither dispersed nor changed in colour. This strengthened his belief that white light yielded colours because it was composite and could be split up into several elementary components. The green, being one of these elementary components, could not be further analysed.

He argued also that, if white light could be decomposed, there must be some way of reproducing it from its components. He therefore made a disc, whose sectors he painted with the colours of the spectrum. He found that, when this was rapidly spun, the individual colours were no longer seen. The confusion of them made the disc appear white.

All this opened the way for a better understanding of colour. The old idea, that coloured bodies imparted something to the light that fell upon them, gave way to the idea that they subtracted something from it. Thus, when white light shines through red glass, the glass allows some colours—the red, and perhaps some orange —to pass; but is opaque to others, and absorbs them. The glass acts as a filter. When we look through it we see, not the original light with some colouring matter added to it, but the original light without its yellow, green and blue elements. Again: a leaf looks green because it absorbs the red and violet light (which it needs for its internal chemical processes), reflecting a preponderance of yellow, green and blue. Chromatic aberration is due to a lens refracting different colours to a focus at different points. The reflecting telescope is free from it, because the law of reflection is the same for light of all colours. It is possible to combine lenses, of different kinds of glass, so that one nullifies the dispersion due to the other without completely nullifying the deviation. Thus achromatic refracting telescopes are possible. Newton was unaware of this.

An elegant theory of the rainbow was devised. This did not just vaguely attribute the bow to the dispersion of sunlight by refraction in raindrops. It was a precise theory, giving figures which could be tested by measurement. It determined the width of the bow, and predicted there could be a complete bow only if the sun's elevation was less than 41°. It gave the order of colours, and accounted for their reversal in the secondary bow.

The study of colour gave science an instrument (the spectrometer) almost as valuable as those that came from the study of reflection and refraction. The spectrometer was not a 17th-century invention, but we may conveniently consider it at this point. It enables light from any source to be precisely analysed into its component colours, and compared with that from any other source.

The principle appears in Fig. 57. Let us first suppose that the light to be tested is of a single colour—red, say. It is allowed to fall on a narrow slit S. The divergent rays from S pass through a lens C, which renders them parallel, and then through a prism P, which refracts them all (since they are of one colour) to the same extent. The object lens L of a telescope then brings them together again, thus forming a red image of the slit at R. This image is examined through a magnifying eyepiece E.

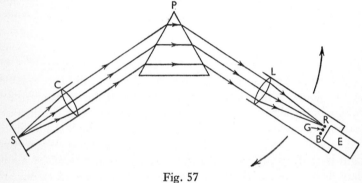

Fig. 57

If we now add green light to the red that falls upon the slit, this will be more sharply bent, and a green image will be formed at G. If blue light is added, it will form an image at B. We shall now see three parallel images of the slit, one in each colour.

The vertical plane in which the images R, G, B are formed is called the focal plane of the telescope. In this plane, inside the telescope, a vertical wire W is placed, which can be seen, with the images, crossing the field of vision from top to bottom (Fig. 58). The telescope can be rotated to left or right, as shown by the arrows (Fig. 57). Its position is marked by a pointer on a circular scale. Let us move it until the wire coincides with the red image, and note the position of the pointer. Suppose, now, that we replace the original source of red light by another. We wish to know whether the new red is the same as the old. We can decide at once, by noticing whether the new image coincides with the wire. If it does, the colours are the same. If we have to move the telescope to make it coincide, then the amount of movement is a measure of the difference in colour. Human judgment is notoriously fallible in matching colours: the spectrometer submits colour to accurate, impersonal measurement; so that observations involving colour may be as reliable as those of other kinds.

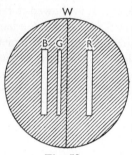

Fig. 58

The results of applying this instrument in astronomy were remarkable. But its revelations were not immediate: they came only after much detailed, unspectacular work. The credit goes to a host of 19th-century opticians, astronomers and chemists. The most eminent, perhaps, were Sir J. Herschel, Foucault, Bunsen, Kirchoff and Lockyer.

The white light given out by an incandescent solid is composed of all colours. When passed through the spectrometer, it produces images of the slit in every possible colour. These, being contiguous, form an unbroken band of colour varying through all shades from red to violet. This is called the continuous spectrum. When sunlight is analysed, it gives a continuous spectrum crossed by many dark lines. These dark lines show that certain shades of colour are either missing or unduly dim. The dark lines are called Fraunhofer lines, having been first carefully studied (1814) by the optician who supplied Bessel's instruments.

The interpretation of Fraunhofer's lines depended on two other discoveries. Firstly: it was found that each chemical element, in an incandescent gaseous state, emits light of a characteristic colour or combination of colours. Sodium, for instance, yields two yellows; mercury yields certain yellows, greens and violets. Secondly: it was found that the vapour of an element can absorb light of the colours which it radiates. Thus, if bright white light, before entering the spectrometer, is passed through a flame containing sodium vapour, the vapour cuts off the characteristic sodium yellows; and the otherwise continuous spectrum of the white light shows dark lines where the sodium yellows are to be expected.

This led to an obvious explanation of the Fraunhofer lines: for they appeared just where the characteristic colours of certain elements should be. The white light from the inner parts of the sun, before reaching us, has to pass through the sun's atmosphere of incandescent vapour. Each element present in this atmosphere will absorb light of the colours peculiar to it: hence the dark lines on the sun's spectrum. By noting the positions of the lines, we can identify the elements in the sun's atmosphere. Similar dark lines appear when the light from other stars is analysed; though the pattern varies from star to star. The spectrometer, therefore, enables us to answer, at least partly, a question which not so long ago seemed unanswerable—what are the heavenly bodies made of? The common sense of 17th-century astronomers repudiated the Aristotelian belief in a quintessence. When it was found that heavenly and terrestrial bodies obeyed the same mechanical laws, it seemed unlikely they were made of altogether dissimilar materials. But this was only a shrewd guess, without positive evidence to support it. Strong positive evidence was at last supplied by the spectrometer. It was further strengthened by a successful prediction. Certain Fraunhofer lines, not associated with any known element, led to the suggestion by Sir Norman Lockyer (1878) that the sun contained an element, undiscovered on earth, which he proposed to call helium. This gas was later found in ordinary air.

*   *   *

WE MUST say something of the hypotheses suggested in the 17th century to account for the propagation of light. Newton favoured a corpuscular emission theory, according to which light was supposed to be a stream of particles, projected by the luminous body. But he held this view with characteristic caution. Hooke and Huygens preferred a wave theory, recognising the analogy between light and sound.

Sound is produced by bodies, such as bells and fiddle strings, in rapid vibration. It is carried to the ear, by a succession of impulses, through the air. The vibration of the string or bell is taken up by the layer of air immediately surrounding it; this layer transmits the vibrations, with a slightly delayed action, to the next layer; and so on. The disturbance, which consists in small but rapid variations of pressure, is thus in time carried to the eardrum, and the sensation of sound is produced. The arrangement shown in Fig. 59 roughly illustrates the passage of a sound wave. Billiard balls, A, B, C, D, . . ., are suspended, not quite touching one another, by equal strings. Let A be pulled aside, as shown by the dotted lines, and let go. The resulting motion will be imparted by A to B, by B to C, and so on; but the swing of each ball will begin slightly later than that of the previous ball. The disturbance will pass along the line, becoming gradually feebler. Two points are important: (i) the passage of the disturbance does not involve any transference of air from place to place; (ii) the individual particles vibrate in the line, AH, along which the disturbance travels. A wave of this kind is called longitudinal. A sequence of such waves, at regular intervals, produces a musical note, whose pitch depends on the frequency with which one wave follows another— the greater the frequency, the higher the note.

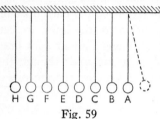

Fig. 59

The wave theorists believed that light was transmitted in a similar way. But the vibrating medium could not be air, since light could travel in a vacuum. They had to postulate a subtle, space-filling ether, which could carry the waves, but which yet did not obstruct the motion of the planets. Huygens, who was the first to work out a detailed wave theory, supposed that light waves were longitudinal like those of sound. But Hooke suggested they might be transverse: i.e. the ether might vibrate at right-angles to the direction in which the waves travelled. The ripples on a pond are of this kind; the individual particles of water move only up and down as the waves pass horizontally. The distance between successive crests is called the wavelength, and the number of crests passing a given point every second is called the frequency. The speed at which the waves advance is equal to the wavelength multiplied by the frequency. It is a fact of experience that the speed of waves in a given medium is fixed; hence an increase of wavelength is always accompanied by a decrease of frequency.

Thus three hypotheses were current in the late 17th century— those of corpuscles, longitudinal waves and transverse waves. All were in keeping with the mechanical spirit of the age; for all pictured light in terms of matter and motion. Each had its good and bad points.

It is obvious, from the existence of clearly defined shadows, that light travels nearly, if not quite, in straight lines. Newton set the weight of his authority against waves of either kind, because he did not see how they could explain this fact. His objection was fair enough at the time. Sound waves can certainly turn corners, and there was then no evidence to suggest why light waves should behave differently. Rectilinear propagation, on the other hand, was a natural consequence of his own emission theory. Despite this difficulty the wave theory had attractions. It could explain variations of colour as variations of frequency. The analogy of colour with pitch was so obvious that this explanation appeared natural and convincing. We must remember, also, that Cartesian ideas were still very much alive; and the Cartesians had an ether already at their disposal, in the fluid of the Vortices.

There was, ideally, an experiment which could decide between the Newtonian and wave hypotheses. Refraction, according to the former, could be explained only by supposing light to travel faster in the optically denser medium. According to the latter, light had to be slower in the denser medium. Although Roemer had estimated the speed of light over astronomical distances by 1676, there was no technique in the 17th and 18th centuries for measuring it over short distances. There was thus an unresolved difference of opinion, until the crucial experiment became practicable in the 19th century. Natural respect for Newton tended to divert attention from the merits of the wave theory, which returned to favour only with the work of Thomas Young (1773–1829), Augustin Fresnel (1788–1827) and J. B. L. Foucault (1819–68).

Young, by his study of interference and diffraction, provided fresh evidence for the wave theory, as well as overcoming one of the main objections to it. He supposed, with Huygens, that light waves were longitudinal and consisted of rapid fluctuations of pressure in the ether. Now sound waves do not cast sharp shadows. They tend to come together again after being parted by an obstacle, and to spread out in all directions after passing through a gap. This effect is called diffraction. It is more pronounced with long waves of low frequency than with short waves of higher frequency. Young realised (with Newton) that light, if it did indeed travel in waves, would, like sound, exhibit diffraction. But he saw that, if the wavelength were sufficiently small, this diffraction might be hardly noticeable. He devised a beautifully simple experiment which did three important things at once. It showed the existence of diffraction: it produced another phenomenon, interference, which was predicted by the wave theory but not by the emission theory: and lastly, it enabled him to estimate the length and frequency of the waves whose reality now seemed so probable.

The principle is shown in Fig. 60. There are three parallel screens, X, Y, Z. A narrow slit, D, in X, with a lamp L behind it, acts as a point source of light. The light falls on two narrow slits,

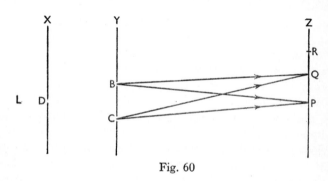

Fig. 60

B and C, close together in Y. If it were to pass straight through B and C without diffraction, we should have a single clear-cut image of each slit on the screen Z. What we find, instead, is a series of alternately bright and dark lines, called interference fringes. This evidently shows there must be some diffraction, or spreading of the light, after it passes through the slits.

As to the alternate bright and dark patches, it is easy to explain them by Young's wave theory. Consider first the rays, BP and CP, which meet on Z at the point P, equidistant from B and C. Each ray consists of pulses of high and low pressure, following one another at regular intervals. Since the rays are of equal length and come from the same source, a pulse of high pressure from B will arrive at the same time as a pulse of high pressure from C. The pulses of low pressure will also coincide. Thus the rays from B and C will combine to reinforce each other, and will produce an illumination according to their sum. But at Q the symmetry is upset since CQ is greater than BQ. If it happens that the difference between CQ and BQ is half the wavelength of the light, then the pulses of high pressure from C will coincide with those of low pressure from B: the rays will destroy each other, and we shall have darkness. At R, where the difference of distance is equal to the wavelength, a pulse of high pressure from B will meet the previous pulse of high pressure from C; and we shall again have the whole illumination. Thus the appearance of the fringes is naturally explained. It is very difficult to explain them by the emission theory.

It is easy to calculate the difference CQ — BQ, from the measured distances YZ, BC and PQ, and so to find the wavelength of light. This is found to vary with its colour, being about 0·000 045 cm for blue and about 0·000 08 cm for red. A typical sound wave, that of the note middle C, has a wavelength of about 4 feet. Thus the wavelengths of light and sound are of entirely different orders. The amount of diffraction, in the case of light, is so small that superficial observation can (misleadingly) suggest an absolutely rectilinear behaviour.

Huygens and Newton were puzzled by the double refraction in crystals of Iceland spar. If such a crystal is placed over a dot on a piece of paper, two images of the dot can be seen—one in the normal place, and an extraordinary one close beside it. When the crystal is rotated in the plane of the paper, the normal image remains fixed, while the extraordinary image moves round it in a circle. Huygens altogether failed to explain this. Newton argued from it that the cross-section of a ray of light, by a plane at right-angles to its path, could not be symmetrical; but he went no further. Now a longitudinal wave cannot lack symmetry in this way. Fresnel, therefore, reintroduced Hooke's idea that light waves were transverse, with the ether vibrations taking place across the line of progress of the waves. This made possible the necessary lack of symmetry, while it did not spoil Young's explanation of interference. (One has only to alter the explanation verbally, by substituting 'crest' for 'pulse of high pressure' and 'trough' for 'pulse of low pressure').

The position of the wave theory was further strengthened by Foucault, who in 1850 devised a way of measuring the speed of light over quite short distances. This made it possible to detect differences in the speed of light in different transparent media. It was found that light travelled less quickly in water than air—a fact which, according to the wave theory, but not according to the emission theory, would explain Snell's law of refraction.

Thus the theory of transverse light waves was pretty well established by the mid 19th century. But there was still a great objection. In order that the ether might carry transverse waves, it needed elastic properties more like those of a solid than a fluid. The Aristotelian-Cartesian *plenum*, which pneumatic scientists of the 17th century had done so much to repudiate, was returning with a vengeance. The space-filling fluid had been banished, only to have its place taken by a still less convenient space-filling solid. Optical facts seemed to imply the existence of such a medium; but how was it to be reconciled with unimpeded planetary motion? The difficulty disappeared when Maxwell's electro-magnetic theory was accepted. This suggested that the passage of a train of light waves involved periodic fluctuations of electric and magnetic tension (whatever they may be) rather than any material vibrations. Electrical and magnetic properties were assigned to the ether, but it no longer needed the elastic properties of gross matter. This was a development of great philosophical importance, though its full significance was not appreciated at the time. The belief that Nature could be described in terms of nothing but matter and motion had become steadily deeper and more widespread since the mid 17th century. With Maxwell's theory we see the first signs of a scientific retreat from this standpoint.

Thus another 17th-century conception, the wave theory of light, became, in its refined electro-magnetic form, an ingredient of modern science. It led to the union of optics with electrical science. This has already had immeasurable social, military and economic consequences, by the technical application of electric waves: above all, it began the movement of scientific thought away from that limited outlook of coarse materialism which, though it was for a time successful and perhaps even *necessary* to progress, is now seen to be inadequate—even for science.

Analogy played a big part in these developments. They were set going by perception of the analogies between light and sound, colour and pitch. But there was trouble whenever the analogies were followed too closely. Perfect analogies appear only in logic and mathematics. Thus there is a perfect analogy, in analytical geometry, between the behaviour of curves and that of their equations. This logically established analogy enables us to infer properties of curves from those of equations with certainty. But the analogies that are helpful in the natural sciences are neither perfect nor logically established. More often than not they are just vaguely *felt*, as the result of a really quite inadequate experience. This may not destroy their value as guides; but it means caution is advisable in following them. It pays to look for them, and examine their suggestions with care. The ability to spot them is one of the greatest gifts a scientist can have. But there must always be independent checks. Analogy is generally invalid as an argument, but frequently invaluable as a source of inspiration.

We may now understand another important astronomical use of the spectrometer. The motion of a star across our line of sight is easy to observe, but its motion directly towards or away from us is not. The changes in apparent size or brightness due to such a motion are too small to be detected; but the Fraunhofer lines can be used to overcome the difficulty. The whistle of a train changes note as it passes: the note is shriller when the train approaches than when it recedes. This is called Doppler's Effect. The reason is that, when the train comes towards us, the impulses which cause the sound reach us in more rapid succession than they would if the train were at rest. Thus we hear a note of higher frequency, and therefore higher pitch. Light waves behave similarly. If their source is approaching, they appear to have more than their normal frequency; if it is receding, they appear to have less. The red end of the spectrum is the low-frequency end, the blue the high-frequency end. Thus the approach of a star makes its light seem slightly bluer, while recession makes its light seem redder.

In detecting these changes of colour, we can use the Fraunhofer lines as landmarks. A given element, say hydrogen, produces lines in a recognisable pattern. In examining the spectrum of a star, we sometimes find what is obviously the hydrogen pattern slightly out of place. If the pattern is shifted towards the red, we can infer that the frequency of the star's light is lowered by its motion away from us. A shift towards the blue suggests the star is approaching. The shift can be measured by setting the star's spectrum beside that showing the hydrogen lines from a stationary source. The velocity of approach or recession can then be calculated.

Doppler's Effect was used to check Maxwell's theoretical assertion that Saturn's ring could not be solid, but must consist of many particles. It was found that the inner parts of the ring revolve faster about Saturn than the outer parts. If the ring were solid, this would evidently not be the case. But the most surprising revelation has been that the extra-galactic nebulae are all apparently receding. The more distant they are, the more rapid their recession. Thus cosmic geometry is complicated by the notion of an expanding universe.

*   *   *

THE SCIENTIFIC self-confidence which gathered force during the 17th century received its first serious rebuff from Bishop Berkeley (1685–1753, Plate 11c), who saw the danger of a naïvely materialistic philosophy. As his attack was founded on the criticism of mathematics and optics, it may suitably be considered now.

Unlike most ecclesiastical opponents of science, he understood what he was opposing. Anyone who reads *The Analyst* or *An Essay towards a new Theory of Vision* will realise that Berkeley could himself have done first-class scientific work. His criticism was keen, rational, moderate and kindly. Much of what he said is still relevant. Although he had a religious axe to grind, he ground it with such skill and good sense that, while defending religion, he also clarified the philosophic foundations of science.

Newton and Locke, although they believed that matter and motion were the concepts in terms of which the science of their time could best express itself, were too well balanced to think these concepts all-sufficient. But their less profound disciples, observing that thought in terms of matter and motion led to unprecedented scientific success, began to suppose it was the only kind of thought worth while. They rashly took the concepts which seemed sufficient for the science of their own day to be the only concepts science would ever need. At the same time, they forgot that scientific success is not the only object of human endeavour. Voltaire, returning to France, preached Locke and Newton with the zeal and indiscretion of a hot gospeller—partly because he recognised their merits; partly to undermine the civil and ecclesiastical authority he hated. The French Encyclopaedists,[1] under his influence, professed a mechanical philosophy like that of Democritus, which implied

[1] Authors of the *Encyclopédie*, published in 35 volumes (1751–80).

that everything, including mind, could be explained by the motion of atoms according to ascertainable laws. They really seem to have thought that the human race was within reach of universal understanding. This philosophy went with an absolute determinism, summed up by Laplace in the paradoxical fancy that an able enough mind (presumably not itself part of the material universe!), given the position, velocity and mass of every particle of matter, could predict the whole future of the universe.

No doubt scientists were wise to renounce metaphysical ambitions, and seek superficial regularities in Nature. They were also wise to select matter and motion as the elementary ideas most likely to serve their limited purpose for the time being. It was quite another thing to regard the *sole existence* of matter in motion as an article of faith; or to infer universal determinism from the discovery of a few regularities, however striking, here and there. Berkeley foresaw such developments and did his best to forestall them. He had little success at the time. Scientists of the 18th and 19th centuries, excited by their own achievements, were not in the mood to pause and consider his wise and gentle remonstrances. They were so sick of the inept interference of philosophers in the past, that they would not grant him a fair hearing. But, if he had returned to meet the pioneers of present-day science, he would have found among them (though not in all their lesser followers) an attitude in many ways like his own. He would have understood Einstein, and even Maxwell, as he could never have understood Laplace. The return of a Newtonian humility to science has been partially due to the long-term influence of Berkeley.

Berkeley's purely destructive thought was altogether good. Perhaps more than any other thinker since Socrates, he resembles 'some medicinal root in pharmacy, whose juice is wholesom for purgation'. In *The Analyst, or a Discourse addressed to an Infidel Mathematician* (1734) he begins by quoting Matthew, 7:5. He accuses mathematicians of being too ready to lay down the law concerning everything else, without first setting their own house in order. He enforces this point with an astute criticism of the argument (*Principia*, Bk. II, Lemma 2) by which Newton tries to establish a fundamental theorem in fluxions; and he has right on his side. In the early days of the calculus mathematicians were often careless of their logic. The fact that their intuition generally led them to correct results gave them no right to complain of those who put faith or intuition before logic in other fields.

In a period of rapid expansion it is natural for scientists of all kinds to let their intuition have its way. Too much attention to logic in the early stages can retard progress. The strict logic is usually imported by later thinkers, consolidating this progress. It was only late in the 19th century, after being used for 200 years, that the calculus acquired a sound logical foundation. Berkeley's plea to the mathematicians is to allow others the liberty they allow themselves; not to be too dogmatic; to beware of drawing supposedly logical conclusions from that which lacks proper logical foundations; to hesitate before extending, to philosophy in general, the results of thought in a particular field. This warning is always relevant in periods of rapid scientific advance like the present. Scientists themselves are now less dogmatic and more reserved in judgment than they were; but the warning is sometimes unheeded by their journalistic and popular following. We must always guard against the indiscriminate acceptance of a new scientific authority in place of the ecclesiastical authority which science did so much to soften.

Opticians, says Berkeley, spend too much time on geometrical theory, and not enough on the psychology of sight.[1] They should carefully consider how the mind interprets the impressions which light makes on the eyes: some of their difficulties would then be resolved. What our mind actually perceives is only a flat picture, made by light which falls on the retina. The various parts of this picture are not at different distances. How, then, do we judge the distances of things we see? The textbook answer is that, when we look at something, we have to squint slightly, in order that the optic axes of our eyes may converge on what we are looking at. The angle between the axes increases as the object approaches. We judge the distance according to the angle.

Berkeley scouts this idea that we make subconscious calculations when we judge distances. He recommends a sense of reality to the opticians. Animals, children, uneducated men, who know nothing of angles, can judge distances as nicely as mathematicians. The best mathematician, having been born blind and suddenly acquired sight, would fail utterly at first. We really judge the distance

[1] *A New Theory of Vision* (1709).

of a thing by the amount of movement we have to make in order to *touch* it. Before we can judge by sight alone, *experience* must teach us to correlate visual sensations with those of touch and muscular action. We must learn to associate small faint images with long walks, large confused images with immediate contact, and so on.

This attack on current optical notions, which Berkeley makes in his first book, is the opening of a brilliantly sustained campaign against scientific materialism. He puts himself in a strong position from the first, by showing scientists he really understands their work, and by addressing them as a fellow empiricist. He admits that experience is the source of knowledge, and sees that no effective criticism of science can rest on the denial of empiricism. He concentrates his attack at the vulnerable point, by warning scientists against a naïve *misinterpretation* of experience.

There is no doubt about the reality of the sensations we call 'seeing a table' and 'touching a table'. Experience tells us that, whenever we have one of these sensations, a voluntary act (such as moving the hand or opening the eyes) will enable us to have the other. May we suppose, therefore, that there is an independently existing 'thing' outside our mind, which in some way *causes* both sensations? Berkeley says we may not. We know the sensations exist together; but we cannot thence infer (with Locke) that they have the same material cause or even that they have material causes at all. In any case we gain nothing by such an inference. All that affects us is the complex of sensations we experience. This *is* reality. In forming the concept of matter, we are not, as the scientists seem to think, grasping the reality behind appearances; but creating a fanciful, unnecessary world to support an already self-sufficient reality.

Berkeley's denial of the reality of matter, which despite Dr. Johnson[1] we must take seriously, is set forth in detail in his

---

[1] 'After we came out of church, we stood talking for some time together of Bishop Berkeley's ingenious sophistry. . . . I observed, that though we are satisfied his doctrine is not true, it is impossible to refute it. I shall never forget the alacrity with which Johnson answered, striking his foot with mighty force against a large stone, till he rebounded from it—" I refute it thus." ' (Boswell, *Johnson*, *aetat* 54.)

'Being in company with a gentleman who thought fit to maintain Dr. Berkeley's ingenious philosophy, that nothing exists but as perceived by some mind,

17

Principles of Human Knowledge (1710) and defended in his *Dialogues*. In assessing it, there are several points to consider. Johnson's experiment with the stone certainly demonstrates the sensation of solidity. But Berkeley never denies this. He stresses the reality of sensations, such as 'feeling a stone' and 'seeing a stone'. What he does deny is our right to infer the existence of matter from such sensations.

Nothing Berkeley says can affect the right of scientists to employ the *hypothesis* of matter in their calculations, if they find this helpful. It is when interpreting the *results* of their calculations that they must be careful. The natural uniformities (or laws), which scientists discover by analysing their experience, may be stated, for mathematical or linguistic convenience, in terms of a hypothetical matter and motion. But calculations based on such laws tell us nothing about an independent, material world; they merely enable us to predict our own future sense perceptions. When an astronomer predicts an eclipse, he may legitimately *imagine* a sun, moon and earth made of gravitating matter and having a certain geometrical disposition. He may calculate when these supposed bodies will come into a straight line. He may announce his conclusion: 'At noon tomorrow there will be an eclipse of the sun'. But all this really means is: 'When we perceive the shadow on the sundial passing the figure XII tomorrow, we may also perceive a dark circle slowly covering a bright circle against a blue background.' And, surely, this is all that matters to us. Such a view of scientific conclusions was again taken by Ernst Mach late in the 19th century. It is now common among scientists.

Thus Berkeley's aim is not to destroy science, but to prevent its losing touch with human needs and problems. Men are *directly* conscious of their own sensations and nothing else. These sensations, and the mind in which Berkeley assumes they take place, are, therefore, the essentials of which we must never lose sight. He fears that the preoccupation of science with its own concept of matter, and the associated mechanical laws, will push mind into the background, and lead to its being regarded as a mere superficial manifestation of underlying material events. He sees the urgent need for reasserting the central human importance of mind

Johnson said to him, "Pray, Sir, don't leave us; for we may perhaps forget to think of you, and then you will cease to exist." ' (*Ibid., aetat* 71.)

before it is too late. He tries to do this by going to the opposite extreme; by making matter ideal; by insisting that it is no more than a figment of mind attempting to interpret experience.

There are three conflicting opinions about mind and matter: (i) the idealist belief: that mind is the ultimate reality, and matter a figment of mind; (ii) the materialist belief: that matter is the ultimate reality, and mind a mere effect of atomic rearrangements; (iii) the dualist belief: that mind and matter are both real, and exist side by side. It is perhaps impossible to decide finally for any one of the three. But the difficulties involved in (i) are no greater than those of (ii) or (iii); and much may be said for Berkeley's view that they are far less.

We may admit that a material, machine-like brain could control bodily functions—acting as an automatic telephone exchange, to receive nervous messages of need, and return appropriate orders for action. But no materialist has yet suggested how such a brain could become the seat of consciousness, and so earn the right to be called a mind.

The unsolved problem for the dualist, who regards matter and mind as essentially different, is to account for the influence each appears to have on the other. How does a mental act of will bring about the motion of a man's legs? The Cartesians, and some other dualists, have tried to overcome this difficulty by the quaint device of psychophysical parallelism. This far-fetched idea supposes a predetermined sequence of physical events on the one hand, and a predetermined sequence of mental events on the other. These two sequences are unconnected, but they keep in step like independent clocks set going at the same time. The laws governing the sequences are such that every physical event is simultaneous with an appropriate mental event. Thus the laws of the physical sequence always happen to decide that my legs shall move at the very moment when those of the mental sequence are deciding that I shall feel the urge to go somewhere. Although the movements of my legs are determined solely by previous physical events, while the wishes in my mind are determined solely by previous mental events, I suffer the *illusion* that my wishes cause my walks—i.e. that mind affects matter. The believer in this theory can not only maintain his dualism, but disclaim moral responsibility for his own wrongdoings. Perhaps it is fortunate the theory lacks plausibility.

Idealism avoids these difficulties. Experience shows that mind has the faculty of imagination. It is therefore easier for the idealist to maintain that matter is a figment of mind, than for the materialist to explain mind by means of matter. And, if the reality of matter is denied, the question how mind and matter affect each other does not arise. But idealism has its own difficulty: namely, to account for the regularity and coherence which are obvious in everyday experience. Science would be impossible without such regularity; and no philosophy is adequate if it fails to allow for the evident possibility of science. Materialists explain the regularity by supposing that experience is perception of an external material world, governed by mechanical laws. They may reasonably object that, if everything were ideal, all experience would have the inconsequence of a dream—it would lack organised shape, like the body of an animal when the invisible supporting skeleton is removed. The idealist must meet this objection, if he wishes to be taken seriously.

Berkeley, at one stroke, answers the objection and reveals the main purpose of all his subtle thought:

> If we follow the light of reason, we shall, from the constant, uniform method of our sensations, collect the goodness and wisdom of the *spirit* who excites them in our minds. (*Principles of Human Knowledge*, Section LXXII.[1])

This is (effectively) the final sentence of a long argument, running right through Berkeley's philosophy, to demonstrate the existence, wisdom and day-to-day importance of God. We must not underrate the similar arguments of others, from Plato to Paley. But it is hard to find another as convincing, or as rich in incidentals. If we accept idealism, says Berkeley, there is only one way to explain the constancy which science reveals in experience; and that is, to suppose our sense perceptions exhibit an intelligible and reliable pattern because they are directly excited in us by a wise and good God. But we *must* accept idealism, since the objections to materialism and dualism are insuperable. Hence we must believe in a wise and good God.

It is easy to pick holes in this argument. What really matters is that, in developing the argument, Berkeley does so much, by the

[1] See also Sections XXX to XXXIII.

way, to suggest how religion and science can proceed together in peace. He moderates the more extravagant claims, both of religious authority and scientific self-confidence. He initiates a kind of criticism which recognises the merits as well as the dangers of empiricism and science. He offers scientists a defensible philosophic position, while protecting religion from the excesses of science.

*   *   *

JUST AS Berkeley is more sceptical than Locke, so David Hume (1711–76) is more sceptical than Berkeley. Locke allows us, from our sense perceptions, to infer the bare existence of matter. He believes we can know nothing about it, except just that it is there. Berkeley forbids us to infer even the *existence* of matter; all he allows us to infer from our sense perceptions is the existence of the mind in which they occur, and the existence of a God to give them order and coherence. Hume maintains that we must be content with sense perceptions alone; we cannot validly infer either mind or matter from them.

But Hume's most important notions are those about cause and effect. When we find an event A invariably followed by an event B, we naturally suppose there is, in the background, some unperceived relation between A and B—of which their constant appearance in succession is only the outward and visible sign—in virtue of which B *necessarily* follows A. We express this by saying that A is the *cause* of B. Hume maintains that we should not infer any relation in the background. There is, he says, nothing but the observed fact of the constant conjunction of A and B in the past. We have no right to believe in a mechanism, behind the scenes, which will ensure repetition of the same constant conjunction in the future. This is a natural extension of Berkeley's idealism. The hidden mechanism, which we incautiously assume to exist behind the scenes, is a *material* mechanism—a mechanical connection of the atomic movements supposedly underlying A with those supposedly underlying B. Deny matter, and you must also deny the existence of any mechanism to explain the constant conjunction of events. Berkeley falls back on God to overcome this difficulty; but Hume's more thorough scepticism will not allow this.

Both scientific prediction and the conduct of daily life rely on the assumption that natural uniformities observed in the past may be expected in the future. We assume that, if B has followed A on many past occasions, the next occurrence of A will probably be followed by an occurrence of B. The strength of our expectation increases with the number of cases in which the sequence AB has already been observed. Whatever Hume may say, we shall retain this assumption, because we cannot live without it. The assumption is a *belief*—since, for lack of any better guide, we must act according to it.

But, although Hume fails to destroy the belief itself, he shatters its supposed intellectual foundations. We must admit, however reluctantly, that we cannot be certain of any mechanism in the background. We may base our calculations hopefully on the hypothesis of such a mechanism; but we can no longer confidently cite the mechanism as reason for the belief. Nor can we establish the belief empirically, by appeal to past experience. The principle to be established is: *Uniformities observed in the past are likely to persist in the future.* If we accept this as a guide for the future because experience has shown it to be a reliable guide in the past, we shall be involved in a vicious circle, since we shall invoke the principle we wish to establish. Thus Hume will not allow us any rational foundation for the chief principle on which our brave new science rests. We cling to it for no intellectually sufficient reason, simply because we have no better principle to live by.

Common sense will not underwrite a scepticism as complete as Hume's. To judge by Johnson's reactions, even Berkeley goes too far for common sense. It was, nevertheless, important that such an extreme scepticism should be shown to be logically defensible. Berkeley and Hume did thought a great service. They repeated, to the scientists, Cromwell's advice to the Assembly of the Church of Scotland: 'I beseech you, in the bowels of Christ, think it possible you may be mistaken!' The effect on science, though not immediate, was in time salutary.

Science was criticised in an altogether different way by Hume's contemporary Rousseau, who did much to propagate the dangerous idea that judgment should be the business of the heart rather than the head. He believed feeling was a better guide than reason. The Romantic movement of the 19th century exhibits the spread of this idea. It is true that the unrestrained feeling of a Blake, a Coleridge or a Beethoven can produce great art. But one need only consider Pope or Mozart to understand that, even in the fine arts, cold reason has its place. The idea that unbridled feeling should take the place of reason in other fields is, to say the least, a questionable one. Rousseau and the Romantics must be held partly responsible for the modern tendency, called the flight from reason, which has since diluted the sanity and moderation sponsored by men like Galileo, Newton, Locke and Berkeley. We can see the dangers— in the intuition of Hitler, the reverence for ideologies, the power of sentimental rhetoric.

Rousseau was a vagabond, knowing little of self-discipline. He lacked the application and stability (if not the brains) for solid academic achievement. He tried to make up for it (not without shallow success) by wrapping vague generalities in emotional language. He tells us (*Confessions*, Bk. VI) that he could never master Latin or co-ordinate geometry. He disliked Euclid, whose object he dismisses contemptuously as only 'a chain of proofs'. He dabbled in astronomy, of which he says he would have become fond if he had 'had the necessary appliances'. But he was 'obliged' to content himself with 'the general idea of the situation of the heavenly bodies'. Yet he dared to write a long *Discourse on the Moral Effects of the Arts and Sciences*. What is more, he won a prize for it at the Academy of Dijon. He describes his state of mind while writing this essay:

> With inconceivable rapidity, my feelings became elevated to the tone of my ideas. All my petty passions were stifled by the enthusiasm of truth, liberty and virtue; and the most astonishing thing is, that this fervour continued in my heart for more than four or five years, in a higher degree, perhaps, than has ever been the case with the heart of any other man. (*Confessions*, Bk. VIII.)

The attempt of anyone in this condition to assess deep and patient scientific thinkers is ridiculous. It might be ignored, but for the fact that it evoked a widespread response.

Rousseau passionately advocates the view, for which he offers no evidence, that primitive ignorance is a state of Arcadian innocence and happiness. Civilisation, on the other hand, brings only artificial pomp and moral depravity. Men are better guided by the impulses of heart and conscience than by steady exercise of reason.

From these dubious premises he easily infers that arts and sciences are futile. At best they are only the superficial pleasures which help us to forget the miseries of civilised life.

This may not be a serious contribution to thought; but it is most effective anti-scientific propaganda.[1] Men fear unemotional scientific thought, because it raises awkward questions and challenges their prejudice. They are easily persuaded that it destroys happiness. Others find the way of learning and reason too dull or difficult: they listen readily to anyone who recommends a more exciting line of less resistance. Thus the seed sown by Rousseau has not failed to find fertile soil. The tendency to prefer instinct to reason has grown greater since he wrote.

Perhaps Rousseau's attack on reason was the expression of disappointment at his own failure to make the grade. Possibly he took the extreme scepticism of Hume's thought as evidence of the total barrenness of reason. In this case, it would seem that the rationalism of Locke and Newton held the seeds of its own destruction. The psychology of the flight from reason is interesting. There is an entertaining, if chastening, discussion of it in *The Comforts of Unreason*, by Rupert Crawshay-Williams. It is important to recognise the flight from reason as a movement to be reckoned with. It may lead either to anarchy, or the rehabilitation of Authority in some form.

*   *   *

PTOLEMAIC ASTRONOMY and Aristotelian physics were ousted by a new astronomy and physics which were irresistible. But in chemistry the old ideas were overthrown before the new were ready to take their place. Boyle, in *The Sceptical Chymist* (1661), wrote a devastating criticism of ancient and medieval theories. But, although he suggested some of the notions on which modern chemistry has since been reared, he did not formulate them precisely enough; and they did not at once take shape as practical working hypotheses from which an altogether fresh start could be made. If you weed a garden and fail to plant a vigorous new growth, the weeds return. The early promise of Boyle's attempt to reform chemistry was unfulfilled, because of its weakness on the constructive side. The old ideas, in a modified form, returned for a

[1] The line missed by Galileo's opponents.

time, because the new ones were not mature enough to keep them
out. There was a period of confusion. It was more than a hundred
years before chemistry began to keep pace with astronomy and
physics.

Alchemy had the transmutation of the baser metals into gold as
its main object. But chemical research was directed to less Utopian
ends by an eccentric Swiss physician, contemporary with Copernicus, who called himself Paracelsus. His full name was Phillipus
Aureolus Theophrastus Bombastes von Hohenheim. He was
Rabelaisian in his capacity for drink and his talent for abuse. There
was a mystical and occult side to him; but he had the great scientific
virtue of preferring first-hand observation to reliance on the
authority of ancient writers—a virtue he advertised by burning the
works of Galen and Avicenna under the noses of their medical
disciples. He was leader of the iatrochemists, who believed that the
main purpose of chemistry should be the preparation of drugs. At
the cost of poisoning an occasional patient, iatrochemistry made
some solid progress. It is important as the first serious break with
alchemical tradition. But it was Boyle who first gave chemistry a
genuinely scientific purpose. He suggested that it should try to
elucidate the differences between substances, simply for the sake of
knowledge. He pointed to it as a branch of natural philosophy, not
the mere servant of cupidity or medicine.

Boyle saw that, before attempting this new purpose, he had to
clear away the archaic theories which held chemistry in chains.
The most widespread was the old Greek theory of the four elements, which had been plausible and useful in its day, and which
was still fortified by what remained of the authority of Aristotle.
The Belgian chemist van Helmont (1577–1644) had revived the
even earlier belief, due to Thales, that everything was ultimately
water. He was led back to this idea by a quantitative experiment:
it was not in his case an idle speculation. He weighed some earth
before and after a willow had been grown in it. He found that the
weight lost by the earth was negligible compared with that gained
by the willow. He presumed, therefore, that the willow had drawn
its substance from the water with which it was supplied. His
deduction was reasonable, since he could not know that plants take
most of their material from the carbon dioxide in the atmosphere.
But he was not justified in founding a general theory on it. His other

argument for his theory depended on the supposed powers of a miraculous universal solvent, or alkahest, the *sal circulatus Paracelsi*, which he claimed to possess—although it has never been rediscovered. This, he asserted, could reduce all substances to their primitive watery form.

The alchemists attributed the properties of metals to two principles—one whose nature was fiery, another whose nature was liquid. The presence of the first explained why the metal could be burnt, or converted into a calx: this happened when the fiery principle was driven out. The presence of the second explained the fusibility and malleability of the metal. These principles were called sulphur and mercury; but they were not the substances now so called. It is, indeed, difficult to understand just how they *were* regarded. They were supposed to be themselves made from the Aristotelian elements; so that they were only the immediate, not the ultimate, constituents of metals. They were also the material forms attributed by mystical imagination to certain abstract qualities. Sulphur was the embodiment of fieriness, mercury that of fusibility. In pictures they were even personified. The differences between metals were explained by supposing that the sulphur and the mercury of one metal differed from those of another, or that sulphur and mercury occurred in different proportions in various metals. Paracelsus added a third (earthy) principle, which he called salt. He thus arrived at the theory of the three principles or *tria prima*. The presence of salt explained why the removal of the sulphur, in combustion, did not leave pure mercury.

The assignment of a specious material reality to abstract notions is called hypostatisation. The *tria prima* are called hypostatical principles, because they are the material forms supposedly assumed by abstract qualities. The danger of confusion is obvious. Despite the fact that abstractions, such as 'beauty', 'fusibility', 'infinity', and 'socialism', have evidently not the same kind of reality as the objects denoted by 'Jupiter' or 'Jack Robinson', much plausible but unsound reasoning is based on the assumption that they have. There is a tendency to believe that a thing must necessarily exist, as a constituent of the physical world, just because there happens to be a word for it. The accidental forms of words and the syntactical forms of sentences are allowed to influence the course of thought: language, which should serve the purposes of thought as a mere means of expression, may suddenly become a dictatorial master. When we say 'this is beautiful', we mean that 'this', if classified according to its effect on our feelings, is to be grouped with certain other objects which (upon request) we could name. But, as soon as we reword our statement in the form 'this has beauty', we are apt (unwarily) to extend its meaning. Our statement now has the same outward form as 'this has legs'; we mistake a trick of language for a turn of thought, and we begin to suppose that beauty has the same kind of reality as legs. Possibly it has: but we should not allow ourselves to be bullied into this opinion by the behaviour of the words we use.

The enduring influence of Plato is apparent in all this. His dialogues are full of unsuccessful attempts to run abstract qualities, like justice, beauty and virtue, to earth. But, despite the monotonous inconclusiveness of the resulting arguments, he never seems seriously to doubt that such qualities actually do exist independently of the objects they are perceived in. He is so obsessed with the 'reality' of his Ideas that he will scarcely admit the reality of anything else. The hypostatical principles clearly have much in common with Platonic Ideas—they are realised abstractions. Their introduction into natural science, which is likely to succeed only by its firm attachment to empiricism, was a retrograde step. It is noteworthy that Paracelsus, like many of the alchemists, was a Neoplatonist. Neoplatonism was mainly developed by the Alexandrian philosopher Plotinus (204–270). It was the last important movement in pagan philosophy. It was one of those attempts, typical of dying cultures, to revive a glorious past. It had considerable influence on Christianity, chiefly through St. Augustine of Hippo. Thus the more mystical parts of Plato's thought came, somewhat modified, into Western Europe at an early date. Aristotle acquired his grip, through Albertus Magnus and Thomas Aquinas, in the 13th century; but Plato's influence was reasserted after the Renaissance, except in orthodox Catholic circles.

Boyle's point of view is expressed, in *The Sceptical Chymist*, by Carnaedes.[1] His first objection to all the ancient theories concerns

1 Boyle, writing when classical literature was more familiar than it is now, had reason for so naming his principal character. The original Carnaedes was an Athenian who taught Greek philosophy in Rome. He was noted for expounding the opinions of philosophers, tongue in cheek, only that he might demolish them with sceptical arguments.

their lack of precision. Their elements and principles, he says, are nowhere unambiguously defined. The Paracelsans invest the words 'salt', 'sulphur' and 'mercury' with different meanings on different occasions: they deliberately fight shy of clear definitions, and cultivate vagueness, so that they may not be open to refutation. As for the followers of 'those unsevered teachers, Truth and Aristotle', they point to green wood burning in a chimney: the flames, they say, are the element of fire, coming out of the wood; the smoke, which mingles with the atmosphere and disappears, is the element of air; water bubbles at the ends of the log; the residual ash is the element of earth. But what right have they to assume that these supposed 'elements' cannot be further decomposed, by greater heat or by some other means? How do they know the 'earth' and 'water' they obtain from one substance are really the same as those they obtain from another? Do not some bodies yield one set of constituents when treated in one way, and another set when treated otherwise? Are there not substances, like gold, that defy the decomposing powers of every known chemical process?

Carnaedes does not deny the significance of van Helmont's experiment with the willow. But, with regard to the alkahest, he simply remarks that, since van Helmont has not left us the recipe, we cannot repeat his observations. Thus van Helmont is subjected to the modern test of scientific good faith, which he fails to pass.

The destructive arguments of *The Sceptical Chymist* are supported by much detail which is of only archaic interest. Boyle's most important contribution to a fresh start in chemistry is to point out that the words 'principle' and 'element', as generally used by his predecessors, represent no concepts of any value to exact science. He sees that scientific chemistry cannot rest on preconceived ideas about the number or nature of the elementary constituents of bodies: we shall make no progress by trying to interpret our experimental results in terms of *a priori* schemes which have no better foundation than philosophic prejudice. In so far as Boyle himself had any use for the notion of an element, he propagated van Helmont's view that any substance should be regarded as an element so long as it resists our efforts to resolve it into simpler constituents. This empirical definition, later adopted by Lavoisier, served chemistry very well for a long time. It cannot enable us to know for certain that a substance is an element; nor can it tell us how many elements there are. We must be content to say, at any given time, that, as far as we know, A, B, C, etc., are elements. We may discover other elements; or we may find that A is, after all, not an element. Our business as chemists must be to decide, experimentally, what bodies are elements according to our definition and what are not. In the case of those that are not, we must try to find which of our supposed elements enter into their composition. We must certainly not suppose that all compounds are made of the same four elements or the same three principles. It is, indeed, possible that we may find compounds which have no element in common—one made of A, B, C; another of P, Q.

The present-day notion of a chemical element is more complex. According to the electrical theory of matter, all substances are ultimately composed of protons, neutrons and electrons. Such particles are the only 'elements', in Boyle's sense, known to modern science. The proton carries a positive electric charge, the electron an equal negative charge. Thus the combination of a proton and an electron is electrically neutral. But the mass of an electron is almost negligible compared with that of a proton. The neutron has nearly the same mass as the proton, but no charge. The nucleus of an atom consists of closely bound protons and neutrons. It is therefore positively charged, and it accounts for nearly all the mass of the atom. If we take the charge on a proton as unit, the charge on the nucleus is equal to the number of protons it contains. This is called the 'atomic number' of the atom. Variation in the number of neutrons will alter the mass of the atom, but not the atomic number. The nucleus is surrounded by a system of electrons. When the atom is in its normal state, the total charge of the electron system just neutralises that of the nucleus. If the atom is ionised (i.e. deprived of one or more electrons) it becomes positively charged. The chemical behaviour of the atom, its mode of combination with other atoms, is determined by the nature of its electron system, which is in turn determined by its atomic number. Thus a chemical element is characterised by an atomic number. Any substance whose atoms all have the atomic number 1 is called hydrogen; the number 2 distinguishes helium; and so on. The atoms of an element are not necessarily all the same. A normal hydrogen atom consists of one proton encompassed by one electron. But the atom of 'heavy hydrogen' has a neutron as well as a proton in its nucleus. Its mass is about double that of an ordinary hydrogen atom; but its electron system and (consequently) its chemical behaviour are the same.

Chemistry is concerned with the differences of substances. In order, therefore, that the notion of an element may be of value for purposes of chemical classification, it is necessary that our analysis of matter shall not be carried so far that these differences disappear. We must recognise degrees of elementariness: one suitable for the purposes of everyday chemistry, the other for the deeper purposes of physics.

The issue was clouded in Boyle's mind by his inability to make this distinction. In thinking of an element as something *absolutely* elementary, he was in vague touch with a physical idea, which went too deep to be of immediate use to chemistry. Dalton conceived a notion of 'element' which was of practical value to chemists. He did this because he was content, for the time being, not to probe too far. He began at the chemical level, with the notion of essentially different atoms of oxygen, hydrogen, etc. He built upwards from these, wisely ignoring such questions as *how* they were different, or whether they were made from the same ultimate stuff. Thus chemistry could proceed, until physics was sufficiently developed to attack these deeper problems.[1]

Boyle did begin to offer chemistry some clear, simple notions and a scientific purpose. He was, however, too much influenced by Francis Bacon, whom he greatly admired. His scientific method was, therefore, too exclusively experimental; and he did not fully appreciate the urgent need for suggestive hypotheses at the earliest possible stage. He saw the physical merits of the atomic theory, but did not give it a form from which verifiable deductions could be made in chemistry. He had some inkling of a new theory of combustion, but did not develop it sufficiently to make it useful. He cleared the ground and dug the foundations; but the building of modern chemistry had to wait more than 100 years for an adequate theoretical scaffolding.

*   *   *

[1] For a discussion of Boyle's too physical attitude to the atomic theory, see Chapter XI of *The Scientific Revolution* by A. R. Hall.

A SATISFACTORY theory of combustion and a precise atomic theory were still needed to set chemistry on its feet. The first came from the French chemist Lavoisier, born 1743 and beheaded by revolutionaries in 1794; the second from the Quaker schoolmaster John Dalton (1766–1844), who died loaded with honours. These two were pre-eminently responsible for filling the void left by Boyle's work of destruction.

It had been supposed, since early Greek days, that combustion was a process of disintegration, in which the burning body yielded up its element of fire. At the same time it often happened that the other elements, originally contained in the body, were separated. Thus many medieval chemists came to regard heat as the one and only means of chemical analysis. Boyle effectively questioned these beliefs, but offered no satisfactory alternative. And, although the Four Elements and the Hypostatical Principles began to fall into disrepute, the old theory of combustion had a further lease of life in the Phlogiston Theory of J. J. Becher (1635–82) and G. E. Stahl (1660–1734). Phlogiston was a fiery principle, very like the sulphur of the alchemists or the Aristotelian element of fire. All combustible substances were supposed to contain it, and to give it up in burning. Bodies which burnt readily were supposed to be rich in phlogiston, others less so: but the quantity of phlogiston which a given body could hold was limited. Phlogiston could not exist in isolation; it had to find a home somewhere.[1] Hence a body would not burn unless there was some other body to absorb the liberated phlogiston. Combustion was not the mere *release* of phlogiston, but the *transfer* of phlogiston, from a body that had much to a body that had less.

This new and more precise version of an old theory accounted fairly well for some of the observed facts, and was widely adopted for over 100 years. It was not the best theoretical guide that chemists could have had: but it was better than no guide at all; and it did serve as a framework into which further experimentation could be fitted with some sort of steady purpose. There was at least, now, an hypothesis capable of establishment or disproof.

The function of air in combustion was to absorb the phlogiston given off by the burning matter. This explained why only a limited

[1] Believers in the theory maintained that the notion of isolated phlogiston was as absurd as that of isolated magnetism.

quantity of matter could be burnt in a closed vessel; since, clearly, the air within the vessel would in time become so saturated with phlogiston that it could absorb no more. The 'phlogisticated air', left in the vessel, was found to extinguish a lighted taper; and it would not support life. It appeared similar to air fouled by the breathing of animals—a fact suggesting that respiration was related to combustion, since it involved the exhalation of phlogiston. Common metals are not combustible in the ordinary sense; but they can be calcined—that is made into an ash or calx—by persistent heat. It was therefore thought that metals consisted of calx and phlogiston, the calx remaining when the phlogiston was expelled. A natural inference was that, if the calx were reheated with a combustible substance like charcoal, rich in phlogiston, then phlogiston should be transferred from the charcoal back to the calx, and the original metal should reappear. This process—the reverse of calcination—is called reduction: the metallurgists had long been aware of its possibility and its practical importance in smelting.

But, although phlogiston explained so much so convincingly, there was one great difficulty. It was found that the calx weighed more than the original metal. This was explained by supposing that phlogiston had negative weight. The Aristotelian concept of levity, obsolete in mechanics, was dragged back into chemistry. This strikingly illustrates the fact that Aristotelian scientific notions were so ingeniously interlocked that they had to stand or fall together. It was impossible, as Galileo saw, to keep some and discard others. In so far as the Scientific Revolution consisted in replacing the Aristotelian system by another, it was still incomplete.

The experiment which led to the abandonment of phlogiston was made by one of its firmest champions, Joseph Priestley (1733–1804). He was a Nonconformist minister, who made himself so unpopular, by opposition to the Established Church and sympathy with the French Revolution, that he had to emigrate to America. His hobby was chemistry—particularly the study of gases. He found that red calx of mercury, when strongly heated, yielded a gas which supported combustion and life better than ordinary air. There was a residue of pure mercury. He naturally supposed that ordinary air contained some phlogiston, since unceasing combustion and respiration, throughout the world, continually fed phlogiston to it. Its power to support combustion and life, however, depended on the fact that it was not saturated with phlogiston, and could still absorb more. It seemed that the new gas was like air, except that it had a greater capacity for phlogiston. He supposed, therefore, that it was just ordinary air without its normal ration of phlogiston; and he called it 'dephlogisticated air'. He did not explain convincingly how this gas could be obtained from the calx. According to the Phlogiston Theory, the calx was one of the *elements*[1] from which metallic mercury was made. It was not easy to say how this supposed element could yield substances different from itself. But Priestley would not give up the theory; he preferred to botch it.

Priestley mentioned his experiment at a dinner given by Lavoisier in Paris. Lavoisier at once saw its fundamental importance. He repeated it, and performed other similar experiments. He interpreted his results with an open mind; not with a mind already steeped in phlogiston, like Priestley's. The outcome was a new theory of combustion—regarding it as a process of combination rather than disintegration. The change of outlook was as radical as that brought about by Galileo in mechanics, when he rejected the Aristotelian belief that force was necessary to maintain uniform motion.

Lavoisier put a known weight of tin into a closed flask. He then weighed flask and tin together. After heating the flask until the tin was calcined as completely as possible, he weighed it again before opening it. The total weight was unaltered. He therefore knew that nothing had been gained or lost by the apparatus as a whole. He noticed, when the flask was opened, that air rushed in. He found that the weight after opening was greater than before; and it was clear that the increase was due to the influx of air. Finally, he removed the calx and what was left of the tin. He found that the weight gained by the tin in calcination was almost equal to that of the air which entered the flask when it was opened. It seemed, therefore, that the calcination of the tin was due to its combination with part of the air.

To confirm this, Lavoisier devised an elaboration of Priestley's experiment with the calx of mercury. He placed mercury M in a flask whose neck was bent as in Fig. 61. The neck opened into a bell jar B, inverted in a trough of mercury T. By means of a fire,

[1] The other being phlogiston.

18

at F, the mercury M was kept near its boiling point for some days. Particles of red calx appeared, floating on the mercury M; while the level of mercury in the bell jar rose, showing that air was used as the calcination proceeded. When calcination had ceased, about 1/6 of the air in the flask and bell jar had disappeared. The residual air would not support combustion or life.

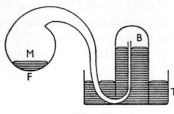

Fig. 61

He collected the red calx, placed it in another vessel and heated it strongly. Mercury reappeared, while a gas, which he collected, was given off. The volume of this gas was about equal to that of the air absorbed during calcination. It would support life much longer than an equal volume of ordinary air, and substances would burn with abnormal brilliance in it. It was Priestley's 'dephlogisticated air', which Lavoisier called 'eminently respirable air'. He later called it oxygen, because of the part he supposed it to play in the formation of acids. He found that, when the oxygen was reunited with the foul air left by the original calcination, a gas was formed which had the properties of ordinary air.

Certain conclusions were now inescapable: and, although the believers in phlogiston put up a tough resistance, Lavoisier lived to see his new theory of combustion generally accepted. It may be summarised as follows:

(i) Air is not an element: it consists in part of oxygen, and in part of another gas or gases.

(ii) Respiration, combustion and calcination alike consist in the combination of certain substances with the atmospheric oxygen—a process often accompanied by the generation of heat. The other constituents of air play no part in respiration or combustion.

(iii) A metallic calx is not an element: it is the compound formed by union of the metal with oxygen.

(iv) The reduction of a calx consists in the separation of the oxygen from the metal with which it is combined. The liberated oxygen may be given off in gaseous form, as when red calx of mercury is heated; or it may combine with some other substance which is present, as it does with the coke or charcoal when iron ore is smelted.

(v) Matter is neither created nor destroyed in combustion. If the products are prevented from escaping, their total mass is found to equal that of the original materials (including the oxygen) which took part in the reaction.

(vi) Phlogiston is not needed to explain chemical processes: there is, indeed, no reason to suppose it exists.

In 1784 Cavendish dethroned another Aristotelian element, by showing that water could be made by combining oxygen with hydrogen.[1]

The work of Lavoisier and Priestley was very important for physiology and the chemistry of life. They knew that respiration was accompanied by a kind of slow combustion, throughout the body, in which oxygen played an essential part. They also knew that air, fouled by the breathing of animals, could be restored to its original freshness by the introduction of green plants. These discoveries began the understanding of a continuous process, called the carbon cycle, fundamental to biochemistry. Animals take in oxygen, which reacts with the organic substances within them, maintaining the chemical balance, and producing the energy, necessary for life. They give out oxygen, combined with carbon, in the form of carbon dioxide. Thus animal life reduces the proportion of free oxygen and increases that of carbon dioxide in the atmosphere.

A complementary process goes on in the leaves of plants, which absorb atmospheric carbon dioxide. From this, and the water and mineral salts which they also take in, plants can build up the complex organic substances they need for their existence. In this process, called photosynthesis, they use the energy which they derive from sunlight. Photosynthesis, in which a necessary function is performed by the green pigment chlorophyll, involves the release of oxygen, as well as the absorption of carbon dioxide. Thus the respiration of animals and the photosynthesis of plants together keep the constitution of the atmosphere roughly constant.

Animals cannot make the complex substances on which all life depends—they can only modify them for their own use. They obtain them, in the first place, by eating plants and other animals.

---

[1] Hydrogen, generated by the action of sulphuric acid on zinc, was then called 'inflammable air'.

Thus carbon continually passes from plants to animals in the form of complex organic compounds, and back to plants as carbon dioxide. Plants, in photosynthesis, store the energy they derive from sunlight. Animals obtain their energy by combustion of the organic compounds made and passed on to them by plants. Oxygen, by taking part in this combustion, enables animals to liberate the energy they need: it is also the agent by which carbon is returned to the plants in usable form.

The material of dead plants and animals is decomposed by soil bacteria. This decomposition is another source of atmospheric carbon dioxide: it also replenishes the soil with the mineral salts—particularly nitrates—needed by new generations of plants.

*   *   *

THE ATOMIC THEORY was one of the most important Greek notions revived during the Renaissance. It must be contrasted with the alternative theory, that matter is continuous, which, mainly through Aristotle and the Stoics, prevailed in ancient and medieval times. According to this continuous theory, matter is infinitely divisible: however finely it may already be divided, further division is always possible. But, according to the Atomic Theory, the structure of matter is granular: continued division will in time lead to ultimate particles, or atoms, which cannot be further analysed.

By derivation, 'atom' means 'that which cannot be cut up'. The fastidious philologist may reasonably point out that the phrase 'splitting the atom', now so familiar, involves a contradiction in terms—splitting the unsplittable is like uttering the unutterable. Particles which a century ago were thought indivisible are now known to be composite; but the old name has clung to them, thereby losing its etymological significance. This does not imply any scientific retreat from the opinion that matter exists in discrete units of some sort, separated by distances which are often great in relation to their size. It implies, merely, that the particles we still *call* atoms are now known not to be the *ultimate* particles we once supposed them to be.

The revival of the Atomic Theory was another important incident in the overthrow of the Aristotelian System; for it involved belief in the existence of empty space between the atoms, which Aristotle would have refused to admit. The atheism of Leucippus and Democritus, abhorrence of which was no doubt largely responsible for the long neglect of their more respectable ideas, was not resuscitated with their atomism. Pierre Gassendi (1592–1655), the Provençal philosopher who reintroduced their ideas, was a Roman Catholic priest; while other prominent 17th-century atomists, such as Galileo, Locke, Newton and Boyle, though variously opposed to orthodoxy, were not atheists—nor even wholehearted materialists. Descartes is notable, among great men of the Scientific Revolution, as an opponent of atomism. He never really broke with Aristotle; and he was too devoted to the explanatory virtues of the *plenum*.

In the early stages of its revival the Atomic Theory had more to do with physics than chemistry. Ideas connected with it, as we have seen, were at the root of the new mechanics: and the elastic properties of gases, in which 17th-century physicists were much interested, were in keeping with the notion that a gas was not a continuous medium, but a chaotic mass of widely spaced particles, moving rapidly in all directions. The existence of spaces between the particles would explain why a gas could be compressed; while the pressure of the gas could be attributed to the continuous bombardment of the walls of the container by the many rapidly moving particles. Dalton was originally interested in the Atomic Theory by reason of its connection with pneumatics: he only subsequently saw its possibilities in chemistry.

When the Atomic Theory began to play a serious part in chemistry, it helped in two ways. It led to a new theory of heat, and to a more precise notion of the nature of chemical combination.

Lavoisier's destruction of the Phlogiston Theory put an end to the belief that fire and heat were material substances—subtle fluids, whose transfer from body to body could explain combustion or change of temperature. Lavoisier still believed in the material nature of *heat* (as opposed to fire). He thought all bodies contained an element, caloric, whose presence tended to make them warm. There was, however, no direct evidence of such an element: it could not be isolated; and changes of temperature were unaccompanied by changes of weight. The caloric theory was, therefore, speculative and unsatisfying.

But if, as now seemed probable, fire and heat were not substances, it was urgently necessary to suggest what else they might be. The Atomic Theory, by its association with the kinetic theory of heat, was able to provide an answer. The kinetic theory supposes that heat consists in the rapid motion, or vibration, of the minute particles of which a body is composed. It is evident (to anyone who reads Locke, for instance) that this notion was familiar before the end of the 17th century. The notion is, indeed, a natural one to those who believe in the atomic constitution of matter. Its plausibility was enhanced by an observation (1798), of the American Benjamin Thompson (1753–1814)—better known as Count Rumford—that there seemed to be no limit to the quantity of heat produced by friction in the boring of cannon. If heat is a fluid, resident in the metal, and able to be extracted from it, there is reason to think that the emission of heat must cease after a time. But if heat is a vibration of the particles of the metal, it is natural to suppose that continued friction will produce continued vibration and, therefore, an indefinite amount of heat. Thus the kinetic theory was able to fill the gap left when chemical research discredited the old fluid theories of heat and fire.

The most important virtue of the Atomic Theory was pointed out in Chapter 4: it can account for the constant physical properties of matter, by supposing all things made from the same ultimate material; yet it can explain the differences between one substance and another, by attributing them to variations, not in material, but in fine structure. Now structural differences are essentially mathematical, since they depend on the *number* and *arrangement* of parts. Dalton first drew attention to the importance of structure as a fundamental concept in chemistry. He thereby gave chemical thought a more mathematical turn, and offered chemists a foundation on which they could build more systematically than before. In the approved scientific fashion, he formulated precise hypotheses, suggested by facts already known, from which it was possible to make logical predictions that could be experimentally tested. It has been necessary to extend and modify his original hypotheses; but, in modern dress, they still play a vital part in chemical theory. His chief contentions were (essentially) as follows:

(i) Matter consists of atoms, which cannot be created or destroyed. Chemical change consists in the combination of atoms which were previously apart, or the separation of those which were combined. There is no change in the atoms themselves.

Thus Dalton's theory at once recognises 'the conservation of matter'. This principle was stated by Lavoisier with reference to combustion; experiment has since confirmed its validity for chemical reactions of every kind. It was a feature of the speculative atomic theory of Leucippus and Democritus.

(ii) The atoms of a given element are all exactly alike; and they differ, particularly in weight, from those of any other element.

This principle has since been modified. It is now known that there are atoms of different weights having the same chemical properties. These are called isotopes. There are also 'isobaric heterotopes', which have the same weight but different chemical properties. The chemical nature of an atom is not, as Dalton thought, precisely correlated with its weight. It is the equality of their atomic numbers, not their atomic weights, which ensures that two atoms shall behave similarly in their chemical relations with other atoms. Dalton could not foresee that his supposedly indivisible atoms would themselves be found to exhibit minute electrical structure. He was therefore unable to form the concept of atomic number. His hypothesis, that specific chemical properties went with a given atomic weight, appeared consistent with experience in his lifetime and for many years after his death. In any case, it did what a good hypothesis should do—it initiated a systematic train of experiments, designed to confirm or disprove it. These experiments, involving the progressively more accurate comparison of atomic weights, in the end yielded results which helped to lead to the modern electrical theory of matter; so that there is now no recognisable boundary between chemistry and physics. The technical and scientific consequences are already immense and portentous.

Dalton devised symbols for the atoms of various elements. Thus he represented atoms of hydrogen, nitrogen, carbon, oxygen, phosphorus and sulphur by ⊙, ①, ●, O, ⊘, ⊕, respectively. This was not the earliest chemical symbolism. The alchemists believed that certain metals were related to the heavenly bodies; and they used the appropriate astrological symbols for these metals. The alchemical symbols, however, just vaguely indicated the substances; whereas Dalton's symbols indicated precisely an atom of each. Dalton's symbols were never generally adopted, since the more convenient practice of representing atoms by suggestive letters[1] was introduced shortly afterwards by the Swedish chemist Berzelius, the originator of modern chemical notation.

> (iii) The smallest particles of a given chemical compound are all exactly alike. Each consists of x atoms of X, y of Y, z of Z, and so on—where X, Y, Z are the elements of which the compound is made; and x, y, z are small whole numbers whose values, for the compound in question, are invariable.

The smallest particles of a compound are now called molecules. Dalton calls them 'compound atoms', but this is not a well chosen phrase. By supposing that the molecules of a compound are structurally identical, Dalton gives precision to the concept of chemical combination, and clearly distinguishes it from mechanical mixture. Thus carbon dioxide is not a haphazard mingling of oxygen and carbon particles: it consists of molecules, all alike, each constructed from just one atom of carbon and two atoms of oxygen. Dalton represented such a molecule by the symbol ○●○; Berzelius wrote CO^2; we now write CO_2.

It follows from this theory that any specimen of carbon dioxide must yield weights of oxygen and carbon in the same proportion as any other. The molecule of water is similarly represented by the formula H_2O. Dalton thought it should be HO: but his error does not invalidate the inference that water always contains oxygen and hydrogen in a constant proportion. A mechanical mixture, on the other hand, may contain its ingredients in any proportion. A mixture of oxygen and hydrogen is like a random crowd of girls and sailors. But water resembles a crowd of sailors, each with a girl on either arm, like the chorus in a comic opera: there are just two girls for every sailor: a fixed pattern of arrangement is apparent everywhere.

The rule that chemical compounds should yield their constituents in fixed proportions is thus a logical consequence of Dalton's theory, and provides a first experimental test for it. It survived this test, conscientiously applied by Berzelius, who carefully analysed many compounds.

Another consequence, also confirmed by Berzelius, is the Law of Multiple Proportions. This applies whenever different compounds,

---

[1] E.g. H for hydrogen; Pb for lead (*plumbum*); Ca for calcium.

P and Q, can be made from the same elements, X and Y. Suppose that, in P, an ounce of X combines with p ounces of Y; while, in Q, an ounce of X combines with q ounces of Y. The Law states that the ratio $p:q$ can always be expressed in small whole numbers. There is (e.g.) a second compound of carbon and oxygen, called carbon monoxide, whose molecule is CO. The weight of oxygen combining with an ounce of carbon in this compound must evidently be just half that which combines with an ounce of carbon in carbon dioxide. The proportion of hydrogen in ethane (C_2H_6) is exactly three-quarters of that in methane (CH_4).

These were not the only criteria by which the theory was established; but they serve as examples. The general correctness of Dalton's views has never since been seriously challenged; their value has steadily become more apparent. It was soon found possible to form and test hypotheses about the geometry, as well as the arithmetic, of molecular structures; and direct evidence has recently been obtained concerning the spatial distribution of atoms in some compounds. The properties of a compound depend, not only on the nature and number of the constituent atoms, but also on how they are put together. Thus ethyl alcohol and methyl ether are both represented arithmetically by the formula C_2H_6O; but they are different substances, whose respective molecular structures are suggested by the formulae

$$
\begin{array}{ccccccc}
\text{H} & \text{H} & & & \text{H} & & \text{H} \\
| & | & & & | & & | \\
\text{H—C—C—O—H} & & \text{and} & & \text{H—C—O—C—H} \\
| & | & & & | & & | \\
\text{H} & \text{H} & & & \text{H} & & \text{H}
\end{array}
$$

The structures of many molecules are now so well known that 3-dimensional models can be made of them.

Such developments underlay the vast growth of 19th-century chemistry and chemical industry. Another stage has now been entered: interest in the electrical structure of atoms is the modern equivalent (and natural outcome) of 19th-century interest in the atomic structure of molecules. This is leading to knowledge of the mechanism by which combination takes place. Chemists can now often predict the properties of substances from their structures, or say in advance how a substance with required properties should be put together.

*   *   *

THE MECHANICAL outlook is as noticeable in biology as in physical science during the 17th century. The tendency was to regard living things, particularly animals, as machines—to study them with reference to the new principles of hydrostatics and dynamics. Borelli, whom we have met as a pioneer of gravitation, wrote a book, *De Motu Animalium* (Rome, 1680–81), on the mechanics of running, jumping, flying and swimming. Descartes regarded the bodies of men and animals as *nothing more* than elaborate machines, entirely subject to physical law. His religious belief enjoined him to equip man with a soul, the seat of consciousness: but this, although resident in his body, was quite distinct from it; and the two could be independently studied. The difficulty he had in explaining their interaction led, as we have seen, to the strange hypothesis of psychophysical parallelism. He attributed no soul or consciousness to animals, which he treated as automata. Thus, in classifying natural objects, he drew his most formidable dividing line between the human race and everything else. Experience has shown it is unwise to attempt rigid classification in any branch of science: but, if a hard and fast line is to be drawn anywhere, the modern tendency would surely be to put it between the living and the inanimate.

The development of such a thorough-going dualism no doubt over-simplified the tremendous problem of life. No adequate study of this problem can ever rest on the complete separation of its physical and psychic aspects—we must keep body and soul together. But the separation was nevertheless of temporary service to science. Scientific progress is mostly piecemeal: it comes from patient concentration on strictly limited objectives. Occasionally there is a great synthesis; the results of many limited inquiries fit together, so that the coherent picture of a wider field appears. But the daily work is that of men, studying particular problems, who do not foresee the *nature* of the synthesis, though they may believe that what they do will form part of *some* wider scheme in the future. The artificial separation of the two main aspects of life could not become a permanent feature of the scientific scheme; but it opened the way for genuine progress in one particular department, at a time when any attempt to treat the problem as a whole would have been premature and unsuccessful. There are now signs that physiology and psychology are ready to come together fruitfully at certain points: but it was necessary that they should first attain maturity apart from one another.

The great triumph of 17th-century physiology, concentrating on animal mechanics, was Harvey's discovery of the circulation of the blood. It was as important in its own field as Copernicus's discovery of the circulation of the earth; though it did not have such repercussions outside science. It inspired physiology, as the heliocentric notion inspired astronomy, because it was the key to so much else. Once the movements of heart and blood were traced, the way was clear for understanding of such processes as respiration and digestion. The behaviour of the blood is so intimately related to almost every other bodily function that solid progress in physiology was impossible while it was misunderstood.

Harvey, like Newton, owed much to his predecessors; but, also like Newton, he ranks above them. The ancients, through Aristotle, Galen and the Alexandrians, handed on an extensive anatomical knowledge, much of it accurate. This was developed during the Renaissance, especially in Italy, where the finest medical school in the world arose at Padua, and where Leonardo made his wonderful anatomical drawings partly from artistic and partly from scientific motives (Plate 13). Harvey studied medicine in Padua, where he met the independent spirit of Vesalius, founder of modern anatomy. He received there the grounding in method, and the up-to-date general knowledge of anatomy and physiology, which equipped him for work on the fundamental problem he eventually solved. It could only be solved by experiments on living animals, or (in the practice of surgery) on living men. He points out that one of the commonest of the errors with which physiology was then bedevilled—the belief that arteries, as their name implies, convey air—was due to the general practice of dissecting animals which had bled to death.

He presents his case with a remorseless logic that cannot be denied.[1] He considers the structure and behaviour of the various

[1] *The Motion of the Heart and Blood in Animals*: first published, in Latin, 1628.

272   *History and Philosophy of Science*

parts of the blood system. He then sets up hypotheses, which he checks experimentally, concerning their mode of operation. He points out that the contraction of the heart coincides with the dilation of the arteries. This implies either (*a*) that the contraction of the heart forces blood into the arteries, or (*b*) that the dilation of the arteries sucks blood from the heart. Observing that the puncture of an artery (which should clearly destroy any powers of suction it may have) does not lessen the flow of blood, he concludes that (*a*) must be the case. It is thus established that the heart is a muscular pump, providing the motive power of the blood system.

The lay-out of the more obvious parts of the mammalian blood system, as revealed by anatomy, is shown in Fig. 62. (There is no attempt to show the actual shapes of the organs.) The heart is

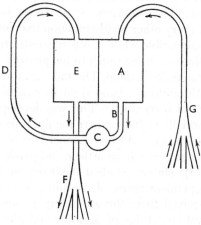

Fig. 62

divided, by an impervious membrane, into two compartments A and E. These are separate force pumps, side by side, of which the left one, E, is the more powerful. Blood vessels B and D connect A to E, through the lungs C. A large blood vessel F, with branches leading all over the body, issues from E; while another branching blood vessel G enters A. The system has one-way valves, so disposed that blood can pass only in the direction suggested by the arrows. The arteries, by which the blood moves away from the heart, have a tougher structure than the veins, by which it moves towards the heart. The veins, moreover, unlike the arteries, contain non-return valves. These valves were described in 1574 by Harvey's teacher, Fabricius; but it was Harvey who first correctly divined their purpose. (Indeed, the disposition of these valves did more than anything else to suggest his discovery to him. In asking what their *purpose* was, he began to form his new ideas. This is one of the rare cases in which science has been advanced by an inquiry into final causes.) The passage of blood from A to E, via C, was discovered by another Paduan, Colombo; but he erred in supposing that blood passed outwards from the heart to the remainder of the body through both veins and arteries.

Having confirmed the existence of this flow of blood, always in the same direction GABCDEF, Harvey approached his final discovery by considering two questions: where does the blood in G come from? Where does the blood in F go to? He estimated the decrease in volume of the heart in its contraction—i.e. the volume of blood discharged at one beat. He multiplied this by the number of beats, and so computed the quantity of blood taken in from G and forced into F in 24 hours. He found this was far more than could possibly be supplied by the food, or consumed in the growth and nourishment of the bodily tissues, in so short a time. In his own words: 'It will be obvious that this can neither be accounted for by the ingesta, nor yet held necessary to nutrition'.

Only one inference seemed possible. There could not be a continual flow of *new* blood, from source to place of use, at this rate: there must be some way by which the blood, forced out through F, could find its way back into G. An unceasing circulation was the only explanation for such a copious flow, *in one direction*, all the time.

But Harvey would not let his thesis—that all the blood sent out through the branching arteries returned through the converging veins—rest solely on a logical argument, however cogent. He undertook a further (experimental) test. He showed that the constriction of an artery led to its becoming empty on the side further from the heart and distended on the side nearer to the heart; while the reverse was true of veins.

Harvey could not trace the path, which he knew must exist, from the fine extremities of the arteries to those of the veins. This path was discovered in 1661, when Malpighi noticed the microscopic capillaries, which connect arteries and veins.

Harvey's discovery was fundamental, because it in time revealed the function of the blood as a carrier. Blood distributes food and oxygen throughout the body: it collects waste products and conveys them to the appropriate excretory organs. The recognition of these facts is the only possible basis for an accurate physiology.

9

THE 19TH CENTURY AND EVOLUTION

THE ESSENTIAL achievements of the Scientific Revolution were two. The first was repudiation of those erroneous Greek ideas which, available only in second-hand scraps during the Middle Ages, had been too uncritically incorporated in medieval scholastic doctrine: the second was a revival of the Greek spirit of free inquiry, typical of Alexandria, in place of a too obsequious reliance on authorities. Dalton's modernisation of the long neglected Atomic Theory marks the end of this epoch, which began with Copernicus: for, although mathematics, astronomy, optics and mechanics had regained their freedom by the end of the 17th century, outmoded ideas remained in chemistry until the end of the 18th.

But by 1800 the physical sciences had all assumed characteristically modern forms and methods. The 19th century was a period of consolidation in these sciences. A vast syllabus of detailed development, based on the fundamental work of the Scientific Revolution, was carried through; while the integration of the various sciences into one great scheme was largely accomplished. Meanwhile, the progress of pure science became more intimately related to that of industrial technology. The opening phase of the Industrial Revolution—the growth of an independent chemical industry; the application of steam power to mining, and of machinery to the manufacture of textiles—overlapped the final phase of the Scientific Revolution. From then onwards the results of scientific research were increasingly applied in industry, while research was aided by the technical devices which industry could put at the disposal of scientists. And, although we need not follow technical developments in detail, it is important to understand how closely science has become entangled with technology in the last 150 years. But the total volume of scientific work has grown so great that, despite the diversion of much effort to technical ends, the accumulation of pure knowledge has been more rapid than ever before. In any case, the quest for pure knowledge has so often led to unforeseen technical applications that men of business are now often anxious to encourage or finance it. Conversely, research with a technical aim continually leads to pure knowledge as a by-product.

*   *   *

BEFORE PASSING to the main subject of this chapter—the impact of Evolution—we must notice the steps by which the physical sciences were welded together during the 19th century. Unification came chiefly from the studies of electricity and heat, which we consider in turn.

The static electricity, produced by friction, had been known since ancient Greek times. Even Thales knew that amber, when rubbed, would attract small objects. The systematic study of static electricity had been begun by Gilbert; and, since his time, much had been found out about it. Franklin showed that lightning was an electric phenomenon; while Priestley, Cavendish and Coulomb found that the force between electric charges, like gravitation, obeyed the Inverse Square Law. The possibility of a steady flow (or current) of electricity was suggested by the experiments of an Italian physiologist, Galvani, in 1786. He found the muscles of a frog's leg were stimulated by contact with wires, of different metals, which were also in contact with each other. Another Italian, Volta, suggested that the energy was produced, not in the frog's muscles, but at the junction of the unlike metals. He made a pile, with layers of zinc, copper and brine-soaked paper. This produced Galvani's effects with greater intensity. It was the earliest electric battery; though its effects were at first thought to be due to a previously unknown cause, labelled 'galvanism'.

It soon became clear that the discovery of galvanism was more important for physics and chemistry than physiology. Volta and others showed convincingly that galvanism was simply electricity in motion. More efficient batteries were made, and the effects of the electric current were enthusiastically studied by many scientists. It was found that the current could decompose many chemicals, and Sir Humphry Davy almost immediately isolated the alkali metals, potassium and sodium, by electrolysis.[1] Berzelius

[1] I.e. electrical separation.

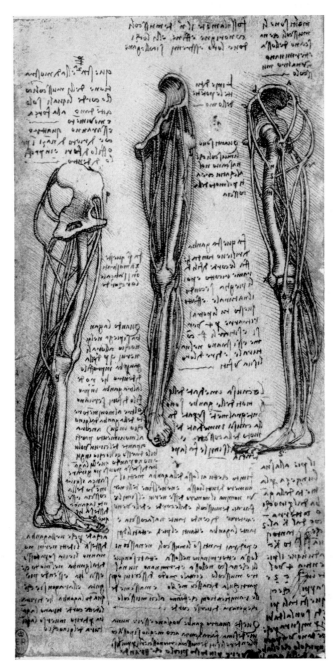

Leonardo da Vinci; *The left leg in three positions*

PLATE 13

Faraday in the laboratory of the Royal Institution

suggested that the elements in chemical compounds were held together by electric force. Michael Faraday (1791–1867, Plate 14)—Davy's successor at the Royal Institution—discovered the quantitative laws of electro-chemistry. He found (e.g.) that if a given current, running for a given time, liberates on one occasion silver and on another chlorine, then the quantities of silver and chlorine liberated are just such as will combine chemically with one another.

Oersted noticed in 1820 that a compass needle was deflected by a neighbouring electric current. This effect was used in electric telegraphy, an invention of great military, political and social importance. But Ampère and Faraday saw more than this in Oersted's discovery. They revealed the full extent of the connections linking electricity and magnetism, thus creating the combined science of electro-magnetism. Two of Faraday's experiments will illustrate the nature and importance of the results obtained. He found that, when a magnet was moved in relation to a coil of wire, an electric current was produced in the coil. Thus mechanical work could produce a current. This opened the way for large-scale generation of electric power: the dynamo is simply a machine by which coils are continuously moved in the presence of magnets. He also found that the starting or stopping of a current in a coil would induce a transient current in a neighbouring but unconnected coil. This led to a technique for transforming large currents at a low pressure into small currents at a high pressure, and *vice versa*—a technique much used in the commercial distribution of electric power. The electric motor, which recreates mechanical work from an electric current, depends on Ampère's observation that a current will exert a force on another current, as on a magnet. The whole of modern electrical engineering springs from these discoveries. We have already seen how the mathematical work of Maxwell surprisingly related electro-magnetism to optics, and suggested the possibility of wireless telegraphy.

Another connection, of theoretical and practical importance, appeared in the discovery that a current heats any conductor through which it passes. A series of astonishingly pregnant inter-relations, involving electro-statics, heat, optics, magnetism, chemistry and mechanics, thus came to light within a few years—through the quaint behaviour of a frog's leg.

19

The study of heat, meanwhile, led to the great unifying principle of the Conservation of Energy. The precise notion of work, in mechanics, was derived from considerations of weight-lifting. The amount of work done in raising a pound through a foot, against gravity, is called a foot-pound. When x pounds are lifted through y feet, the work done is xy foot-pounds. The notion of energy comes from that of work: the energy of a mechanical system is its capacity for doing work. A raised weight can do work by falling, a compressed spring by expanding, a spinning flywheel in being brought to rest: all three possess energy. The energy of the raised weight or the spring, which depends on position or configuration, is called potential energy; that of the flywheel, which depends on its motion, is called kinetic. These two kinds of energy are interchangeable. The potential energy of a spring can be used in giving kinetic energy to a clock: the kinetic energy of a cyclist is converted to potential energy as he freewheels up hill.

It is obvious that mechanical work, done in rubbing things together, can produce heat; and the introduction of the steam engine showed that heat could yield mechanical work. The engineers of the Industrial Revolution, anxious to raise the efficiency of their machines, were interested in the question of how much work could be extracted from a given quantity of heat. This problem led to the far-reaching science of thermodynamics. The pioneer was J. P. Joule (1818–89), a pupil of Dalton.

Joule took, as unit of heat, the amount of heat needed to raise the temperature of a pound of water by 1°F. He warmed water by stirring it with paddles, driven by falling weights. Allowing for loss of heat, he showed that a fixed amount of work always produced the same quantity of heat. He concluded that 772 foot-pounds of work were equivalent to a unit of heat. The accepted value is 778; but his inaccuracy is immaterial. The important point is his demonstration that heat was not just vaguely related to mechanical work, but could be exchanged for work at a fixed, ascertainable rate. It seemed that heat was actually a *form* of energy. This conclusion agreed well with the kinetic theory, according to which heat could be the concealed kinetic energy of rapidly vibrating molecules. The work of rubbing or stirring would naturally increase molecular agitation, and hence raise the temperature.

Joule obtained a similar result when he examined the heating effect of an electric current. He found that a given quantity of electricity, passing through a given conductor, yielded a constant quantity of heat. Since this heat was already known to be equivalent to a definite amount of mechanical energy, it followed that the electric current also had a fixed mechanical equivalent. The direct conversion of mechanical energy into electricity, and *vice versa*, was demonstrated by Oersted, Ampère and (above all) Faraday. The thermocouple, discovered by Seebeck (1822), exhibits direct conversion of heat to electricity. Two wires of different metals are joined to form a closed circuit. If one junction is heated, while the other remains cool, a current flows in the circuit.

Observations of this kind led Joule and Helmholtz to believe that energy exists in many forms: elastic, gravitational, thermal, kinetic, electric, magnetic, radiant, chemical, etc. Loss of one kind of energy always entails the appearance of *a definite amount* of some other kind. Energy cannot be created or destroyed, but only transformed. Further experience, in every branch of science, has confirmed this. This principle in its original form, stating the strict equivalence of mechanical energy and heat, is the First Law of Thermodynamics: in its more general form, with reference to energy of all kinds, it is the Conservation of Energy. Thus thermodynamics has revealed an apparently universal law, governing all natural events—even those involving life. It is not a mechanical or astronomical or physiological law; nor even an electro-chemical or thermodynamic or thermo-electric law: it is, without qualification, a *scientific* law, entering every field of natural knowledge. It brings together, not only the various physical sciences, but the physical and the life sciences. The carbon cycle involves continual exchanges of energy—from radiant to chemical form in photosynthesis; from chemical to thermal and kinetic forms in animals, who live on the products of photosynthesis.

As thermodynamics was developed by Helmholtz, Clausius and Kelvin, another far-reaching general principle appeared. Although energy cannot be destroyed, it can be dissipated or disorganised, and thereby rendered useless. Energy is valuable to animals, and particularly men, only when available for the maintenance of warmth, and the movement of ponderous objects—e.g. their own bodies or the supplies they need. The availability of energy for such purposes depends upon its organisation: we need energy of the right kind concentrated in the right place.

Two examples may help to make this clear. A massive body in motion has kinetic energy which can be harnessed to do useful work. Now let this body be stopped by collision with a pile of sandbags. There is no loss of energy: the kinetic energy becomes heat, which slightly warms the body and the sandbags. Thus the organised progress, of many molecules moving together in one direction, has been transformed into random vibration. The energy is still there; but it can never again affect the large-scale world, because the organisation cannot be restored. It is distributed, for good, among microscopic particles whose helter-skelter movements can serve no common purpose.

Or again, consider a system of bodies, one of which is hot, while the others are comparatively cool. This is not the kind of situation that occurs by chance. The molecules of the system vibrate at different speeds. Chance, among such vast numbers, would allot about the same proportion of rapidly moving molecules to each body. Hence the temperatures would be nearly equal. The concentration of more rapidly moving molecules in one place is a clear sign of organisation. Now our knowledge of heat engines shows that an organised situation of this kind is necessary to their operation. They can deliver useful mechanical work only where heat can pass from a hot body to a cool one. They cannot utilise disorganised—i.e. uniformly distributed—heat.

The second general principle in thermodynamics is that, although the energy of the universe remains constant, its degree of disorganisation tends always to increase.[1] Nothing is said about the origin of such organisation as there already is; but observation indicates that natural processes, like combustion and the passage of heat from hot bodies to cold, are continually destroying this organisation. Local pockets of reorganisation are not uncommon. They are often associated with living things. Photosynthesis is a good example of this. But the overall trend is always towards disorganisation; towards that uniform distribution of energy which we should expect to occur by chance. It has been suggested that this is the one essentially irreversible process in virtue of which time acquires its apparent singleness of direction: a *general* increase of

[1] This degree of disorganisation is sometimes called 'entropy'.

organisation would seem like a return to the past; but we do not experience such increases.

This raises questions of extra-scientific interest. It suggests that the universe is tending to a state in which all its energy will be concealed in the random motion of minute particles: events on a large scale, involving the co-ordinated behaviour of many particles, will become less frequent and ultimately cease. The pattern that makes the world so enchanting and exciting will disappear. Its end will be an eternal monotony. The atheist will use this for evidence that there is no mindful God: his opposite will answer that, as organisation has been created in the past, so it may be recreated in the future. Reorganisation would be within the power of a being gifted with sufficiently acute faculties. Maxwell imagined a daemon, at the door between two rooms, one empty and the other filled with particles of gas in random motion—fast and slow mingled according to chance. When a fast-moving particle approaches, the daemon lets it pass into the empty room; but he shuts the door against the slower particles. In the end he has hot gas in one room and cold in the other: the energy is usable again. This fancy may suggest why local reorganisation is often associated with life. Reconcentration of energy, as when one gathers sticks to make a fire, depends ultimately on powers of will and choice, and would seem to imply the exercise of mind. Chance, by nature indiscriminate, cannot accomplish it.

*   *   *

R. W. SOUTHERN (*The Making of the Middle Ages*, Chapter V) says:

> At the deepest levels of experience, in intimations of the nature of God and the economy of the universe, in new insights into the powers and powerlessness of man, the changing scene of history has its focus and its justification.

Anyone who assesses the history of 19th-century science with this precept in mind, is likely to regard the growth of evolutionary ideas as the movement of greatest importance. The technical and intellectual developments in physical science had far-reaching effects: but it was biology, in its evolutionary aspect, that really shook the 19th century as astronomy shook the 17th. The whole world of thought was stirred up; violent controversy and animosity were raised; the disturbance is obvious in politics, philosophy, literature, sociology, religion.

Evolutionary ideas entered modern science unobtrusively, through astronomy and geology. Their full significance appeared only when they were seriously adopted in biology. Before discussing their growth, however, we must consider some general notions of change, stability and progress.

Change may be monotonic, periodic or random. Monotonic change occurs when individual variations are all in one direction; so that, even when they are themselves small, their effect is cumulative and, ultimately, drastic. Periodic change occurs when there is a repeated cycle of variations; so that a given state of things, having once appeared, must in time reappear. Random change occurs when individual variations are equally likely to be great or small, this way or that. These three kinds of change are exemplified, respectively, by the cooling of a red-hot poker, the swing of a pendulum, and the shifting pattern in a kaleidoscope.

Purely monotonic change is uncommon. But the overall effect will be monotonic if there is a *majority* of variations in one direction; and this is what we usually find when we examine natural changes which *appear* monotonic. Thus, although loss of entropy occurs occasionally in certain regions, gain of entropy is the overwhelming general rule; hence the change of entropy throughout the observable universe is effectively monotonic.

Purely periodic change, on the other hand, is common. It is seen (e.g.) in the vibration of a tuning-fork, or the apparent motion of a planet. There are also many cases of *approximately* periodic change. Thus changes of season are not, in detail, the same from year to year; but, for most practical purposes, we may treat them as periodic.

The overall effect of periodic change is to maintain a kind of dynamic stability. There is fluctuation from extreme to extreme: but between the extremes is an average state, to which the system subject to periodic change has a constant tendency to return. A fluctuation of long period, observed for a comparatively short time, can be mistaken for a monotonic change. This happened with Newton, who supposed that the gradual variations (in eccentricity and inclination) of the planetary orbits were cumulative, and might disrupt the Solar System. Laplace, who could take a broader view, knew they were periodic.

Periodic fluctuation sometimes takes place about a mean which is itself subject to monotonic change. The average population of a holiday resort, for instance, may steadily increase over the years; but there will be seasonal fluctuations superimposed on the underlying monotonic change. In such cases, the seasonal fluctuations, especially when irregular in magnitude, can often mask the more important monotonic change in the background.

Random change, when widespread, can produce a most remarkable stability. This paradox is best explained by examples. Suppose an angry bee is let loose in a room whose volume is 1000 cubic feet. Assuming it buzzes round, and its changes of speed and direction are random, then there is no means of predicting where it will be at any given time. But let there be a million such bees in the room: we can then predict with great confidence that at any given time, in any given region whose volume is one cubic foot, there will be about 1000 bees. Or suppose that someone sets an alarm-clock with his eyes shut. He cannot know when it will ring. But, if he surrounds himself with a million such clocks, he can be sure of 12 hours' continuous noise. Of course, they *might* all go off at once; or there *might* be 5 minutes in which all were silent: but the possibility of such coincidences can be confidently ignored, because the odds against them are so great.

These are cases of statistical uniformity. Such overall uniformity results from the random behaviour of very many things: it can be predicted with more assurance than any other physical phenomenon; and the assurance increases with the numbers involved. There are many natural instances of it. It is particularly evident in the behaviour of gases. A cubic centimetre of gas, under normal conditions, contains about $2 \cdot 7 \times 10^{19}$ molecules in random motion.[1] The walls of the container suffer continual bombardment by rapidly moving particles, and this produces the pneumatic pressure. The pressure at any point depends on the severity of the bombardment. We can predict with virtual certainty that this pressure will be the same everywhere; simply because the (calculable) chance of a significant difference, where such vast numbers are involved, is infinitesimal.

[1] If the molecules in 1 c.c. of gas were evenly distributed throughout the atmosphere, there would be thousands within the space of an ordinary room.

Change and progress should not be confused: progress implies change, but change does not necessarily imply progress. There can be progress only when there is a purpose or ideal to be approached. Purpose depends on judgments of moral, aesthetic or economic value, which are not the business of science. The question of progress is therefore not purely scientific.

These remarks may help to resolve an apparent inconsistency. Obviously the universe exhibits change: if it did not, nothing would ever happen. Yet, if we enquire whether we live in a stable or changing world, the question seems to have some significance. How is this? Clearly, we assign different meanings to the word 'change' in different contexts. When we speak of a changing (as opposed to a stable) universe, the change we mean is not a periodic fluctuation, or a set of random movements which effectively cancel one another out: it is a persistent, monotonic change. It is natural for scientists, studying the present world, to wonder whether there has been such change, or whether things have always been much the same as now. The evidence everywhere, especially in geology and biology, leaves little doubt about the answer. There have been sweeping changes in the past, and there is change proceeding still. Subsidiary questions of great importance arise. Has change in the past been catastrophic, the result of occasional great upheavals; or has it been evolutionary, a continuous process only noticeable over long periods? If it is evolutionary, what governs it? Is there evidence of purpose in it; does it, in any sense, imply progress? These questions, known to Greek philosophy, received little attention during the long reign of ecclesiastical authority. They reappeared to dominate thought in the 19th century. They then turned out to have an emotional content which made them more than mere new subjects for dispassionate scientific inquiry. The scientific answers, as in Galileo's time, conflicted with literal interpretations of Scripture: though, as England was now the main theatre of conflict, religious opposition came more from Fundamentalism than Catholicism. Men were as bewildered now, about their origin, as they had been, in the 17th century, about their cosmic position. Political thinkers of right and left adapted evolutionary ideas to their purposes. The righteous indignation of Gladstone, the uninstructed sarcasms of Disraeli and Wilberforce, the ravings of Nietzsche and the controversial virtuosity of Huxley all added to

the fun, while Darwin cultivated orchids (or barnacles) in
scientific detachment.

*   *   *

THE EVOLUTIONARY idea attained prominence in modern science
with the nebular hypothesis of Laplace and Kant. This sprang
from Laplace's mechanical instinct and Kant's flair for spotting
analogies. It has not survived as they put it forward; but, in modified form, it still lives. They explained the present pattern and behaviour of the Solar System by supposing it to have begun as a
rotating cloud of incandescent gas. Many nebulae had been discovered by Herschel, and it seemed natural to suggest that some
might be embryo solar systems. In cooling, such a cloud would
condense and shrink, forming a more concentrated fluid mass, and
becoming gradually more like a sun. Its angular momentum would
be constant[1]; hence its decreasing size would entail increasing
rapidity of spin. In time its rotation might become so rapid that the
cohesive forces could no longer hold it together; small pieces would
then be thrown off, which would quickly cool and solidify. A
solar system—a large central sun, surrounded by small, cool
planets, all revolving in the same sense—might be thus evolved.

Later mathematical investigations suggest that the evolution of a
galaxy of stars may perhaps take place by condensation from cosmic clouds and nebulae; but that the sequence of events supposed
by Laplace and Kant will not take place on the small scale involved
in the formation of a single solar system. Jeans therefore supposed
that the planets might have been torn from the sun by the gravitational pull of another star, passing unusually close to it. It seems,
however, that the chemical constitution of the earth is very different from that of the sun: in particular, the sun contains a much
greater proportion of hydrogen. Theories which suppose the earth
was once part of the sun are therefore now less favourably regarded: an altogether different theory has arisen. From time to
time new stars suddenly appear and die down, or faint ones flare up

---

[1] Angular momentum may be described as 'quantity of rotation'. Its constancy, in an isolated system, is implied by Newton's Laws. This means
that loss of size, in such a system, must involve increased angular velocity. Anyone who ties a weight to a string, and swings it so that it winds round his
finger, will find the revolutions of the weight become faster as the radius of its
path grows less.

with transient brilliance. These exploding stars are called novae: their eruptions are so violent that, for a short time, their radiation may equal that of a whole galaxy. It is thought that the sun may once have been part of a double star, and that its companion exploded like a nova: most of the pieces were projected into space, but a few remained to circle the now lonely sun as planets.

These theories of evolution in astronomy have influenced conjecture about life in other worlds. This is an intriguing problem; though we cannot do more than hazard doubtful guesses, based on limited knowledge and questionable assumptions. Life, in any known form, can flourish only in a certain small range of physical conditions. The temperature must be such that water can exist as a liquid, and such that the fundamental organic compounds shall not disintegrate—as they readily do when overheated. There must be an atmosphere containing oxygen and carbon dioxide. The gravitational field must be strong enough to retain this atmosphere, but not so great that living things are unstable or immobile under their own weight. Thus life in stellar conditions is out of the question. It can only occur on some kind of planet; and, even then, the size of the planet and its distance from the local sun must be within narrow limits. The possibility of life on other worlds, therefore, depends on whether planets more or less like the earth exist elsewhere. If they do, there seems no reason why life should not have appeared on them as it has here. The prospects in other parts of our own system are not good: Venus and Mars are the only possible places; and conditions on them seem likely to suit only a rudimentary vegetable life. Are there other systems like our own? The Kant-Laplace hypothesis implies that the evolution of a sun is naturally accompanied by that of a solar system: planetary systems are as manifold as stars; so that, even if planets resembling the earth occur in only a small proportion of them, the total number of such planets will be large. This lends plausibility to Bruno's speculation about the multiplicity of inhabited worlds. Jeans' hypothesis leads to an opposite conclusion. Stars are so widely scattered that the close approach of any two is about as likely as the close approach of two corks adrift in the Atlantic. Planets will therefore be rare; and planets like the earth rarer still. The nova theory tends to bring us back where we were. Novae, observed in the spiral nebulae as well as the Galaxy, are quite frequent; while double stars are also common. Thus planetary systems are likely to occur often.

*   *   *

EVOLUTION ON the grand scale, in the heavens, is a fascinating subject: but the evidence for it is tenuous and indirect; so that what is said about it always contains an element of dubious speculation. It is only when we come back to earth that we can examine questions of past, present and future change with anything like the thoroughness needed for firm scientific judgment. On the terrestrial scale, too, these questions assume an urgent human interest which, despite their cosmic insignificance, forces us to take them seriously. The really reliable evidence of great change in the past is geological: we can only shrewdly guess that the Galaxy was once a cloud of incandescent gas; but we can scarcely doubt that the earth itself is very different from what it was once. The strata of its surface contain fossil remnants of living things now unknown; marine deposits are found far inland; formations of hard rock have aspects which suggest they were once molten. Such evidence was gathered, in detail and quantity unknown before, by the industrious naturalists of the 18th and early 19th centuries—many of them gifted amateurs, like Gilbert White of Selborne, or the Prussian traveller von Humboldt.

But, though it became impossible to doubt great changes in the earth's surface, there was disagreement about their nature and causes. The Catastrophists supposed that great upheavals, separated by long periods of little change, had periodically devastated the earth's surface and destroyed life. A new creation of living things had taken place after each great flood or earthquake. The various strata, with their peculiar fossils, were taken as evidence of this: it was assumed that they held the entombed remains of specially created populations, cut off by successive cataclysms.[1] On the other hand, the Uniformitarians (as early evolutionists were called) thought the changes of the earth's surface were all due to the gradual action of causes still in operation—erosion, ordinary volcanic action, the deposition of silt, and so on. This opinion involved the implication, if not the open statement, that the different forms of life resulted from a similar process of gradual modification, and not each from a distinct act of creation.

[1] This apparently scientific evidence for Genesis infuriated the partisan Voltaire.

In the 18th century, and the early 19th, as interest in geology first became widespread, Catastrophism found favour, not only with the majority of educated men, but also with many influential scientists, such as Cuvier in France, Werner in Germany and Buckland in England. There were two main reasons. Firstly, Catastrophism was easy to reconcile with faith in the scientific accuracy of the Bible. Genesis clearly points to many separate acts of creation: it also mentions at least one great cataclysm—the flood survived by Noah. There was thus a tendency to associate Catastrophism with piety and orthodoxy, while evolution was thought to suggest heresy or atheism. Secondly, there was the serious difficulty of time. The causes, still in action, to which evolutionists attributed the changes of the past, operate very slowly. The evolutionary explanation of the earth's history demands a vast extent of time; and this seemed as unacceptable in the 18th century as the vast extent of space seemed in the days of Copernicus and Bruno. Until the middle of the last century, the chronology of the devout was that of Archbishop Ussher, whose biblical researches led him to believe the earth was created in 4004 B.C. The authority of Newton was added to that of Ussher: for, although Newton made some use of astronomical methods in chronology, he still regarded them as subsidiary to the biblical method. He may have questioned the Archbishop's figures here and there: but he supported the biblical method, and thought the results were of the right order. Even when 19th-century physicists began to come to the rescue, with rational estimates of the earth's age, they were not entirely reassuring. The allowance of time they offered was not liberal by evolutionary standards; and it was obvious they were not too sure of themselves. In 1862, for instance, Kelvin, by considering the earth's rate of cooling, concluded it had existed in a solid state for rather less than 200 million years. As he later reduced the estimate to between 20 and 40 million, it was clear that what physics had to say on this subject was still very unreliable. This was not the sort of independent evidence with which evolutionists could confront their stern opponents. The early evolutionists had to admit limitless time by an act of faith, just as early Copernicans had to admit limitless space.

Another objection against great stretches of geological time was that it seemed impossible for the sun's radiation to be so long maintained. Where could the necessary energy come from? Satisfactory solutions of these problems have only recently appeared. The decay of radio-active elements in the earth's crust has now enabled us to make more reliable, and much more generous, estimates of its age: while nuclear physics reveals an ample source of heat for the sun. But, with all this so far in the future, it is not surprising that 18th-century pioneers of evolution—like the Edinburgh geologist James Hutton and the French naturalists Lamarck and Buffon—had so little influence in their own day. Nor is it surprising that Lyell and Darwin, the men who did most to make evolution a real force in thought, were almost obsessed with the need for gathering masses of detailed evidence before presenting their case. Like Pooh Bah, they sought 'corroborative detail intended to give artistic verisimilitude to a bald and unconvincing narrative'. They were painfully aware of the delicate problem of persuasion that lay before them; and the tact with which they wrote was as carefully studied as the many specimens they collected.

Sir Charles Lyell (Plate 15a) learnt geology from the Catastrophist Buckland at Oxford. He was soon converted to the evolutionary view; partly by Hutton's *Theory of the Earth*, and partly by the discoveries[1] which he and his friend G. P. Scrope made in their scientific travels. His book *Principles of Geology* (1830–33) deeply influenced the great evolutionists who followed him. Its main thesis was that past changes in the earth's surface could be explained by the gradual operation of causes still at work —no other causes need be invoked. Darwin read it during his voyage of exploration to South America, as naturalist in H.M.S. *Beagle*. He never ceased to emphasise his debt to it. He returned (1836) in time to help Lyell and Scrope canvass their views before the Geological Society in London. There was still powerful opposition; but, from then onwards, the general acceptance of evolution, as a principle governing the *inorganic* world, was only a matter of time.

It was impossible that Lyell should so carefully study evolution in geology without wondering whether it might also take place among living things. In order not to aggravate inevitable opposition to his main thesis, he refrained from pressing this additional point too far: but his candour prevented him from keeping it

[1] Particularly those concerned with the effects of water.

altogether in the background; and his readers quickly saw the implication of his references to it. There were signs of protest from the orthodox; but the minds of men like Darwin, Wallace and Huxley were electrified. Darwin, with characteristic modesty, was indeed ready to offer Lyell half the credit for *The Origin of Species*.

There were two main problems. First, to establish the *fact* of biological evolution, past and present; second, to reveal the causes. Darwin saw that it was useless to treat these matters separately: the only way to convince the world was to give it hard facts and satisfactory explanations *together*. Lamarck asserted his belief in animal evolution; but his facts were insufficient and his explanation dubious. Buffon hinted at it with a hesitation like that shown by Descartes over Copernican astronomy. Others speculated about it,[1] but were too vague to be taken seriously. The present causes of change in the earth's crust are fairly obvious: all Lyell had to do was show they were sufficient to explain the past. The causes of biological evolution are less obvious, and it would be rash to say they are fully understood even now.

The key notion of Natural Selection, which made the modern evolution theory possible, came independently to Darwin and A. R. Wallace (Plates 15b, 15c). The same fertile thought-connection occurred to both—namely, that of Lyell's *Principles* with Malthus' *Essay on Population*. Wallace had the idea in 1858, while sick in the East Indies. He sent a short account of it to Darwin, who had noted the same conclusions in 1842, but, instead of publishing them, had settled down to the immense task of marshalling the detailed evidence. Wallace did not know this. There could have been a dispute like that of Newton and Leibniz; but this was prevented by the tact and generosity of those involved. It was agreed that Wallace's paper should be read, with Darwin's early notes, before the Linnaean Society. Darwin was not ready to produce the massive work he had planned; but he was persuaded to write an abstract, which appeared as *The Origin of Species* in 1859. Much of the detail which he omitted was published later in separate books, Wallace, who described himself as 'a young man in a hurry'. always insisted on Darwin's major part in the affair.

*   *   *

1 It is interesting that one of these was Goethe. Scientific poets are uncommon; though Lucretius, Omar Khayyam and Robert Bridges are examples.

THE *Origin* first gives evidence for the existence of variation—
the occasional appearance, in every species, of individuals which,
in some respect, differ noticeably (though slightly) from their
fellows. Darwin found much evidence in the records he kept on
board the *Beagle*, in his experience as a pigeon breeder, and in his
experiments with plants in his garden. But he was not content with
his own observations: he corresponded with dog, horse and cattle
breeders; he read and noted the books of travellers and naturalists;
he went to other scientists for information—notably Sir Joseph
Hooker in botany and Thomas Huxley (Plate 15d) in zoology.

Having to his satisfaction established the apparently universal
occurrence of variation, Darwin remarks that we must be content
with it as an empirical fact: our present knowledge does not reveal
its causes. He does, indeed, consider evidence which suggests that
variation is more marked in some conditions than others. Thus it is
accelerated by change of environment, as in domestication: it is
more frequent with creatures of simple structure than with those
more complex. But we do not know *why* it occurs, and we cannot
foresee its nature: we must accept it as an undoubted, but
unexplained, fact.

The experience of gardeners and farmers shows that plants or
animals can be considerably changed within a few generations by
selective breeding. We can steadily improve the speed of horses by
breeding only from the fastest in each generation, or their strength
by breeding only from the strongest. In the same way, by observing
favourable variants and cultivating their descendants, we can
quickly improve the scent of roses or the taste of strawberries. The
inference is that creatures which slightly excel their fellows in
some particular quality have a tendency to pass on their excellence
to their offspring. If this were not so, there would be no cumulative
effect.

It is important to notice that variation *by itself* is unlikely to produce any important change in a race. Variations in one direction
will tend to neutralise those in another, so that the total effect is
negligible. The selective breeding, which propagates variations of
one kind and cuts off those of another, is also absolutely necessary:
for this is what makes the change monotonic and therefore
significant.

Thus two propositions are now established: (i) That *evolution* is rapidly effected among domestic creatures, by breeders who take selective advantage of the unpredictable variations which seem always to occur. (ii) That *variation* takes place among wild as well as tame creatures—though not perhaps to the same extent. Darwin next enquires whether there is *evolution* among wild creatures. He maintains there is, and offers evidence of four main kinds for his opinion. Firstly, the geological record, although incomplete, suggests evolutionary rather than catastrophic change. In particular, the most recent fossils of a district are generally those of creatures very similar to, though not exactly like, the present inhabitants. Secondly: there is the evidence of geographical distribution. The creatures of neighbouring islands are often nearly, but not quite, the same. This suggests that the islands were once connected, and that their similar inhabitants are the differently evolved descendants of common ancestors. Again: although the fishes on the east and west coasts of South America are in general very different, this is not the case on opposite sides of the Isthmus of Panama. Probably, therefore, the isthmus was once covered by sea; and the separated, slightly different, descendants of certain common ancestors now live on opposite sides of it. On the other hand: we find entirely different populations in the widely separated continents of Australia, South Africa and South America, although the similarities of climate might lead us to expect similar inhabitants. Thirdly: there is the evidence of vestigial structures, like the ear muscles in man—now useless, but presumably inherited from ancestors who needed them. And structural resemblances in widely different species—as in the forelimbs of man, rabbit, bat, whale and frog— forcibly suggest common ancestry.

Finally: Darwin considers the extreme difficulty of classification in zoology and botany. If species are immutable—each descended, without change, from a specially created pair of ancestors —then, surely, classification should be easy: it should be no harder to say, of a creature, what species it belongs to, than to say, of a word, what part of speech it is. But, in fact, as discovery proceeds, species and varieties often appear to merge into one another. Between two distinct organisms, A and B, it is sometimes possible to interpolate a series of organisms, P Q R S . . ., such that the differences between successive links of the chain are scarcely noticeable. The naturalist, who confidently assigns A to a category

(a) Lyell

(b) Darwin

(c) Wallace

(d) Huxley

FOUR GREAT EVOLUTIONISTS

PLATE 15

(a) Gibbon

(b) Chimpanzee

(c) Orang-Utan

(d) Gorilla

ANTHROPOID APES

PLATE 16

(a) Lyell

(b) Darwin

(c) Wallace

(d) Huxley

FOUR GREAT EVOLUTIONISTS

PLATE 15

(a) Gibbon

(b) Chimpanzee

(c) Orang-Utan

(d) Gorilla

ANTHROPOID APES

PLATE 16

α and B to another category β, may be quite unable to decide at what point in the graded series an organism ceases to belong to α and begins to belong to β. This is just what we should expect if continuous evolution is going on.

Some general remarks about classification are relevant at this point. The number of different living types known, even in the 17th century, was so great that ancient methods of classification, handed down (with modifications) from Aristotle, were patently inadequate. The confusion was such that it was difficult for scientists to be sure what creatures other scientists were talking about. The great classifying naturalists of the 17th and 18th centuries, especially John Ray and Linnaeus, rendered fine service by straightening out this muddle. The wide generalisation of the evolutionists, on which modern biology rests, would have been impossible without the previous efforts of those who rationalised, however imperfectly, the systems of grouping and nomenclature. Their work enabled their successors to take that clear comprehensive view of living Nature without which a unifying theory could never have been suggested: it also encouraged co-operation in biology, by facilitating the exchange of ideas. On the other hand, a life devoted to classification may well engender an inflexible attitude of mind. There is a strong human desire for order, simplicity and completeness—a desire which often seeks relief in disciplined works of art. But, as science proceeds, it appears that there is no answer to this desire in the complexities of Nature. Man, trying to foist on Nature an order he can comprehend, seems always doomed to partial failure. The diagonal of the square resisted the charming simplicity of Pythagorean arithmetic: the movements of planets would not conform to the geometry of sphere and circle, and we now know they also disagree with the mechanics of Galileo and Newton: Dalton's sharp distinction of elements has become blurred. The attempt to force living things into man-made categories, though necessary to progress for the time being, led Linnaeus and others to approach Nature rather as grammarians approach words. Their opposition to evolutionary ideas came partly from unwillingness to admit the complex untidiness of Nature. Darwin recognises this when he says that many naturalists look upon a human classificatory system as if 'it reveals the plan of the Creator': they tend to assume that God has arranged things as simply as they would

20

themselves have done. Classification is invaluable so long as it adapts itself to the growth of knowledge, but obstructive when its advocates attach too much importance to it. Evolution, by tracing groups of creatures back to common ancestors, provides a more realistic basis for modern systematics. But Linnaeus, despite anti-evolutionary views, was such a fine instinctive judge of structure that much of his great practical system can remain undisturbed.

To return to the main argument. Variation and evolution clearly take place in wild Nature. But variation alone cannot account for evolution: by itself it would produce the overall stability that goes with random change. There must be some other natural cause at work, to do what the breeder does with flocks and herds. It is here that Malthus comes into the picture. With reference to mankind he points out that, given a constant birth-rate, population will tend to increase according to the law of compound interest. If there is no check, therefore, there will soon be more men than the earth can hold. This pressure of population leads to fierce competition for commodities and space, and many perish. Men are steadily killed off by famine, by the disease which comes of overcrowding, and by wars waged for economic power. Only the most favoured survive the struggle: and, even among these, there are always some, near the boundary, living in the worst bearable conditions. If their lot is improved, there will always be others willing to take their place, even at this lowest level, for the sake of bare existence.

We need not ask how far Malthus is trying to console Dives for the fate of Lazarus; nor how far his theory is invalidated by failure to foresee the use of birth-control. What matters is that Darwin and Wallace saw the wider application of his notions. Most wild creatures reproduce their kind at such a rate that only a fraction can survive. There is an intense struggle for existence: living things strive against each other and against their inorganic environment, and all but the toughest are eliminated. Variation must occasionally produce creatures which have some slight advantage over their fellows in the search for food, the fight against enemies, or the endurance of hardship. These fortunate individuals will have more chance of living to propagate their kind. Relentless competition will ensure more breeding from these slightly favoured creatures than from others, whose lives will tend to be shorter. *Natural Selection* will do what the breeder's artificial selection does with domestic creatures. It will take longer; because the breeder breeds *exclusively* from favoured individuals, whereas Nature breeds only *slightly more* from the favoured than the unfavoured. But in time the effect will be the same, and the character of the race will be modified.

It is also easy to see how a single race, instead of being simply modified, may be separated into several distinct varieties by this same combination of causes. Let us suppose (e.g.) that variation here and there produces two qualities—an extra turn of speed (P), and slightly better vision (Q)—both useful in the hunt for food. Let us call the possessors of P the p's, the possessors of Q the q's, and the unmodified creatures the x's. The p's will secure more of the faster running prey, while the q's will secure more of the less easily seen prey. Thus both p's and q's can secure more than their fair share of food; and this need not involve much competition between p's and q's, since they seek different varieties of prey. But the x's must compete either with p's, for the faster running prey, or with q's, for the less easily seen prey. In either case they will suffer disadvantage. The p's and q's, whose offspring are likely to inherit P or Q, will tend to live longer and be more prolific than the x's. The proportion of x's in the population will decrease, and they will gradually die out. Instead of a homogeneous race, there will then be two distinct varieties—a fleet-footed type and a keen-sighted type. Further evolution will tend to make these varieties even more distinct. Competition is fiercest between creatures which are most alike, because their needs are similar. It will therefore be advantageous for a p to be as different as possible from the q's, and *vice versa*. The most divergent types will have the best chance of survival; any intermediate types which may appear will suffer greater competition and tend to die out. The p's and q's, which were at first only well-marked varieties of the same species, may in time become so different that they constitute distinct species. This division of species into other species need not mean an increase in the total number of existing species, since the evolution of the new species will be accompanied by the extinction of old species which are less well adapted: it will simply mean that one set of species is gradually replaced by a new set. The effect of competition will always be to eliminate those types between which there is most rivalry; and Organic Nature will tend to adjust itself so that the

total amount of competition is a minimum—i.e. so that the amount
of differentiation is a maximum.

This simple idea—that competition does in wild Nature what
the breeder does among domestic creatures; so that there is 'descent with modification through variation and natural selection'[1]—
is the central theme of the *Origin*. It is so simple that Huxley remarked how stupid he was not to have thought of it long ago himself. Yet it is so convincing that it was able, against widespread
opposition, to put organic evolution on the map. In doing so, it
profoundly affected thought. After announcing it, Darwin devotes
the rest of his book to following its subtle implications, answering
objections against it, and showing how it explains the mass of
curious fact accumulated by naturalists.

With due respect for *Das Kapital*, it may be granted that the
Origin was the most influential book of the 19th century. It is a
literary work of art, worth anybody's time to read. In the introduction Darwin does all he can to give credit to others, and to de-
precate his own originality. In the following chapters he handles a
mass of wonderfully apt detail with such skill that the reader can
never miss the wood for the trees. The sheer merit of the exposition is overwhelming. And there is none of that deliberate pom-
posity one so often has to suffer when eminent Victorians attack
serious subjects. It was probably a good thing for science that
Wallace's intrusion caused Darwin to argue his main theme in a
less elaborate setting than he originally intended it to have. The
Origin might have been far less effective in four volumes than in
one.

*   *   *

THE *Origin* is reticent about the most delicate matter of all—the
bearing of evolution on the ancestry of Man. But the trend of
thought is obvious between the lines. One cannot fail to connect
the general evolutionary idea—the descent of species from common ancestors—with the evident resemblance of men to certain
apes (Plate 16). And Darwin's argument that the social instincts of
ants and bees have been evolved by natural selection, not in the
competition between individuals, but in that between communities,

---

[1] These are Darwin's words. Herbert Spencer coined the famous phrase
'survival of the fittest'.

must suggest a similar origin for human conscience and moral sense. These ideas were certain, in time, to come into the open and provoke bitter controversy. As acknowledged leader of those who felt bound 'to go the whole orang', Darwin accepted responsibility for carrying his theory to its logical conclusion. He wrote *The Descent of Man* (1871), in which human evolution is fearlessly suggested. The controversial burden fell mainly upon Huxley, who proved remarkably fit to survive under it.[1] But, before turning to the social, religious and political implications, we must consider some further scientific questions which are much to the point. These are connected with the historically important differences between Lamarck and Darwin.

There are two ways in which a creature may come to differ from its fellows. It may, for no apparent reason, be different at birth; or it may become different during life, by the habitual exercise of some part or faculty—as a blacksmith becomes strong in the arm, or a blind man unusually sensitive in touch. Differences at birth may be called 'spontaneous variations'. This does not imply that such variations have no cause, but merely that their causes are unknown or obscure. Differences arising from habit are called 'acquired characteristics'. Lamarck believed that acquired characteristics could be inherited; and he took such inheritance as the main cause of evolutionary change. In his view, individual creatures strove consciously to adapt themselves to their conditions of life: the results of their efforts were inherited and improved by their successors. Giraffes continually stretched their necks in reaching for high foliage; and each generation passed on its slightly greater length of neck to the next. Darwin did not deny this possibility; but he attributed evolutionary change mainly to the inheritance of such spontaneous variations as chanced to have survival value in the struggle for existence. Giraffes which happened (through no effort of their own) to be born with the inheritable quality of long-neckedness were less likely than their fellows to die young—and more likely, therefore, to have young.

It is certainly difficult to see how external modifications, due to exercise or habit, can affect a creature's genetic constitution and so be passed on. Experiment, since Lamarck's time, has confirmed this *prima facie* judgment, by showing no significant inheritance of

[1] See, e.g., *Evolution and Ethics*, and *Man's Place in Nature*.

such modifications. Lamarck's notion has therefore never seemed convincing. But there is much evidence that the spontaneous variations, on which Darwin chiefly relied, are in fact the outward signs of genetic modification and are *necessarily* inheritable. In its main features Darwin's theory, which proved generally acceptable from the first, has thus received generous support from work done since his time. But for non-scientific reasons there have been attempts to revive Lamarck.[1]

*   *   *

IN SUMMING up the present position, it may be said that the *fact* of biological evolution is now established beyond reasonable doubt. It also seems certain that natural selection is the main directing influence. But, before leaving the scientific side of the subject, we must glance at two lines of investigation whose recent interlacing has begun to reveal the nature of the variations which give natural selection its opportunity. One is cytology, which considers the behaviour and minute structure of living cells. This began among the early microscopists, but was not advanced enough for its bearing on evolution to be evident in Darwin's time. The other is the study of heredity on lines suggested by Gregor Mendel, Abbot of Brünn. Mendel's significant and beautiful work was published in the journal of a local naturalists' society, where it lay neglected until 1900. Thus Darwin, although Mendel's contemporary, knew nothing of it.

Living things consist of units called cells. Some are single-celled, but the majority are multicellular. The growth of multicellular organisms takes place by the division and differentiation of cells. The organism begins as a single cell. This divides into two; each of these divides again; and so on. As they multiply, the individual cells develop differently, becoming suited to the formation of the creature's various parts. Those cells which form the main structure are called body cells. But there are others, called sex cells or gametes, set aside for the eventual purpose of reproduction. These are essentially different from the body cells.

All body cells are in certain respects similar. Each is a blob of protoplasm, containing a nucleus. Threadlike objects, of varying

[1] As in Bergson's idea of Creative Evolution, or the preface of Shaw's *Back to Methuselah*.

size and shape, appear in the nucleus at times of cell division. These are called chromosomes, because their ready acceptance of dyes makes them easy to watch under the microscope. The chromosomes occur in pairs—two alike of each kind. Their number varies from species to species; but, in a given species, it is the same for every cell. Fig. 63 represents a body cell with 4 pairs of chromosomes. When the cell divides, each of its chromosomes divides longitudinally. Thus two daughter cells are formed, each having a chromosome content similar to that of the parent cell.[1]

The sex cells at first resemble body cells. But each suffers, once only, a special maturation division. In this division, the cell separates into two mature gametes. But the chromosomes do not

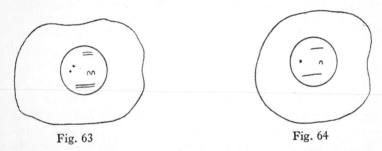

Fig. 63   Fig. 64

split. Instead, one of each kind goes to each daughter cell. Thus mature gametes, male or female, contain only one of each kind of chromosome. Fig. 64 represents a gamete of the creature whose body cells resemble Fig. 63.

A new creature is formed by union of a male gamete (sperm cell) with a female gamete (egg cell). These unite to make a single cell, having the normal ration of 8 chromosomes—one of each kind from the father, one of each from the mother. This new cell then forms the new creature by a succession of ordinary growth divisions. The death of a creature involves that of its body cells. But material from some of its gametes is passed on to its descendants, giving rise to other sets of mortal body cells, and to other gametes which again pass on. Thus the individuals of each

[1] Unicellular creatures *reproduce* themselves by a process similar to that by which multicellular creatures *grow*. In this case, however, the daughter cells part company and become separate unicellular creatures, instead of remaining together to produce a more complex organism.

generation are built of body cells which serve their turn and perish. But the chain of gametes is deathless from generation to generation. Hence arises 'the continuity of germ plasm' in a race. The understanding of this at once robs Lamarck's notions of their plausibility. Changes due to environment or use will generally affect only certain body cells—e.g. those of the blacksmith's muscles or the scholar's brain. They may greatly alter the appearance or behaviour of the individual who suffers them. But they cannot affect inheritance, because this is determined solely by the nature of the gametes. Environment might, conceivably, change the gametes. In this case it could affect the offspring without noticeably affecting the parent. But Lamarckian inheritance, of outward changes caused by use or disuse, would seem to be impossible.

A creature inherits *potentialities* rather than qualities. These reach it in the gametes it receives from its parents; and they decide its genetic constitution. But it may not exhibit all of them as actual qualities. Thus mathematical capacity, inherited from the father, may, through lack of education, be dormant in the son. A tendency to fair hair, inherited from the mother, may be overcome by a stronger tendency to black hair, inherited from the father. But the *capacities* for mathematics and fair hair remain undiluted in the gametes, and are passed on. Either may at any time be fully realised in a descendant not subject to the inhibiting conditions.

Thus there are two essential principles to be observed in the study of heredity: (i) Hereditary potentialities never blend genetically; they pass, unadulterated, from gamete to gamete; the passage of any one of them, from creature to creature, through the most complex series of cross-breedings, may be traced independently, without reference to the others. (ii) A creature does not, in general, exhibit every quality to which it inherits a tendency; the realisation of the tendency may be prevented by an unfavourable environment or the presence of a dominant contrasting tendency; a creature's outward aspect is no sure guide to its genetic make-up.

These facts were discovered by Mendel in his classic experiments with garden peas, though he knew nothing of the cell mechanism behind the facts. The flowers of the pea contain male and female gametes, and are normally self-fertilising. But interbreeding is possible, if flowers of one plant are artificially inseminated with pollen from another. Mendel first studied the inheritance of a single pair of contrasting characters, tallness and shortness. He began with a parent generation (P) of two strains, tall and short. Each strain was pure-breeding—the talls, when self-fertilised, produced only tall descendants; the shorts produced only short descendants. We may call them 'pure talls' and 'pure shorts'. He then raised a first filial generation (F_1), by crossing talls and shorts. The members of F_1 were all tall, but it was soon clear that they were not pure talls. For, when self-fertilised, they produced a second filial generation (F_2) consisting of talls and shorts in the ratio 3:1. Let us call these F_1 talls 'mixed talls'. Mendel next found that the F_2 talls were not all the same: one in 3 was pure, while the others were mixed. But all the F_2 shorts were pure. The family tree, Fig. 65, shows these results diagrammatically. A pure tall is denoted by TT, a pure short by tt, a mixed tall

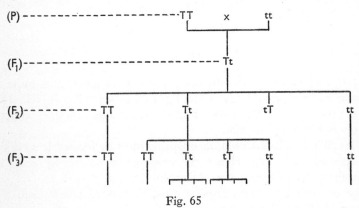

Fig. 65

by Tt or tT. The multiplication sign indicates a cross between two plants. Where an 'unmarried' plant has descendants, they result from self-fertilisation.

Mendel concluded that there were distinct hereditary factors for tallness (T) and shortness (t), T being 'dominant' and t 'recessive'. If a plant inherited T from both parent cells, it would be a pure tall; if it had t from both, it would be a pure short. If it had T from one and t from the other, it would be a mixed tall: it would itself be tall, because T was dominant over t; but it could transmit either T or t (impartially) to its descendants. He observed that a short must always breed true. There cannot be a mixed short, because the dominance of T ensures that any plant which has T in its genetic make-up must show it, even when t is also present.

The hereditary factors are now called genes. If we suppose that genes are carried on chromosomes, those of contrasting characters inhabiting similar chromosomes, then the mechanism of cell division offers an elegant and convincing explanation of Mendel's facts. The key to the whole matter is the maturation division, which

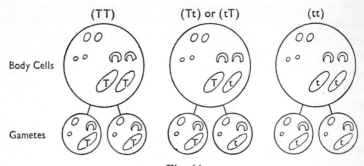

Fig. 66

leaves each gamete with only one set of chromosomes. Fig. 66 represents the types of body cell and gamete associated with TT, Tt and tt plants.[1] A TT has only T gametes, a tt only t gametes, and a Tt equal numbers of each.

If a TT is self-fertilised, its offspring must be formed from a T sperm and a T egg. Hence the offspring is necessarily a TT. Similarly, the offspring of a self-fertilised tt must be a tt. If a TT is crossed with a tt, the offspring must be formed either from T sperm and t egg or from t sperm and T egg. Hence the offspring, as in Mendel's F_1, will all be Tt. But if a Tt is self-fertilised, or bred with another Tt, there are 4 possibilities:

(i) T sperm united with T egg . . . . . result a TT
(ii) T sperm united with t egg . . . . . result a Tt
(iii) t sperm united with T egg . . . . . result a tT
(iv) t sperm united with t egg . . . . . result a tt

We may reasonably suppose that there is a random association of sperm and egg cells in the process of fertilisation. The 4 possible

[1] It is assumed that the characters T and t are carried on the long chromosomes. The pea actually has more than 4 pairs of chromosomes, but the depiction of these would needlessly complicate the diagram.

combinations will then be equally likely; and the proportions of TT, Tt and tt among large numbers of offspring will be nearly 1:2:1, as Mendel found in his F_2.

Mendel subsequently examined the consequences of more complex genetic mixtures, involving several pairs of contrasted characters, in the parent generation. He found again that the hereditary factors kept their identity through a succession of separations and recombinations; and that the various possible types of offspring appeared in simple numerical proportions in F_1, F_2, etc. The chromosome theory predicts these proportions correctly in each case. It also explains 'linkage'—certain characters are always inherited together, because their genes inhabit the same chromosome. The details are beautiful and subtle; but the interested reader must consult a book on genetics. The theory has been so successful that much of it may now be regarded as established fact. In certain cases, particular genes have been located on particular chromosomes, and even in particular places on those chromosomes.

Knowledge of Mendelism can help the plant or animal breeder who, by crossing and selection, seeks a variety with certain qualities. But it would seem that he can obtain nothing really new: all he can do is make fresh combinations of qualities which exist genetically in his original stock. This involves a difficulty for the evolutionist. Even with a genetically very mixed race, the number of possible combinations is finite. One might suppose that natural selection, having established the fittest of these combinations, could do no more. Evolution would then cease, except in so far as changing physical conditions encouraged the return of combinations previously ill-adapted. But, whatever the circumstances, the extent of change would remain within the limits of the genetic material available. Another awkward question is how any genetic differences ever arose at all. Nature avoids stagnation, however, by the device of gene mutation. Individual genes unpredictably change their character from time to time. Thus new hereditary elements are occasionally introduced into a race. The chemical and physical nature of genes is not yet fully understood. Little is known, therefore, about the cause of mutations, though it has been found that their frequency is increased by certain kinds of radiation. It would seem that gene mutations are in fact the 'spontaneous variations' of which Darwin's intuition suggested the existence and importance.

Mendelism introduces serious mathematics into biology—the kind of mathematics, involving statistics, probability, permutations and combinations, which deals with discrete objects in large numbers. This is different from the mathematics of continuous change, which grew up in the service of Newtonian physics. Mendelism, with its distinct and indestructible genetic units, ranks philosophically with the atomic, kinetic and Quantum theories, in suggesting an ultimately discontinuous Nature. Ironically, the mathematics of continuity has begun to acquire sound logical foundations just as science is beginning to have less use for it.

*   *   *

As TO the effects of Evolution on thought in general, we can only give the briefest sketch of them here. Perhaps its deepest, if not its most spectacular effect, was to re-emphasise the opinion of those old philosophers whose intuitive belief in the essential unity of the World convinced them that it must be understood as a whole or not at all. Greek efforts to understand the world in this way, though imaginatively and intellectually remarkable, were premature. In Alexandria, therefore, the keenest minds, impressed by the noble failure of speculative philosophy to gain its end, were devoted for a time to detailed problems of exact science. This happened again in the 16th and 17th centuries, when it became clear that medieval scholasticism had likewise failed to achieve a satisfactory synthesis. There are, indeed, two different intellectual approaches to the problem of understanding the universe—a comprehensive, philosophical approach and a detailed, scientific approach. History exhibits a series of swings from one to the other and back.

The antagonism between philosophy and science, at first sight, seems stronger than ever in the 19th century. It is hard to imagine more contrast in outlook than that illustrated by (say) Hegel and Lord Kelvin. Yet, beneath the surface, there are signs of coming reconciliation—signs that the detailed *methods* of science may in time bring about the comprehensive *purpose* of philosophy. Scientists were at first like isolated groups of men trying to cut clearings in different parts of a jungle; but, by the mid 19th century, the clearings were so large that they began to run into one another. The physical sciences were no longer separate: different lines of research were leading to the same broad general notions, such as those of energy, entropy and the atomic structure of matter. Evolution was thus fortunate in coming to the fore just when great unifying principles were the scientific fashion. It did more than any other single notion to stress the oneness of the cosmic scheme.

There appeared to be evolution in the organic as well as the inorganic world, in social and mental as well as physical development. It even seemed possible that life might have been evolved from inanimate matter, without direct divine intervention, by a natural process. Simple organic compounds had already been artificially produced. There was no apparent reason why more complex organic substances should not in time be similarly made. The difference between living and inanimate matter might, perhaps, be *only* one of chemical complexity. The chance mingling of atoms could hardly fail, in the vast course of geological time, to produce molecules of the requisite complexity. Life would then automatically appear, and organic evolution begin. Belief in the spontaneous generation of life, which goes back at least to the early Ionian philosophers, seemed at last to have some scientific plausibility. There were (and are) vitalists, maintaining that matter, whatever its chemical constitution, can come to life only with the addition of a 'vital principle' unknown to physical science. The question whether life can be completely explained in terms of physics and chemistry is still unsettled. But the mere idea that it *might* be so explained was enough to suggest a single great process of development, from primitive nebulae to self-conscious animals. Thus scientists, practising their peculiar method of concentration on limited problems, were gradually forced back, despite themselves, to the philosophic conception of science as an indivisible whole. One result has been the recent tendency of scientists and mathematicians,[1] especially in later life, to cultivate philosophy. On occasion, perhaps their excursions were as ill-advised as those of old philosophers into natural science: that is a matter of opinion. What seems certain is that philosophers and scientists are beginning to look on one another more as partners than competitors. Scientists are inclined to admit the possibility and value of the philosopher's all-embracing view, while philosophers have more respect for the scientific method as a means of getting the detailed

[1] E.g. Clifford, Huxley, Whitehead, Russell, Eddington, Poincaré, Mach.

knowledge on which a satisfactory synthesis must rest. Mutual contempt is giving way to amicable division of labour in a common cause. Philosophers are much less cautious than scientists in the interpretation of scientific results. They make daring inferences where the scientist withholds judgment. But speculation beyond the bounds of science is their job: it satisfies a genuine human need, while suggesting ideas of value to future scientists. Speculation based on science is, in any case, a sounder proposition than the old science based on speculation.

*   *   *

EVOLUTION REVIVED the old conflict of science with orthodoxy. The question which received most public attention was that concerning the literal truth of the Creation story in Genesis—was Man specially created, or was he the modified descendant of some less upstanding animal? The open battle at the British Association meeting in Oxford (1860), just after the appearance of the *Origin*, raged about this very point.[1] It was not really very important; for it could be dismissed by treating the Bible story as poetic allegory —an expedient soon approved by the majority, even of the most devout.

But there were deeper questions. 'The argument from design', a standard intellectual ground for belief in God, was quite upset. This maintained that the wonderful interrelation of things was evidence that the universe had been created by a conscious being of infinite capacity. Every creature was perfectly adapted to its neighbours and environment; everything supported, and depended on, a myriad other things. Creation was an inconceivably complex and delicately adjusted work of art, which men could barely begin to comprehend: it could only be the product of a superhuman mind. This idea was incompatible with Darwinism. Existing things, it was admitted, were supremely well fitted to each other. But there was no *intention* about this; it was inevitable, simply because natural selection destroyed whatever failed to fit. A universe

---

[1] Although *The Descent of Man* was still unwritten, Evolution was already being ridiculed as 'the monkey theory'. Samuel Wilberforce lowered the level of the proceedings (in a manner reminiscent of Caccini) by asking whether it was through his grandfather or his grandmother that Professor Huxley claimed descent from an ape.

of mutually adapted creatures was the predictable outcome of natural causes. A maladjusted universe would, indeed, be far more astonishing.

There is no escape from this difficulty. You can either have Darwinism or the argument from design, but not both; and the evidence for Darwinism is very strong. But perhaps the dilemma is not as awkward as it seems. Darwinism does not involve denial of God; it involves only the rejection of one argument for the existence of God. In any case, belief in God does not usually rest on purely intellectual foundations: most believers regard intellectual reasons as subsidiary to those of faith. And, if the argument from design is in fact fallacious, honest theologians will no doubt agree that science has done theology a service by destroying it.

Another difficulty was that Evolution seemed to deny any fixed purpose, and therefore any genuine progress, in the universe. An organism may be said to make *biological* progress whenever it becomes better adapted to its surroundings: but the kind of change involved in adaptation will vary with the physical conditions; it may at one time lead towards increasing complexity and higher mentality, while at another it favours simplicity and mental degeneration. One can imagine conditions, tolerable to a crude unfeeling organism, which a more sensitive type could not survive. It is true that specialisation makes for efficiency; physiological processes are better carried out if each is performed by an organ exclusively devoted to it. There is thus reason to suppose that natural selection will favour creatures with many highly specialised organs, rather than those in which a few organs have to do everything. But the identification of progress with mere increasing complexity, which appears to be the creed of some biologists, is a bleak, unsatisfying notion.

It may be held that purpose has now appeared as a by-product of blind evolution. The self-conscious mind, originally developed because it happened to have survival value, has done its work so well that it need no longer be continuously employed on practical problems of self-preservation. It has acquired leisure, which it devotes to reflection. It has used its leisure to conceive standards of 'good', and plans for securing this 'good'. Dr. Julian Huxley has recalled attention to this view:[1]

[1] Letter in the *Sunday Times*, 3 February 1957.

The real wonder of life is the fact that the automatic and non-purposeful process of biological evolution should eventually have generated true purpose in the person of the human species.

This idea may appeal to the thorough-going humanist. It flatters human self-respect and justifies human endeavour. It can lead to a valuable, constructive philosophy. But it can hardly satisfy the Christian or other deeply religious man.

Orthodoxy (like Descartes) sets a hard line between men and other creatures, by insisting that men alone have souls. Degrees of soul are not admitted: a soul is something that a creature has completely or not at all. This again can hardly be reconciled with Darwin's theory, which supposes a chain of creatures, each infinitesimally different from the next, leading up to Man from something which was certainly not a man. The awkward question is: At what point in this series of creatures did the soul first appear? There is no difficulty for those who admit the possibility of a rudimentary soul, which can attain maturity by evolution. But such an idea was not consonant with orthodox 19th-century opinion. A related source of disagreement was Darwin's suggestion, elaborated by Clifford and others, that the human moral sense has grown gradually from such altruistic instincts as favoured *racial* survival in the struggle for existence.[1] This contradicts the belief that Man acquired knowledge of good and evil, once for all, when he ate the forbidden fruit. But the difficulty is perhaps no greater than that of the Creation story.

Biologists and their supporters did not always observe those standards of objectiveness in debate which, as scientists, they should have accepted. This, though not excusable, is understandable. They met insufferable prejudice and ignorance in some of their opponents. Biology was, moreover, years behind physical science in its growth: at the time of the Evolution controversy it had just gained the naïve self-confidence of adolescence—it was approaching the stage reached by physical science in Laplace. Darwin and Wallace were always distinguished for scrupulous moderation; but evolutionary philosophers often went further than the facts entitled them (even as philosophers) to go. Ernst Haeckel,

[1] Darwin: *The Descent of Man*, Ch. V.   Clifford: 'On the Scientific Basis of Morals', in *Lectures and Essays*. Wallace would not go the whole way with Darwin in this matter: see his *Darwinism*, Ch. XV.

the German prophet of Evolution, asserted the purely physical origin of life with provocative arrogance.[1] He also maintained, with insufficient reason, that the stages in the evolutionary development of a race are repeated in the embryological development of its individuals. This led some biologists, relying on a questionable analogy, to base the study of evolution too much on that of embryology. The English reader may find examples of dogmatic bitterness on the scientific side in Winwood Reade's book *The Martyrdom of Man*. Even Huxley, whose integrity is beyond question, was occasionally carried away by his zeal as defender of a cause. He coined the word 'agnosticism' for the detached attitude which prefers honest ignorance to dubious self-persuasion. But his agnosticism sometimes seems less rigorous in scientific than in other matters; and he tends to claim for scientists an authority he would have thought preposterous in the Pope or General Booth.

But, despite difficulties, there seems no compelling reason why belief in evolution should not accompany a genuinely religious outlook. The case is like that of gravitational astronomy. Newton and Laplace showed how the Solar System might function without daily divine intervention; Darwin and Wallace did the same for living Nature. The *ultimate* need for God was not repudiated in either case. Evolution does not explain creation: it merely throws light on the *immediate means* by which a wonderful pattern has been (and is being) woven from raw materials already created. A creation continually developed by evolution is no less admirable or mysterious than the seven days' wonder of Genesis; and it offers quite as much scope for religious reverence.

The daily interference of gods with mundane affairs is a notion natural to men who fear, or fail to understand, their environment. It is the earliest of scientific theories; for it is designed to serve the two characteristic purposes of all science—the explanation and control of phenomena. The god behind the lightning, wind or harvest is admittedly a superficial explanation: but it does hold out some hope that the lightning, wind or harvest may be indirectly influenced by human acts of sacrifice and propitiation. This idea was everywhere present in myth, and it passed into nearly all the more sophisticated religions. It became so deeply ingrained that it

[1] As one of Haeckel's opponents put it: 'There is no God—and Haeckel is His prophet.'

21

persisted long after science had suggested more effective hypotheses. Its continued struggle for survival was behind much of the religious opposition to Evolution: for Evolution does more than any other scientific theory, except perhaps Universal Gravitation, to deny the daily occurrence of *direct* divine action.

The present findings of science may be tentatively interpreted as suggesting that God, foreseeing the outcome He desired, has created a universe which can safely be left to work out its own destiny according to general laws laid down in the beginning by Him. This universe may seem purposeless to the limited intelligence, regarding it from within. But that is because the limited intelligence, although it can partially discover some of the general laws, can foresee only their immediate and not their final consequences. The suggestion that God works in this way does not belittle His majesty or importance. The foresight which seems to make miraculous intervention unnecessary is as wonderful as any miracle.

If these notions are not to anybody's taste, he should remember there is no logical compulsion about them. But they offer a possible foundation for religious belief, consistent with certain scientific findings which it seems unreasonable to reject. The difficulty, for holders of such a belief, is to find a satisfactory basis for conduct: the scheme, at first sight, seems to leave no room for individual responsibility. It may, however, be argued that the evolution of intellect and moral sense is an essential part of the process by which God's final purpose is to be attained. By proper use of these faculties, an individual can hasten the process: by neglecting them, he can retard it; though he cannot prevent its *ultimate* success. The laws governing evolution may be such that *in the long run* the majority of men must come to make proper use of their faculties; yet individual conduct may help to decide when, if not whether, this shall happen.

Misplaced human pride was probably the real motive behind much that masqueraded as religious opposition to Evolution. Men supposed the Evolutionists were degrading them. Huxley denies this in an eloquent passage:[1]

> Is it, indeed, true, that the Poet, or the Philosopher, or the Artist whose genius is the glory of his age, is degraded from his high estate

[1] *Man's Place in Nature*; Lecture II.

by the undoubted historical probability, not to say certainty, that he
is the direct descendant of some naked and bestial savage, whose intelligence was just sufficient to make him a little more cunning than
the Fox, and by so much more dangerous than the Tiger? Or is he
bound to howl and grovel on all fours because of the wholly unques-
tionable fact, that he was once an egg, which no ordinary power of
discrimination could distinguish from that of a Dog? Or is the
philanthropist, or the saint, to give up his endeavours to live a noble
life, because the simplest study of man's nature reveals, at its foundations, all the selfish passions, and fierce appetites of the merest
quadruped? Is mother-love vile because a hen shows it, or fidelity
base because dogs possess it?

Huxley then suggests that Man's past rise, from something lower,
should encourage him to hope he may rise yet higher.

*   *   *

POLITICAL THINKERS tended to notice only such scraps of evolutionary lore as suited their opinions. Those, like Herbert Spencer,
who believed in *laissez faire*, stressed the virtues of unimpeded
natural adaptation. They thought government interference should
be minimised, so that society could adjust itself according to
'natural laws'. Spencer lived too early to be much influenced by
Darwin. His idea of evolution was mainly Lamarckian; he thought
the adaptation of an organism was due to its conscious efforts to fit
itself to its surroundings. Survival was the prize of those whose
efforts were most successful. Darwinians, on the other hand, supposed that individual fitness was the result of spontaneous variation rather than conscious effort. Nature (they argued) produces
successful types by trial and error; she experiments with creatures
of every kind, and lets competition eliminate the failures. But,
whatever their opinions concerning the mechanism of evolution,
believers in *laissez faire* agreed that Nature should as far as possible
be uninhibited—there should be no interference with the struggle
which selected those who (by luck or virtue) were best suited to the
world. Free competition must inevitably breed a race of successful
individuals: and, since a race of successful individuals is likely to
be a happy race, free competition should further the Utilitarian
ideal—the greatest happiness of the greatest number. Industrial
legislation, State education and municipal sanitation are bad: they

encourage indolence; they lessen the survival value of desirable qualities like ingenuity, industry and independence; they must produce a race of mediocrities. The necessary extinction of the unsuccessful, no doubt, involves some suffering; but the greatest possible excess of happiness over misery will in the end be secured by non-intervention.

This argument would have been more convincing if its advocates had really been prepared to allow free competition. But the competition they envisaged was far from free; the game was to be played according to certain rules. It was legitimate to leave the unemployable to starve, or to hold a man to a ruinous contract which he had been inveigled into signing without fully understanding it; but straightforward murder and theft were discouraged. There was, therefore, a false analogy: for natural selection, among wild creatures, operates in conditions of total anarchy, in which the skilful murderer and thief take full advantage of their talents. In any case, the whole argument begs the question. It defines the good as what is best fitted to survive free competition, and then prescribes free competition as a means of attaining the good.

J. S. Mill's mistrust of State intervention was inherited, through his father, from Utilitarians and classical economists—men like Malthus, Ricardo, Adam Smith and Jeremy Bentham. His advocacy of individual liberty, however, is tempered by practical sense and humanity. He sees that absolute individual liberty is incompatible with any kind of society, and he asks how it should be limited. Mill's answer is that a man should be entirely free in actions which affect no one but himself and those (of mature judgment) who willingly co-operate; but he must be restrained in actions harmful to others who do not consent. Thus, if a man likes to get drunk, that is his own business; but if, in consequence, he neglects his family, society has a right and duty to intervene. The application of this principle steers Mill away from *laissez faire*; for there are few actions that affect no one but the agent and his voluntary associates. Thus, despite his background, Mill suggests compulsory education (with State aid where necessary), a law forbidding improvident marriages, and even some government control of the distribution, if not the production, of wealth. The intended apostle of individualism becomes a mild socialist. It is only with regard to freedom of thought and expression that he admits no compromise. The evolution of right opinions is only possible, he maintains, if there is a free struggle for existence among ideas of every kind. Those ideas which are most firmly established, by a long history of service to mankind, may yet contain elements of error; the most bizarre notions may contain elements of truth. No idea, however quaint, must be denied the right of competition with its rivals in the field of open discussion: what is best in thought will then survive. Even the most universally accepted ideas, which seem beyond all reasonable doubt, need the constant opposition of cranks and paradoxers, in order that they may not become deadened by being taken too much for granted.

Mill forms a link between those who think primitive Nature should have a free run and those who think Man should take the reins. This question is ably discussed by Huxley,[1] who argues cogently against *laissez faire*. The early development of life took place by blind evolution: it was the result of natural selection operating on such chance variations as happened to fit some creatures better than others to existing ecological or climatic conditions. The state of things directly produced by this blind process is called by Huxley the State of Nature. Sociability and cunning were qualities which turned out to have great survival value in the State of Nature. The evolution of these qualities gave incidental rise (in Man) to moral sense, reflective thought and the capacity for aesthetic enjoyment. A new element has thus been introduced into the Cosmic Process. A creature has appeared who, through his mental powers, can adapt external conditions to his needs, instead of relying on his own chance adaptation to external conditions. He creates for himself an environment which Huxley, comparing it to a garden in the midst of a wilderness, calls the State of Art. There is conflict between garden and wilderness, in that primitive Nature will quickly restore the wilderness if there is any slackening of the gardener's efforts. The gardener's most pressing task is to mitigate the struggle for existence within the garden; for, once the struggle reappears, the finer garden plants will have no chance against the coarser creatures of the wilderness.

The word 'natural' is ambiguous. It may be used, in a broad sense, with reference to any part or product of the general Cosmic Process; or, in a restricted sense, with reference only to the

[1] See, particularly, the 'Prolegomena' to *Evolution and Ethics*.

products of blind evolution. Huxley makes this distinction clear. In contrasting the State of Nature with the State of Art, he asserts (merely) that the garden is unnatural *in the restricted sense*; it is the product, not of Nature working directly through blind evolution, but of Nature working indirectly through the human intelligence which blind evolution has permitted to emerge. But, *in the broader sense*, the garden is as 'natural' as the wilderness; both are products of the general Cosmic Process, and the struggle between them is just one of the many struggles that contribute to the Process. Exponents of *laissez faire* equivocate with the word 'natural'. The force of their argument, that society should be allowed to develop 'naturally', depends on the tacit understanding of 'natural' in the widest sense: but their policy consists in readmitting the primitive struggle to the garden—i.e. in trying to restore conditions which are 'natural' only in the narrow sense. It is they, not their opponents, who really meddle with the Cosmic Process. Man's intelligence, his moral and aesthetic standards, are products of the Cosmic Process as surely as the leopard's spots or the elephant's trunk; and they should be allowed to play their full part in its continuation. To hinder the organisation of the garden is to deny Man the advantage of those mental powers which natural selection has sanctioned; it is like painting over the leopard's spots or amputating the elephant's trunk.

Huxley was not primarily a political or social thinker. But his point of view is worth special notice because, unlike many others, he understood Evolution, not as a vague philosophic creed, but as a scientific theory dispassionately founded on fact. He had himself handled the evidence, and indeed discovered much of it: he knew its strong and weak points: he could judge the validity or doubtfulness of conclusions drawn from it. It is therefore important that he set his authority against the idea that Evolution gave Government an excuse for handing its responsibilities over to 'Nature'.

Most political theorists agreed with Huxley that the garden should be maintained, if not improved; but they disagreed with each other about how it should be done. Their understanding of Evolution was generally superficial, and each drew attention to the aspect which seemed to support his prejudice. Socialists emphasised the survival value of co-operation, as practised by ants, bees and wolves. They wished to eliminate competition between men, in order that humanity might prosper in its struggle with environment. Thus they could invoke topical evolutionary ideas in support of that principle of organised mutual aid through which they thought they saw the way to human wellbeing. The more conservative, while admitting the need for some co-operation, still saw virtue in competition as a means of encouraging the evolution of efficient individuals within the race. Huxley supports this opinion. He points out that the primitive struggle for bare existence has not seriously affected civilised Man for centuries: all that remains is the milder struggle for enjoyment; and this may be valuable as a spur to individual self-improvement. Nationalists and militarists, whose ideal unit was the Nation rather than the Human Race, and who had little use for any but the martial virtues, advocated a garden in which the internally organised cabbage patch should be left to fight the internally organised strawberry bed for supremacy. Marxists thought the evolutionary struggle should be between classes.

There has been some tendency, especially among thinkers of the left, to revive Lamarckism, for propaganda purposes, without regard for the scientific state of the case. The modern statistical study of genetics has sprung from the work of Mendel and Sir Francis Galton. It confirms Darwin's belief that hereditary qualities are, in general, those which are innate: it contradicts Lamarck's idea that the effects of environment and nurture are passed on. The inference, for anyone bent on permanent improvement of the Race, is that it will pay to offer special opportunity to those who owe their excellence to accidents of birth or breeding. This does not imply that excellence occurs only within a single income-group or social class; nor need it involve the total neglect of the less gifted: but it does suggest the maintenance of an aristocracy based on birth and patronage.[1] Such a notion cannot please egalitarians. Their case is strengthened if they can show that better living conditions and mass education have a permanently beneficial, not just a transiently palliative, effect. According to Lamarck, the benefits of nurture will be cumulative, as egalitarians would like to think: but modern genetic science suggests that they will affect only those who directly receive them—they may brighten many lives for the time being, but we must look to breeding if we seek improvements.

1 State (as well as private) patronage is envisaged.

which will persist from one generation to another. A notable attempt to revive Lamarckism was that which raised the recent Lysenko Controversy in Russia. This is thoroughly considered in Dr. Julian Huxley's *Soviet Genetics and World Science*. It evokes disturbing memories of what happened in the 4th and 5th centuries, and again in the 16th and 17th. The idea that science should prefer the cynical maintenance of orthodoxy to the honest search for truth, and that it deserves persecution if it refuses, is still far from dead.

A remarkable product of evolutionary thought was Nietzsche's gospel of the Superman. Nietzsche was a classical scholar with a poetic imagination and a profound reverence for the aristocratic cultures of Greece and Rome, cultures based on educated leisure for the few and slave labour for the many. He turned to evolutionary biology with the dangerous enthusiasm of the superficially informed amateur. In particular, he was affected by Galton's notion of eugenics—the planned improvement of the human race by rigorously selective breeding. He was deeply influenced by Schopenhauer's assertion of the fundamental importance of Will as a cosmic force, and also by the ideal of the romantic hero set forth by such barbaric artists as Byron and Wagner. He tried to unite these diverse ideas in his philosophy.

The Superman was to be the dominant species of the future, evolved from Man, but as far superior to Man as Man is to the apes. Nietzsche imagined him with the essential qualities of Alexander the Great, Leonardo da Vinci and Charles Bradlaugh; a superb artist-warrior, without belief in God, interested only in his own self-fulfilment. The evolution of the Superman was to be on Lamarckian lines, consciously striven for: it was the one object worthy of human endeavour, for which no sacrifice was too great. The duty, therefore, of those who were conscious of their own superiority, in intellect, physique, energy or will-power, was to form themselves into a master class of 'higher men', devoted to the sole purpose of developing their own hero-like qualities. The herd, whom Nietzsche called 'the bungled and botched', were of no value except as slaves to minister to these higher men; their welfare was of no account beside the success of a single hero, because this success was a step towards the advent of the Superman, which was all that mattered. Religions—especially those, like

Christianity, which encouraged sympathy, humility or kindness—were a bar to progress, since they sapped the admirable quality of ruthless self-assertion in the masters: they might, however, be of temporary use for keeping the masses contented with their servile lot. Nietzsche had a further grudge against Christianity for the part it played in interrupting the tradition of pagan civilisation. His opinions of men like St. Paul and St. Augustine are scarcely printable.

Such was the message of the Prophet Nietzsche, for which he thought mankind should render him eternal gratitude. It was humanism gone mad: not the healthy independence, typical of Athens or the Renaissance, which freed men from superstition and arbitrary authority; but an insane selfhood. Nietzsche wrote an autobiography, blasphemously entitled *Ecce Homo*, in which the first three chapters are 'Why I am so wise', 'Why I am so clever', 'Why I write such excellent books'. Further comment seems unnecessary. It may, however, be remarked that, although Nietzsche was himself an internationalist, and although there is some nobility in his ideal of conscious human self-evolution, his influence, both great and evil, was exerted mainly through movements of racial pride, like Prussianism, Fascism and Aryanism.

10

EPILOGUE: 20th-CENTURY TRENDS

A BOOK of this size, covering so much ground, can deal with 20th-century science only in barest outline. There are many popular books on the subject. But let us face the fact that recent ideas in physics, chemistry and astronomy cannot be fully understood without highbrow mathematics. The same is becoming true even in biology. Another scientific revolution has occurred in the last 60 years. It differs from that of the 16th and 17th centuries, in that scientists have brought it upon themselves by their own discoveries. It is not the result of an influx of ideas from outside. It is nonetheless a revolution. It involves a thorough change in fundamental concepts and ways of thought. New instruments, like the radio-telescope and electron microscope, are as full of possibilities as the optical telescope and microscope once were.

The science of the 17th, 18th and 19th centuries took space, time and matter as its basic concepts. The concept of matter, as a coagulation of simple indivisible atoms, appeared to offer no serious difficulty. It was assumed to be within the grasp of normal understanding, and to correspond closely to something which existed independently in the physical world. The extension and duration of matter gave rise to ideas of measurable space and time. These ideas, again, seemed straightforward enough for immediate use, without subjection to any deep analysis. Material objects existed in different places and at different times—there were spatial and temporal relations among them. Changes in these relations suggested the concept of measurable motion. The concept of mass arose from the observation that every body had a measurable inertia, or unwillingness to have its motion changed by other bodies. Heat, sound and elasticity were 'explained' in terms of matter and motion. It seemed certain that electricity, radiation and gravitation would in time be similarly 'explained'. The mechanical world was ruled by the principle of Universal Causation. Every event had a cause, and given causes always had the same effect. An event was, quite simply, a rearrangement of material particles. The work of science was to reveal the relations between events. These relations might be complex and difficult to trace; but scientists had no serious doubts about the nature and objectiveness of the events among which the relations held.

Three shattering developments came early in the 20th century. These were Relativity, Quantum Theory, and the electrical theory of matter. Each exposed the inadequacy of concepts which science had long taken for granted. Trusted foundations were undermined.

The new theory of matter, due particularly to J. J. Thomson and Lord Rutherford, began with the study of electric discharges in a high vacuum. This revealed a particle, the electron, much smaller than the atoms of chemistry. The study of radio-activity offered further evidence. It was soon clear that chemical atoms could not be regarded as the final constituents of matter. Other sub-atomic particles, such as the proton, neutron and positron, appeared. The atom was neither solid nor simple. It seemed to be a complex structure, consisting mainly of empty space, and capable of disruption. This was not all. The discovery that the ultimate particles of matter were smaller than had been supposed, though interesting, was not revolutionary. But the attempt to predict the behaviour of sub-atomic particles by Newtonian mechanics failed. This was serious. A new quantum mechanics had to be applied, which suggested that such particles were not definite things, in definite places, having definite velocities. The mere act of observation affected their behaviour. It was impossible to know both the position and velocity of an electron exactly, because measuring the one was liable to change the other. And, though electrons often behaved like particles, they seemed at times to exhibit interference as if they were groups of waves. It was also found that mass could be annihilated, with the appearance of an equivalent in radiation.

Thus the analysis of ordinary matter was apparently leading to something that differed *in kind* from ordinary matter. The ultimate particles seemed not to have those properties, such as permanence, unique position and amenability to Newtonian Law, which had come to be regarded as essential to all matter. Such properties now appeared to be statistical. They existed in large portions of matter (where the average behaviour of many particles was involved), but not in the individual particles. The accepted notion of matter, as something simple and readily understood, was destroyed. It had to be admitted that matter was highly complex. Its constituent particles seemed to have incompatible properties, and no satisfactory physical picture of them could be formed.

The long-standing belief that radiation travelled in continuous waves was also questioned. To account for certain phenomena, the Quantum Theory[1] supposed that light was transmitted in successive discrete packets of energy, called photons. Here was a return to something like the old emission theory. Although many optical phenomena suggested light was undulatory, there now seemed to be occasions on which it behaved like a shower of corpuscles. This paradox, which is like that of the electron, was vaguely perceived by Newton. But until early in the 20th century the evidence for a purely undulatory theory nevertheless steadily gained strength.

The Theory of Relativity was meanwhile criticising the concepts of space and time. It was found that the measured velocity of light was independent of the observer's velocity in relation to the source. It was also found impossible to detect motion of the earth through the luminiferous ether. Since the earth moves round the sun, it would seem that there should at some time of year be such a motion. Einstein showed how these anomalies might be avoided, if certain assumptions about space and time were abandoned. The word 'distance' is significant only in so far as it indicates the result of measurement. Now, as Einstein pointed out, an observer, measuring the distance between two points, will obtain a result depending on his state of motion. Other observers, with other velocities, will obtain different results. Since there is no such thing as absolute motion, we have no criterion for preferring one result to another. We must admit that the distance between two points has no absolute value—it is a relation involving the observer, not an objective relation between the points. The assumption, hitherto general, that there is any such thing as *the distance* between two points, is illegitimate. The same is true of time intervals. Observers, in different states of motion, who measure the time between two events, will disagree; and their estimates will be equally legitimate. If, however, an observer measures both the distance and time

[1] Initiated by Max Planck in 1901.

between two events, and combines his results mathematically in a certain way, he can obtain a quantity called the 'separation' of the events. This separation is found to be the same for all observers. Whenever two observers differ in their estimates of distance, there is a compensating difference in their estimates of time; and they obtain the same separation. Thus separation has an absolute quality which distance and time, individually, have not. In order to take an objective view of the World, we must treat space and time together, ceasing to think in terms of either apart from the other. We must concentrate on the separation of events in 'space-time'.

These notions led to a new theory of gravitation. The separation of two neighbouring events, about which all observers agree, is given by a mathematical formula (called the metric), involving the measured distances and times about which they *disagree*. Each observer puts his personal estimates of distance and time into the formula, which is so designed that they all calculate the same separation. It is found that the metric varies from region to region. In regions destitute of matter it is analogous to the Pythagorean formula for distance in ordinary geometry. But, in the vicinity of matter, the agreement between observers can only be secured by using a modified metric. The necessary modifications depend on the distribution of the matter, and can be determined from it. Thus the geometrical properties of space-time, epitomised in the metric, are affected by the presence of matter. When modified, the metric becomes analogous to those formulae which, in ordinary geometry, give the distance from point to point over a curved surface. This is what is meant by saying that space-time is 'curved' in the presence of matter. Any attempt to visualise the curvature is vain and misleading. The mathematical technique for calculating separation in the neighbourhood of matter is analogous to that for calculating distance over a curved surface. That is as far as the analogy goes.

Let A_0, A_1, A_2, ..., A_n be points in close succession on a planet's orbit. The planet's arrival at A_0 (at time t_0) is an event, which we denote by E_0. Events E_1, E_2, ..., E_n are similarly defined. Let the separation of E_0 from E_1 be S_1; let that of E_1 from E_2 be S_2; and so on. Then $S_1 + S_2 + \cdots + S_n$ will be the total separation, measured along the planet's course. Einstein's law of gravitation states that the path and speed of a planet are so adjusted that the total separation, measured over any section of its course, shall be a maximum. Any deviation from the actual path or speed would mean a decrease of total separation. This course of maximum separation, which is natural to the planet, will be affected by the proximity of other bodies, because their distribution will determine the nature of the metric in the neighbourhood of the planet. Einstein does not try to explain *why* the planet follows a course of maximum separation, or *why* the presence of matter alters the metric. He is content to offer mathematical rules for adjustment of the metric and calculation of the planet's behaviour. He asserts that predictions based on these rules will agree with observation.

This geometrical theory of gravitation recalls the Greek idea of 'natural' motions. Pythagoras and Plato believed that circular motion was 'natural' to the heavenly bodies, because the circle was a perfect figure. Aristotle believed that a stone fell because of its 'natural' tendency to its proper sphere. No outside agent was needed to keep the planet in a circle or pull the stone to earth. Galileo and Newton reformed science by supposing that the only 'natural' motion was uniform motion in a straight line. Any other motion had to be attributed to some force which compelled the body out of its 'natural' course. They had to postulate a force of gravitation, which was always suspiciously elusive. Einstein made the concept of force unnecessary, by returning to the idea that there were various kinds of 'natural' motion in various parts of the universe. But, instead of superstitious or aesthetic reasons, he offered something more practical—mathematical methods, by which the 'natural' motion in any given region could be precisely calculated from the local distribution of matter.[1] The only justification of these methods is that they predict future sense perceptions correctly. This aptly illustrates the preference of modern science for pure description, and its unconcern with metaphysical explanations.

Except in matters of atomic smallness or cosmic magnitude, the observable predictions of the new theories agree with those of the old. Where there *are* differences, the new theories are superior. They have led to practical developments of immense consequence,

[1] The necessary pure mathematics had already been created by the non-Euclidean geometers, just as the mathematics needed by Kepler had been created by the Greeks.

especially in the atomic field. But Newtonian science remains adequate for many purposes, such as those of ordinary engineering.

The philosophic change is profound. Despite its expanding power, science is at last fully conscious of its own limitations. Now that unforeseen complexity and difficulty have obscured concepts once thought simple, the physical scientist has given up trying to picture the objects whose interrelations he studies. He creates a mathematical structure, in which ideal elements $(a, b, c, \ldots)$ are connected by a pattern of relations. He has reason to suppose that there are corresponding natural objects $(a', b', c', \ldots)$ connected by a similar pattern of relations. Study of the mathematical relations between $a, b, c, \ldots$ may enable him, by analogy, to predict the effects of $a', b', c', \ldots$ on our senses. But, concerning the objects $a', b', c', \ldots$ themselves, he can only say 'what they are, yet I know not'. The modern scientist's account of Nature has much the same relation to Nature as the score has to a symphony. The dots on the paper are in no way like musical notes. But the geometrical relations among the dots have a structure similar to that of the relations of pitch and time among the notes. If one dot is above another, the corresponding note is higher in pitch. If one dot is to the right of another, the corresponding note is later in time. Dots in the same vertical line correspond to simultaneous notes; those in the same horizontal line to notes of equal pitch. The score cannot enable a man, born deaf, to form any conception of a musical note. But it *can* tell him that the symphony is a structure involving at least two essentially different types of relation among the unknown elements of which it is composed. The study of many scores may show him that certain rules of construction are always followed. Experience may teach him, given a score, to *predict* the antics of a conductor or the emotions of an audience, though he cannot understand the *reasons* for their behaviour.

The new way of thought in physics has created wider interest in the ideal structures of pure mathematics, which, despite their abstractness, are now seen to be of vital importance. Great impetus has been given to study of the logical foundations of mathematics. This subject had some attention in the 19th century. But its more general significance became evident in the work of Whitehead and Russell, whose *Principia Mathematica* appeared in 1910. The use of symbols in mathematics and logic was subjected to searching analysis. Light was thus thrown on the nature of language, the way it functions as an instrument of thought, and the fallacies connected with its misuse. This unspectacular development, through its effects on philosophy, must in time have repercussions in almost every intellectual field.

*   *   *

CHANGES IN outlook and method have been accompanied by changes in motive. The interests inspiring science are of two kinds, intellectual and technological. Babylonian and Egyptian science was dominated by the latter. It was pursued for its usefulness in surveying, building, navigation and medicine; or for the power it gave to the priests who cultivated it. Greek interest was almost purely intellectual. In Roman and medieval times, with such science as there was, the intellectual interest gave way again to the practical. Since the Renaissance the two motives have always been present together, and their union has led to increasingly rapid development. But their relative importance has changed. In the 16th and 17th centuries, with Greek influence still strong from the Renaissance, intellectual curiosity was perhaps the main force. Since then the urgency of technical demands, military and economic, has so grown that intellectual curiosity now takes second place. The jealousy of modern governments for scientific secrets is very like that of ancient hierarchies. Science is publicly valued as an aid to wealth and power. It is too generally associated with factories, bombs, hygiene or artificial manure. Its place, beside religion, philosophy and the arts, among the elements of gracious civilisation, is forgotten. Educated men in ancient Greece or Renaissance Europe would not have dreamt of ignoring science. Aristotle, Leonardo, Bacon, Milton, Locke, Berkeley and Voltaire accepted it as an integral part of the culture they represented. But now, despite its immense effect on daily life, it is becoming intellectually a thing apart.

This is due to its intrinsic difficulty, as well as over-emphasis of its purely practical aspect. Five hundred years ago a first-class mind could master the bulk of existing knowledge. But the modern scholar cannot know the whole, even of his own subject. He *must* be a specialist. We depend increasingly on the expert who knows more and more about less and less. The intellectual society of today consequently tends to break up into smaller societies, each preoccupied with its limited domain, and ignorant of what the rest are doing. Scientists are apt to go their technical way without regard for human problems; while artists and men of letters are often unaware of the wonderful contribution that science has made, and can still make, to the cultural heritage. There *are* some unifying forces, such as the increasing co-operation of science and philosophy, already mentioned; but they are not sufficiently strong or widespread. It is urgently necessary to restore the unity of intellectual life. Unless we do so, we shall soon lose most of what is best in Western civilisation.

The problem is educational. How can we avoid the ill effect of necessary specialisation? The standard remedy is superficial study of many subjects. But a wide and balanced outlook is not to be had in this way. It comes, rather, from the proper study of a single subject. Students of different subjects are like men exploring the branches of neighbouring trees. A man cannot understand other people's problems by interrupting his own work to climb a few feet up their trees. His time will be better spent on his own tree. As he climbs higher, he will find its branches interlaced with those of the others. As he works downwards, tracing its roots, he will find them entangled with other roots, nourished in the same soil. The individual trees are now so extensive that few men have time or ability to reach many of the upper branches. It is comparatively easy to learn something of the roots. Here, surely, in the historical approach, lies the practical solution of the problem. Let everyone know the history of his own subject. He will find its origins in the same human problems and purposes as have given rise to other subjects. He will see that other men, with similar motives, are often seeking the same ends by other means. He will regard their efforts with sympathy. He will know that, by persevering in his own way, he may in time meet them again high above the ground.

We must make sure, by some such means, that men of science shall have more in common with other men of thought. Perhaps then they will have less to do with men of power. We must realise Clifford's hope: 'Dynamics and Prose Composition have met together; Literature and Biology have kissed each other. Perhaps not yet, but the good time is coming.' We may then avoid another (possibly not distant) Dark Age.

22

BOOKS FOR REFERENCE OR FURTHER READING

Books mentioned in the text or footnotes are omitted from this list, which does not, in any case, pretend to be exhaustive. It is only a small selection from the books which, without being too technical, give historical background or additional scientific detail.

BACON, F. *The Advancement of Learning*
BALL, W. W. R. *A Short Account of the History of Mathematics*
BELL, E. T. *Men of Mathematics*
BENN, A. W. *History of Modern Philosophy*
BEVAN, E. *Stoics and Sceptics*
BONNARD, A. *Greek Civilization*
BREWSTER, SIR D. *Memoirs of the Life, Writings and Discoveries of Sir Isaac Newton*
BURCKHARDT, J. *The Civilization of the Renaissance in Italy*
BUTTERFIELD, H. *Origins of Modern Science*
CROMBIE, A. C. *Augustine to Galileo*
DAMPIER, Sir W. *A History of Science*
DE MORGAN, A. *A Budget of Paradoxes*
DRAPER, J. W. *The Intellectual Development of Europe*
DREYER, J. L. E. *History of Astronomy from Thales to Kepler*
EDDINGTON, SIR A. S. *Space, Time and Gravitation; The Nature of the Physical World*
FARRINGTON, B. *Greek Science*
GOLDSCHMIDT, R. B. *Understanding Heredity*
GREENSTREET, W. J. (Ed.) *Isaac Newton, 1642–1727*
HEATH, SIR T. *A Manual of Greek Mathematics*
HOLMYARD, E. J. *Makers of Chemistry*
HUME, D. *A Treatise of Human Nature*
HUXLEY, J. *Evolution, the Modern Synthesis*
IRVINE, W. *Apes, Angels and Victorians*
JACOB, E. F. *The Renaissance*
JEANS, SIR J. *The Growth of Physical Science; The Stars in their Courses*
JUDD, J. W. *The Coming of Evolution*

KANT, I. *Critique of Pure Reason*

LACK, D. *Evolutionary Theory and Christian Belief*

LIVINGSTONE, R. W. (Ed.) *The Legacy of Greece*

POINCARÉ, H. *Science and Method; Science and Hypothesis*

RUDNICKI, J. *Nicholas Copernicus* (Trans. Massey)

RUSSELL, B. *History of Western Philosophy; Human Knowledge; Introduction to Mathematical Philosophy; Mysticism and Logic; Our Knowledge of the External World*

SAMBURSKY, S. *The Physical World of the Greeks*

SHERWOOD TAYLOR, F. *The Alchemists*

SINGER, C. W. *A Short History of Science*

SMITH, P. *A History of Modern Culture, 1543–1687*

SPENCER JONES, SIR H. *General Astronomy*

TOULMIN, S. *The Philosophy of Science*

WELLS, H. G. *A Short History of the World*

WHITEHEAD, A. N. *Introduction to Mathematics; Science and the Modern World*

WOOD, A. *Thomas Young, Natural Philosopher*

INDEX

Where, among several references, some are of special importance, these are in heavier type.

340   *Index*